CHECKLIST OF
THE FLORA AND FAUNA
OF WICKEN FEN

The 'jizz' of three of Wicken Fen's familiar breeding birds – the sedge and reed warblers and the marsh harrier – is brilliantly captured in this sketch by Eric Ennion. The swallowtail butterfly, with its caterpillar below it on the foodplant, milk-parsley, was a resident species in 1946 when Ennion drew it but it is now extinct at Wicken. Attempts to re-establish it have so far ended in failure but it is hoped that they will eventually be successful.

Courtesy: Hugh Ennion

CHECKLIST OF
THE FLORA AND FAUNA
OF WICKEN FEN

compiled and edited by

Laurie Friday and Basil Harley

in association with the
Management Committee of Wicken Fen,
a property of the National Trust

2000

Harley Books (B. H. & A. Harley Ltd)
Martins, Great Horkesley,
Colchester, Essex CO6 4AH, England

Text set in Sabon by
Saxon Graphics Ltd, Derby

Text printed by St Edmundsbury Press Ltd,
Bury St Edmunds, Suffolk

Colour reproduced and printed by
Hilo Colour Printers Ltd, Colchester, Essex

Bound by Woolnoughs Bookbinders Ltd
Irthlingborough, Northants

Designed by James Shurmer

Checklist of the Flora and Fauna of Wicken Fen
published by Harley Books in association with
the Management Committee of Wicken Fen,
a property of the National Trust.
© L. E. Friday & B. H. Harley, 2000

British Library Catalogue-in-Publication Data
applied for

ISBN 0 946589 61 5

CONTENTS

This Checklist is published as a companion volume to *Wicken Fen: the making of a wetland nature reserve* (Friday, 1997), which tells the story of the Fen from its formation, through its acquisition by the National Trust from 1899 onwards, to the present day.

INTRODUCTION

Wicken Fen is one of the oldest and most intensively studied nature reserves in the British Isles. From the middle of the nineteenth century, it has been a prized collecting and recording ground for naturalists. As the Fenland all around was drained for agriculture, the Fen became an isolated refuge for the characteristic species of fen habitats.

The earliest records that can confidently be located within the present reserve are plant records to be found in the notebooks and herbarium specimens of C. C. Babington, who first began to visit the Fen in pursuit of beetles in the 1820s. In the following decades, insect collecting became the chief attraction, and the Fen was celebrated for the richness of its lepidopteran and coleopteran fauna (see Friday, 1997).

The first co-ordinated attempt to catalogue the whole range of species at Wicken Fen was begun in 1923 by J. S. Gardiner and A. G. Tansley, professors of Zoology and Botany respectively at the University of Cambridge. The results, compiled by a team of naturalists who between them specialized in a wide range of organisms, was published in six volumes of *The Natural History of Wicken Fen* (Gardiner & Tansley, 1923; Gardiner, 1925–32).

In 1938, a comprehensive review of the Natural History of Cambridgeshire was published in the Victoria County History series in which many additional records for the Fen appeared (Salzmann, 1938). The publication of a series of guides to the flora and fauna of Wicken Fen provided another impetus for collecting and recording during the 1960s and 1970s: a botanical and topographical guide appeared in 1966 (Bingley & Walters, 1966), followed by guides to molluscs (Paul, 1967); vascular plants (Walters, 1967); birds (Easy & Kirkland, 1967); bryophytes (Lock, 1968); triclads (Ball, 1968); spiders (Duffey, 1970), butterflies and day-flying moths (Smart, 1972); microlepidoptera (Emmet, 1972); lichens (Laundon, 1973); mammals (Flowerdew, 1980); dragonflies (Moore & Bennett, unpubl.); and a new guide to the birds (Thorne & Bennett, 1995).

From its earliest days, the Wicken Fen Management Committee has appointed Botanical and Zoological Secretaries to keep records and to issue permits for collecting and recording, and, during the 1980s, specialist recorders were appointed to assist with the collection of invertebrate records. A new and pressing challenge to document the Fen's species is presented by the call to draw up a Biodiversity Action Plan for Cambridgeshire (Cambridgeshire Biodiversity Steering Group, 1997). It is not possible to conserve rare species unless their distributions, past and present, are known, and no habitat can successfully be managed without a detailed knowledge of the species it contains. No stately home should be without a comprehensive inventory of its contents; nor should a National Nature Reserve – particularly one belonging to the National Trust – be without an up-to-date checklist.

The checklists as they appear here are simply lists, although we have indicated those species with Red Data Book status (see Conservation Status (p. xii) for an explanation of Red Data Book classification). For many records we have no information on the precise locality of the specimens, but, in most cases, we have dates and names of collectors. We hope eventually to publish fuller lists, with such information, for each group in turn. We have also embarked on a project to enter the records on to a database to facilitate the retrieval and transmission of information.

An unexpectedly lively debate ensued when we tried to decide in what order to present species and the problem grew as we asked more recorders for their views. Lepidopterists, orthithologists and some botanists strongly favoured a rigid 'taxonomic' order. Other botanists, notably those with ecological leanings, preferred a straightforward alphabetic list, with little if any higher taxonomic sorting. Some dipterists and others fell somewhere in between. We have decided to order each list according to the various taxonomic works referred to in the References. The arrangement of higher taxa broadly follows the 'Five Kingdoms' of Margulis & Schwarz (1988) with minor variants.

In *The Natural History of Wicken Fen*, L. E. S. Eastham summed up the state of faunal records for Wicken Fen seventy years ago (Eastham, 1932). He enumerates 'over two thousand insects, ... 161 spiders, 37 molluscs ...' and goes on to speculate that 'Rich as this fauna may seem, it probably represents only a half of that which probably exists [on the Fen]'. Many of the lists we publish here are indeed more than twice as long as those Eastham knew: there are, for example, more than five thousand insect species (of which more than one third are Diptera), 227 spider species and 87 molluscs. These changes are partly attributable to the considerable efforts of colleagues who have responded to our call for new records, but they also reflect real ecological changes over the past seven decades, during which a large proportion of the open sedge fields have been overwhelmed by scrub (see Friday, 1997; Friday & Colston, 1999).

No species list is ever complete. Some groups lend themselves to extensive and thorough recording, being relatively large, showy and static (like vascular plants) and we expect only a few more species to be added to the lists of these presented here. For other groups, however, it seems unlikely that we will ever feel that we are near to completing the list; this is particularly true of the more problematic groups of insects, such as parasitic Hymenoptera, and the more esoteric phyla of microscopic organisms, especially among the Protoctista. We have no records at all for the phyla Nemotoda and Gastrotricha, although the Fen undoubtedly contains many billions of these creatures. The completeness of our lists for many groups depends largely on the interests of those associated with the Fen and on occasional visits by experts from further afield. Indeed, our records for some groups, such as the Psocoptera, are derived entirely from the efforts of single collectors who have had the foresight to publish their lists.

With these limitations in mind, we present these lists with the caveat that omission does not imply absence and we hope that readers will feel challenged to fill gaps wherever these fall within their own field or to draw our attention to errors. Records for all groups, and requests for permits to record at Wicken Fen may be sent to:

The Property Manager,
Wicken Fen National Nature Reserve,
Lode Lane, Wicken,
Cambridgeshire CB7 5XP

LAURIE FRIDAY & BASIL HARLEY

ACKNOWLEDGEMENTS

We are very grateful to a small army of naturalists; by acting as recorders for specific groups, or by agreeing to update and check existing records, or by helping with nomenclature and classification, the following people have made it possible to present these lists:

Algae: J. H. Belcher, E. J. Cox, D. John, L. Johnson, C. D. Preston, E. Swale, D. Williams; (Charophytes): J. A. Moore, C. D. Preston.

Ciliates: A. Warren.

Dinophytes and *Euglenophytes*: K. Wolowski.

Fungi: R. W. G. Dennis, H. J. Hudson, A. J. Silverside, B. M. Spooner.

Lichens: J. R. Laundon, O. W. Purvis.

Bryophytes: J. M. Lock, C. D. Preston, the late H. L. K. Whitehouse.

Vascular Plants: T. J. Bennett, J. O. Mountford, C. D. Preston, S. M. Walters.

Rotifera: R. M. Pontin.

Mollusca: M. J. Bishop, M. P. Kerney, R. C. Preece.

Arachnida: E. Duffey, D. R. Nellist.

Cladocera: J. H. Bratton, J. Hearn.

Copepoda: G. A. Boxshall, D. W. Sutcliffe.

Ostracoda: H. I. Griffiths, P. A. Henderson.

Isopoda: S. J. Gregory.

Myriapoda: S. J. Gregory, S. P. Hopkin, H. J. Read.

Collembola: S. P. Hopkin.

Ephemeroptera: J. E. Harker.

Odonata: T. J. Bennett, N. W. Moore, D. J. Painter.

Orthoptera: A. Colston, J. H. Bratton.

Hemiptera: W. A. Foster, N. A. Straw.

Thysanoptera: W. D. J. Kirk.

Neuroptera: C. W. Plant.

Trichoptera: D. J. Painter, I. Wallace.

Lepidoptera: T. J. Bennett, A. M. Emmet, R. Revell, the late C. C. Smith, D. E. Wilson.

Coleoptera: A. B. Drane, G. N. Foster, H. Mendel, M. G. Morris, R. D. Pope.

Diptera: D. M. Ackland, P. J. Chandler, J. H. W. Cole, R. H. L. Disney, J. W. Ismay, P. H. Langton, I. F. G. McLean, I. Perry, J. Robbins, A. E. Stubbs.

Siphonaptera: R. S. George.

Hymenoptera: S. A. Corbet, G. R. Else, M. R. Shaw, D. A. Sheppard, P. F. Yeo.

Pisces: D. C. Aldridge, D. J. Painter.

Aves: T. J. Bennett, M. D. Lester, C. J. R. Thorne.

Mammalia: J. R. Flowerdew.

Invertebrate Site Register: S. Ball.

Wicken Fen Zoological Records: M. de L. Brooke, Y. Z. Erzinçlioğlu, W. D. J. Kirk, S. A. Corbet.

Librarians: Natural History Museum (General Library): P. Cooper; (Entomology Library): J. Harvey; (Botany Library): M. Beasley; Royal Entomological Society: B. Pedersen; United Oxford & Cambridge University Club: J. Owston.

To any others who have contributed records or help in other ways but who are not included in the above list we offer apologies for their omission and grateful thanks for their valued assistance.

Finally we express our gratitude to the Managers of the Balfour-Browne Fund of the University of Cambridge for their generous donation towards the cost of the colour cover.

CONSERVATION STATUS

Many species of plants and animals at Wicken Fen are scarce both nationally and internationally. Their threat status is shown after the name, using the categories produced by the World Conservation Union. The key to these is printed below.

For stoneworts, bryophytes and vascular plants the categories, outlined in Hodgetts *et al.* (1996) and Palmer *et al.* (1997), are as follows:

Extinct –
taxa no longer known to exist in the wild

CR (critically endangered) –
taxa which face an extremely high risk of extinction in the immediate future

EN (endangered) –
taxa which face a very high risk of extinction in the very near future

VU (vulnerable) –
taxa which face a high risk of extinction in the medium-term future

LR/nt (lower risk – near threatened) –
taxa which are at lower risk than above but close to qualifying as vulnerable

N (nationally scarce) –
taxa which are thought to occur in no more than 30-100 10km squares

For the animal kingdom the categories are derived from the Red Data Books
(e.g. Shirt, 1987) and the published reviews of threatened species (e.g. Parsons, 1993) and can be summarized as follows:

Extinct –
formerly breeding in Great Britain but now believed to have died out;

RDB1 (endangered) –
taxa in danger of extinction in Great Britain, existing in five or fewer 10km squares;

RDB2 (vulnerable) –
taxa believed likely to move into the endangered category if causal factors continue operating;

RDB3 (rare) –
taxa with small populations in Great Britain, not in categories above but at risk and existing in fifteen or fewer 10km squares;

RDBK –
insufficiently known taxa suspected of belonging to categories above but about which information is lacking;

Na – Nationally Notable (Scarce): Category A –
taxa uncommon in Great Britain and thought to occur in 30 or fewer 10km squares or, for less well-recorded groups, within seven or fewer vice-counties;

Nb – Nationally Notable (Scarce): Category B –
taxa uncommon and thought to occur in no more than between 31 and 100 10km squares or, for less well-recorded groups, within between eight and twenty vice-counties;

N – Nationally Notable (Scarce) –
notable taxa which are estimated to occur in between 16 and 100 10km squares in Great Britain for which no attempt has yet been made to sub-divide the category between Notable A and Notable B.

TYPOGRAPHICAL TREATMENT AND CONVENTIONS IN THE CHECKLIST

(i)

There are fifteen categories of classification in the checklist, the typesizes for which are as follows:

1	**SUPER KINGDOM**	14 point bold caps
2	**KINGDOM**	12 point bold caps
3	*GROUP OF PHYLA*	10 point italic caps
4	**PHYLUM**	10 point bold caps
5	**Subphylum**	10 point bold u/lc
6	SUPERCLASS	10 point caps
7	***CLASS***	10 point bold italic caps
8	Subclass	10 point u/lc
9	**ORDER**	9 point bold caps
10	**Suborder**	9 point bold u/lc
11	***Group of Super families***	8 point bold italic u/lc
12	*SUPERFAMILY*	8 point italic caps
13	**FAMILY**	8 point bold caps
14	Subfamily	8 point u/lc
15	*Genus and species*	7 point bold italic u/lc

Each of the fourteen higher levels is treated differently typographically. This is to enable users of the list, with the aid of this key, to distinguish between such categories as Phylum, Class, Order, Superfamily and Family, among others.

At the lowest level, current generic and species names are printed in bold italic upper and lower case but those of synonyms are in ordinary italics in parentheses. In some groups synonyms, following convention, are preceded by an equals sign (=).

(ii)

Family names can also be identified by their termination. In the Plant Kingdom, all family names end in -ACEAE; in the Animal Kingdom, in -IDAE. No families are included for the Fungi Kingdom, the customarily used higher division being the Order, with the termination -**ALES**. In the first two Kingdoms, nomenclature is less easily categorized by termination and, for general purposes, does not usually go below Phylum (-**PHYTA**, -**PODA**, -**INA**, -**PHORA** and -**OTA**) and Class -*PHYCEAE* (for Algae) and -*MYCETES* (for classes formerly in the Fungi).

However, the Stoneworts, which strictly belong to the Algae, are treated differently. The name for that order, like those in the Fungi, ends in **ALES**, and that for the family, like the higher Plantae, ends in **ACEAE**.

(iii)

Certain abbreviations, other than those explained above in the Introduction under Conservation Status, or at the beginning of the major groups in the checklist, are occasionally used in the text.

The symbols indicating extinctions; early or last records; sources of particular records, or misidentifications are not always used in the same way within each group, so it is necessary to check the introductory sections of these to be sure of their meaning.

For localities: Adventurer's Fen is shown as Adv.Fen; Burwell Fen as Burw.Fen; St Edmund's Fen as St Edm.Fen; Wicken Fen as W.Fen.

(iv)

♂ = male

♀ = female

s.str. = sensu stricto

s.lat. = sensu lato

agg. = aggregate of closely similar species

(v)

Authors of species names are abbreviated. Those for algae, fungi and plants are as recommended by Brummitt & Powell (1992); abbreviations of authors of names of animal species are based on the same principles.

THE CHECKLIST

PROKARYOTA
(Monera, bacteria)

Lists: Griffiths (1925), George (1963)

CYANOPHYTA
(cyanobacteria, formerly known as blue-green 'algae')

Croococcus turgidus (Kütz.) O. Nägeli
Cylindrospermum stagnale (Kütz.) Born & Flahault
Gomphosphaeria aponina Kütz.
Lyngbya ochracea (Kütz.) Thur.
Merismopedia glauca (Ehrenb.) O. Nägeli
Microcystis elabens Bréb.
Oscillatoria princeps Vaucher
Phormidium angustissimum West & G. S. West
  autumnale (C. Agardh) Gomont
  laminosum (C. Agardh) Gomont
  luridum (Kütz.) Gomont
  retzii (C. Agardh) Gomont
  tenue (Menegh.) Gomont
  uncinatum (C. Agardh) Gomont
  valderianum (Delp.) Gomont
Pseudanabaena catenata Lauterb.
Rivularia dura Roth
Spirulina major Kütz.
Tolypothrix lanata J. Wartm.

EUKARYOTA
(superkingdom, to which all forms of life other than
Prokaryota belong)

PROTOCTISTA
(Protista, Protozoa)

Lists: Griffiths (1925), Sandon, (1928), George (1963), J. H.
Belcher, C. D. Preston. The arrangement of the higher taxa
(phyla and classes) is broadly in accordance with Margulis *et
al.* (1990), with the exception of the various phyla containing
photosynthetic members and known collectively as Algae.
These are arranged in the classification and order adopted in
the forthcoming British Freshwater Algal Flora (Whitton &
John, in preparation).

ALGAE
(group of algal phyla)

BACILLARIOPHYTA
(diatoms)

Checklist: Hartley (1986)

BACILLARIOPHYCEAE

Achnanthes bioretti H. Germ.
  (=*Navicula roteana* Kütz.)
  clevei Grunov
  conspicua A. Mayer
  exilis Kütz.
  hungarica (Grunov) Grunov
  minutissma Kütz.
  parvula Kütz.
  rossii Hust.
  wickenensis J. R. Carter
Amphipleura pellucida (Kütz.) Kütz.

Amphora normanii Rabenh.
  ovalis (Kütz.) Kütz.
  pediculus (Kütz.) Grunov
  perpusilla (Grunov) Grunov
  veneta Kütz.
Caloneis bacillum (Grunov) Cleve
  fasciata (Lagerst.) Cleve
  leptosoma (Grunov) Krammer
  ventricosa (Ehrenb.) F. Meister
  ventricosa var. *alpina* (Cleve) R. M. Patrick
Campylodiscus hibernicus Ehrenb.
Cocconeis pediculus Ehrenb.
  placentula Ehrenb.
  thumensis A. Mayer
Craticula cuspidata (Kütz.) D. G. Mann
  halophila (Grunov) D. G. Mann
Ctenophora pulchella D. M. Williams & Round
  (=*Synedra pulchella* Ralfs ex Kütz.)
Cyclotella krammeri Håk.
  meneghiniana Kütz.
  socialis Schutt.
  (=*radiosa* Lemmerm.)
Cymatopleura elliptica (Bréb. ex Kütz.) W. Sm.
  librile (Ehrenb.) Pant.
Cymbella affinis Kütz.
  aspera (Ehrenb.) H. Perag.
  cesatii (Rabenh.) Grunov
  cistula (Ehrenb.) Kirchn.
  cornuta (Ehrenb.) R. Ross
  cymbiformis C. Agardh
  inaequalis (Ehrenb.) Rabenh.
  leptoceros (Ehrenb.) Kütz.
  microcephala Grunov
  obtusa W. Greg.
  obtusiuscula Kütz.
  parva (W. Sm.) Kirchn.
  tumidula Grunov
Denticula tenuis Kütz.
Diadesmis perpusilla (Kütz.) D. G. Mann
  (=*Navicula perpusilla* (Kütz.) Grunov)
Diatoma hyemale (Roth.) Heib.
  tenue C. Agardh
  vulgare Bory
Diploneis elliptica (Kütz.) Cleve
  oculata (Bréb.) Cleve
  ovalis (Hilse) Cleve
Encyonema prostratum (Berk.) Kütz.
Epithemia adnata (Kütz.) Rabenh.
  turgida (Ehrenb.) Kütz.
Eucocconeis flexella (Kütz.) Cleve
  (=*Achnanthes flexella* (Kütz.) Brun)
Eunotia arcus Ehrenb.
  curvata (Kütz.) Lagerst.
  curvata var. *capitata* (Grunov) Woodhead & Tweed
  flexuosa Kütz.
  gracilis F. Meister
  pectinalis (O. Müll.) Rabenh.
  pectinalis var. *minor* (Kütz.) Rabenh.
  vanheurckii R. M. Patrick
Fallacia pygmaea (Kütz.) Stickle & D. G. Mann
  subhamulata (Grunov) D. G. Mann
Fragilaria capucina Desm.
  var. *acuta* (Ehrenb.) Rabenh.
  var. *mesolepta* (Rabenh.) Rabenh.
Fragilariforma virescens (Ralfs) D. M. Williams & Round
  (=*Fragilaria virescens* Ralfs)
Frustulia vulgaris (Thwaites) De Toni
Gomphoneis olivaceum (Hornem.) P. Dawson ex R. Ross & P.
  A. Sims
Gomphonema acuminatum Ehrenb.
  angustatum (Kütz.) Rabenh.

1

augur Ehrenb.
gracile Ehrenb.
longiceps Ehrenb.
parvulum (Kütz.) Kütz.
truncatum Ehrenb.
vibrio Ehrenb. var. *intricatum* (Kütz.) R. Ross
Gyrosigma attenuatum (Kütz.) Rabenh.
Hannaea arcus (Ehrenb.) R. M. Patrick
Hantzschia amphioxys (Ehrenb.) Grunov
Luticola mutica (Kütz.) D. G. Mann
Mastogloia smithii Thwaites ex W. Sm.
    var. *lacustris* Grunov
Melosira varians C. Agardh
Meridion circulare (Grev.) C. Agardh
Navicula bryophila J. B. Petersen
  cari Ehrenb.
    var. *cincta* (Ehrenb.) Lange-Bert.
  cryptocephala Kütz.
  digito-radiata (W. Greg.) Ralfs
  graciloides A. Mayer
  gregaria Donkin
  grimmei Krasske
  menisculus Schum.
  minuscula Grunov
  oblonga (Kütz.) Kütz.
  placentula (Ehrenb.) Kütz.
  pseudolanceolata Lange-Bert.
  radiosa Kütz.
    var. *tenella* Grunov ex Van Heurck
  rhynchocephala Kütz.
  salinarum Grunov var. *intermedia* (Grunov) Cleve
  tripunctata (O. Müll.) Bory
Neidium dubium (Ehrenb.) Cleve
  iridis (Ehrenb.) Cleve
Nitzschia acicularis (Kütz.) W. Sm.
  amphibia Grunov
  apiculata (W. Greg.) Grunov
  denticula Grunov
  dissipata (Kütz.) Grunov
  dubia W. Sm.
  frustulum (Kütz.) Grunov
  gracilis Hantzsch
  ovalis Arn. ex Cleve
  pusilla Grunov
  recta Hantzsch ex Rabenh.
  sigmoidea (Nitzsch) W. Sm.
  vermicularis (Kütz.) Hantzsch
Pinnularia abaujensis (Pant.) R. Ross
  appendiculata (C. Agardh) Cleve
  biceps W. Greg.
  brebissonii (Kütz.) Rabenh.
  gentilis (Donkin) Cleve
  gracillima W. Greg.
  lata (Bréb.) W. Sm.
  major (Kütz.) W. Sm.
  subcapitata W. Greg.
  sudetica Hilse var. *leptogongyla* (Cleve) A. Cleve
Placoneis clementioides (Hust.) E. J. Cox
  (=*Navicula clementioides* Hust.)
  gastrum (Ehrenb.) Mereschk.
  (=*Navicula gastrum* (Ehrenb.) Kütz.)
  pseudanglica (Lange-Bert.) E. J. Cox
Pseudostaurosira brevistriata (Ehrenb.) D. M. Williams & Round
  (=*Fragilaria lapponica* Grunov)
Rhoicosphenia abbreviata (C. Agardh) Lange-Bert.
Rhopalodia gibba (Ehrenb.) O. Müll.
  gibberula (Ehrenb.) O. Müll.
    var. *parallela* (Grunov) H. Perag. & Perag.
Sellaphora bacillum (Ehrenb.) D. G. Mann
  (=*Navicula bacillum* Ehrenb.)

laevissima (Kütz.) D. G. Mann
  (=*Navicula laevissima* Kütz.)
pupula (Kütz.) Mereschk.
  (=*Navicula pupula* Kütz.)
Simonsenia delognei (Grunov) Lange-Bert.
Stauroneis acuta W. Sm.
  agrestis J. B. Petersen
  borrichii (J. B. Petersen) J. W. G. Lund
  smithii Grunov
Staurosira construens (Ehrenb.) D. M. Williams & Round
  (=*Fragilaria construens* (Ehrenb.) Grunov)
Staurosirella pinnata (Ehrenb.) D. M. Williams & Round
  (=*Fragilaria leptostauron* (Ehrenb.) Hust.)
  vaucheriae (Kütz.) J. B. Petersen
Surirella biseriata Bréb. ex Godey
  brebissonii Krammer & Lange-Bert.
  linearis W. Sm.
    var. *constricta* Grunov
Synedra acus Kütz.
  amphicephala Kütz.
  capitata Ehrenb.
  miniscula Grunov
  parasitica (W. Sm.) Hust.
  rumpens Kütz.
  ulna (Nitzsch) Ehrenb.
Tabularia fasciculata (C. Agardh) D. M. Williams & Round
  (=*Synedra fasciculata* (C. Agardh) Kütz)
Tryblionella acuminata W. Sm.
  (=*Nitzschia angusta* (W. Sm.) Grunov)
  var. *acuta* Grunov
  (=*Nitzschia angustata* var. *acuta* Grunov)
  acuta (Cleve) D. G. Mann
  (=*Nitzschia acuta* Hantzsch ex Cleve)
  gracilis W. Sm.
  (=*Nitzschia tryblionella* Hantzsch var. *debilis* A. Mayer

CHRYSOPHYTA
(golden algae)

CHRYSOPHYCEAE
Anthophysa vegetans (O. F. Müll.) F. Stein
Dinobryon sertularia Ehrenb.

CRYPTOPHYTA
(cryptomonads)

CRYPTOPHYCEAE
Rhodomonas minuta Skuja var. *nannoplanktica* Skuja

DINOPHYTA
(dinoflagellates, dinomastigotes)

DINOPHYCEAE
Ceratium cornutum (Ehrenb.) Clap.
Gymnodinium viridae Penard
Gymnosium cieisw Penard
Peridinium bipes F. Stein
  cinctum (O. F. Müll.) Ehrenb.
  marssonii Lemmerm.

XANTHOPHYTA
(yellow-green algae)

XANTHOPHYCEAE
Vaucheria dichotoma (L.) C. Agardh

CHLOROPHYTA
(green algae)

VOLVOCALES
Chlamydocapsa ampla (Kütz.) Fott
    (=*Gloeocystis gigas* (Kütz.) Lagerh.)
Chlamydomonas monadina F. Stein
    (=*cingulata* Pascher)
Haematococcus pluvialis Flot.
Pandorina morum Bory
Phacotus lenticularis F. Stein

TETRASPORALES
Apiocystis brauniana (O. Nägeli) in Kütz.
Asterococcus superbus (Cienk.) Scherff.

CHLOROCOCCALES
Ankistrodesmus falcatus (Corda) Ralfs
Botryococcus braunii Kütz.
Characium ambiguum J. Herm.
  heteromorphum Reinsch
  ornithocephalum A. Braun
Coelastrum cambricum W. Archer
    (=*cubicum*)
  microporum O. Nägeli
  sphaericum O. Nägeli
Crucigenia quadrata Morren
  rectangularis (O. Nägeli) Gay
Crucigeniella appendiculata (Lemmerm.) Komárek
    (=*Crucigenia apiculata* (Lemmerm.) Schmidle)
Dictyosphaerium pulchellum Wood
Muriella magna F. E. Fritsch & R. P. John
Nephrocytium agardhianum O. Nägeli
Oocystis solitaria Wittr.
Pediastrum boryanum (Turpin) Menegh.
  duplex Meyen
  tetras (Ehrenb.) Ralfs
Polyedriopsis spinulosa (Schmidle) Schmidle
Radiococcus nimbatus (De Wild.) Schmidle
Scenedesmus acuminatus (Lagerh.) Chodat
  bijugus (Turpin) Kütz.
    (=*bijugatus* West & G. S. West)
  denticulatus Lagerh. var. *linearis* Hansg.
  obliquus (Turpin) Kütz.
  quadricauda (Turpin) Bréb.
Siderocelis ornata (Fott) Fott
Tetraedron caudatum (Corda) Hansg.
  incus (Teiling) G. M. Sm.
  trigonum (O. Nägeli) Hansg.
Tetrastrum staurogeniaeforme (Schröd.) Lemmerm.
Treubaria triappendiculata C. Bernard

OEDOGONIALES
Bulbochaete rectangularis Wittr.
  sessilis Wittr.

ULOTRICHALES
Geminella interrupta (Turpin) Lagerh.
Hormidium flaccidum (Kütz.)
Microspora stagnorum (Kütz.) A. Braun
Radiofilum flavescens G. S. West

CHAETOPHORALES
Aphanochaete repens A. Braun
Chaetopeltis orbicularis Berthold
Chaetophora elegans (Roth) C. Agardh
  incrassata (Huds.) Hazen
  pisiformis (Roth) C. Agardh
Pleurastrum terrestre F. E. Fritsch & R. P. John

CONIUGATOPHYTA
(conjugating green algae, gamophytes)

CONJUGATOPHYCEAE

ZYGNEMATALES
(desmids)

DESMIDIACEAE
Closterium acerosum (Schrank) Ehrenb.
  acutum (Lyngb.) Bréb.
  parvulum O. Nägeli
  pronum Bréb.
Cosmarium angulosum Bréb.
  basilicum G. S. West
  bioculatum Bréb.
  difficile Lütkem.
  granatum Bréb.
  laeve Rabenh. var. *septentrionale* Wille
  praemorsum Bréb.
  punctulatum Bréb.
  reniforme (Ralfs) W. Archer
  subtumidum Nordst.
  tetraophthalmum Bréb.
Euastrum insulare (Wittr.) Roy
Gonatozygon monotaenium de Bary
Hyalotheca dissiliens (Sm.) Bréb.
Mougeotia calcaria (Cleve) Wittr.
  elegantula Wittr.
  gracillima (Hassall) Wittr.
  parvula Hassall
Pleurotaenium trabecula (Ehrenb.) O. Nägeli
Spirogyra sp.
Staurastrum inflexum Bréb.
  orbiculare Ralfs var. *depressum* Roy & Bisset
  paxilliferum G. S. West
  punctulatum Bréb.

CHAROPHYTA

CHARALES
Check list: Moore (1986)
Dates refer to last records
Conservation status: Hodgetts *et al.* (1996)

CHARACEAE
('charophytes', stoneworts)

Chara aspera Dethard. ex Willd. var. *aspera* [1949] (N)
    var. *curta* (Nolte ex Kütz.) A. Braun ex Leonh [1899]
    (LR/nt)

globularis Thuill. var. *globularis*
    var. *virgata* (Kütz.) R. D. Wood
hispida L. var. *hispida*
    var. *major* (Hartm.) R. D. Wood
    var. *rudis* A. Braun [1935] (**LR/nt**)
pedunculata Kütz. (**N**)
vulgaris L. var. *vulgaris*
    var. *contraria* (A. Braun ex Kütz.) J. A. Moore
    var. *crassicaulis* (Schleich. ex A. Braun) Kütz.† [1882]
    var. *longibracteata* (Kütz.) J. Groves & Bull.-Webst.
    var. *papillata* Wallr.
Nitella flexilis (L.) C. Agardh var. *flexilis*
    tenuissima (Desv.) Kütz. (**EN**)
Tolypella nidifica (O. Müll.) Leonh. var. *glomerata* (Desv.) R. D. Wood (**N**)

EUGLENOPHYTA
(euglenoid flagellates)
Additional records by K. Wolowski (pers.comm.)

EUGLENOPHYCEAE

Euglena acus Ehrenb.
    agilis Carter
    caudata Hübner
    deses Ehrenb.
    gracilis Klebs
    mutabilis Schmitz
Phacus acuminatus Stokes
    longicauda (Ehrenb.) Dujardin
    parvulus Klebs
    pleuronectes (Ehrenb.) Dujardin
Trachelomonas oblonga Lemmerman
    planctonica Swirenko
    similis Stokes
    volvocina Ehrenb.

RHIZOPODA
(amastigote amoebas)
List: Sandon (1928)

Amoeba sp., hyalodiscus type
Amoeba sp., limax type
Amoeba albida Nägler
Difflugia constricta (Ehrenb.)
    globula (Ehrenb.)
Euglypha compressa Carter
    ?*laevis* ((Ehrenb.)
    rotunda Wailes
    tuberculata Duj.
Hartmanella hyalina Alexeev
Lecythium hyalinum Hertw. & Lesser
Nuclearia sp.
Trinema enchelys (Ehrenb.) Leidy
    lineare Lenard

ZOOMASTIGINA
(zooflagellates, craspedomonads, choanoflagellates)
List: Sandon (1928)

Allantion tachyploon Sandon
Bodo edax Klebs
    saltans Ehrenb.
Cercobodo vibrans Sandon
Cercomonas sp.
Dimastigella trypaniformis Sandon
Helkesimastix faecicola Woodcock & Lapage

Heteromita lens O. F. Müll.
Mastigamoeba sp.
Monas sp.
Naegleria gruberi (Schard.) Wilson
Oikomonas termo (Ehrenb.) Martin
Petalomonas angusta (Klebs) Lemm.
Phalansterium solitarium Sandon
Proleptomonas faecicola Woodcock
Sainouron mikroteron Sandon
Salpingoeca gracilis H. W. Clark
Scytomonas pusilla Stein
Spiromonas angusta (Duj.)
Tetramitus spiralis Goodey

CILIOPHORA
(ciliates)
List: Sandon (1928)

Balantiophorus sp.
    (=*Cyrtolophosis* sp.)
Colpoda cucullus (O. F. Müll.) Gmel.
    steinii Maupas
Enchelys sp.
Hypotricha sp.
Oxtricha pellionella (O. F. Müll.) Borror
Vorticella microstoma (Ehrenb.)

OOMYCOTA
(water moulds, downy mildews)

OOMYCETES
'Mastigomycetes'

PERONOSPORALES

Albugo candida (Pers.) Kuntze
Peronospora alta Fuckel
    farinosa (Fr.) Fr.
    (=*effusa* (Grev.) Tul.)
    parasitica (Pers.) Fr.
Plasmopara crustosa (Fr.) Jørst.
    (=*nivea* (Unger) J. Schröt.)
    densa (Rabenh.) J. Schröt.
Pseudoperonospora urticae (Lib. ex Berk.) E. S. Salmon & Ware
    (=*Peronospora urticae* Lib.)

FUNGI

Lists: Corner (1934) and Stenton (1953), updated by H. J. Hudson, with further additions taken from Gardiner (1932), the records of the Herbarium, Royal Botanic Gardens, Kew, and from A. J. Silverside (pers.comm). Classification for taxa (genera and above) follows Hawksworth (1995). The Oomycota, which have traditionally been included in the Fungi, are transferred to Protoctista.

Species' and authors' names have been checked by R. W. G. Dennis and B. M. Spooner, and by A. J. Silverside.

Records by reliable recorders, subsequently considered doubtful or requiring further evidence, are included but shown in square brackets. The identity of four species recorded is quite unknown. Their names are given in quotation marks.

Conservation Status: Ing (1992)

ASCOMYCOTA

ASCOMYCETES
'Discomycetes' (cup fungi)

LEOTIALES

Albotricha acutipila (P. Karst.) Raitv. (on *Phragmites australis*)
(=*Dasyscyphus acutipilus* (P. Karst.) Sacc.)
Ascocoryne sarcoides (Jacq.) Groves & Wilson
(=*Coryne sarcoides* Jacq.)
[*Belonidium leucostomum* (Rehm) Raitv.]
(=*Urceolella leucostoma* (Rehm) Boud.)
(=*Dasyscyphus leucostomus* Rehm)
Belonioscypha culmicola (Desm.) Dennis
(=*Cyathicula culmicola* Desm.)
Belonopsis excelsior (P. Karst.) Rehm
(=*Belonium excelsior* (P. Karst.) Boud.)
(=*Niptera excelsior* (P. Karst.) Dennis)
filispora (Cooke) Nannf.
(=*Belonium filisporum* (Cooke) Sacc.)
Bisporella citrina (Batsch) Korf & C. W. Carp.
(=*Calycella claroflava* (Grev.) Boud.)
Calloria neglecta (Lib.) B. Hein
(as anamorph =*Cylindrocolla urticae* (Pers.) Bonord.)
'*Calycella uliginosa* (Fr.) Boud.'
Calycellina indumenticola Graddon (on *Salix cinerea*)
Catinella olivacea (Batsch) Boud.
Ciboria amentacea (Balb.) Fuckel
Cistella grevillei (Berk.) Raschle
(=*Trichopeziza grevillei* (Berk.) Sacc.)
(=*Dasyscyphus grevillei* (Berk.) Massee)
Cudoniella clavus (Alb. & Schwein.) Dennis
(=*Ombrophila clavus* (Alb. & Schwein.) Cooke)
Cyathicula coronata (Bull.) de Not.
(=*Crocicreas coronatum* (Bull.) S. Carp.)
cyathoidea (Bull.) Thüm. (on *Filipendula ulmaria*)
(=*Crocicreas cyathoideum* (Bull.) S. Carp.)
Durella connivens (Fr.) Rehm (on *Salix cinerea*)
Encoelia furfuracea (Roth) P. Karst.
'*Helotium*' *cruentatum* P. Karst. (on grass sp. (Poaceae))
'*Helotium tetra-ascosporum* Rea'
Heterosphaeria patella (Tode) Grev.
Hyaloscypha hyalina (Pers.) Boud. agg.
Heyderia sclerotipus (Boud.) Benkert (**LR/nt**)
(=*Mitrula sclerotipus* Boud.)
Hymenoscyphus epiphyllus (Pers.) Rehm ex Kauffman
herbarum (Pers.) Dennis
imberbis (Bull.) Dennis
(=*Ombrophila imberbis* (Bull.) Boud.)
laetus (Boud.) Dennis (on *Viburnum opulus*)

phyllogenus (Rehm) Kuntze
phyllophilus (Desm.) Kuntze
salicellus (Fr.) Dennis
scutula (Pers.) W. Phillips
vernus (Boud.) Dennis
(=*Ombrophila verna* Boud.)
virgultorum (Vahl) W. Phillips
(=*calyculus* auctt., non Sowerby)
Lachnum (=*Dasyscyphus* pro parte)
albotestaceum (Desm.) P. Karst.
apalum (Berk. & Broome) Nannf.
(=*Erinella apala* (Berk. & Broome) Nannf.)
bicolor (Bull.) P. Karst.
calyculiforme (Schum.) P. Karst.
controversum (Cooke) Rehm (on grass sp. (Poaceae))
corticale (Pers.) Nannf.
(=*Lachnella canescens* Cooke)
crystallinum (Fuckel) Rehm
dumorum (Roberge) Huhtinen
elongatisporum Baral
(=*L. roseum* misident.)
mollissimum (Lasch) P. Karst.
(=*Lachnella leucophaea* (Pers.) Boud.)
nudipes (Fuckel) Nannf.
(=*Dascyscyphus spiraeicola* (P. Karst.) Sacc.)
palearum (Desm.) P. Karst.
(?=*Dascyscyphus patens* (Fr.) Rehm)
sulfureum (Pers.) P. Karst.
(=*Erinella nylanderi* Rehm)
sulphurellum (Peck) Raitv.
(=*Dasyscyphus cruciferus* (W. Phillips) Sacc.)
tenuissimum (Quél.) Korf
virgineum (Batsch) P. Karst. (on *Rubus* sect. *Corylifolii*)
Mollisia benesuada (Tul.) W. Phillips
cinerea (Batsch) P. Karst. (on *Salix cinerea*)
clavata Gremmen (on *Rubus* sect. *Corylifolii*)
hydrophila (P. Karst.) Sacc. (on *Phragmites australis*)
juncina (Pers.) Rehm
ligni (Desm.) P. Karst.
Niptera lacustris (Fr.) Fr.
[*melatephra* (Lasch) Rehm]
(=*Mollisia melatephra* (Lasch.) P. Karst.)
pulla (W. Phillips & Keith) Boud.
Orbilia curvatispora (Boud.) (on *Salix cinerea*)
delicatula P. Karst.
(=*xanthostigma* (Fr.) Fr. sensu auctt. angl.)
inflatula (P. Karst.) Boud.
(=*Hyalinia inflatula* (P. Karst.) Boud.)
leucostigma (Fr.) Fr.
Pezicula frangulae (Fr.) Fuckel
Pezizella amenti (Batsch) Dennis
eburnea (Roberge) Dennis
effugiens (Desm.) Rehm
(=*Urceolella effugiens* (Desm.) Boud.)
rubescens Mouton (on *Quercus robur*)
vulgaris (Fr.) Sacc.
Phialina ulmariae (Lasch) Dennis
(=*Urceolella deparcula* (P. Karst.) Boud.)
Polydesmia pruinosa (Berk. & Broome) Boud.
Pseudopeziza calthae (W. Phillips) Massee
(=*Phacidium calthae* W. Phillips)
trifolii (Biv.) Fuckel
Pyrenopeziza fuckelii Nannf.
millegrana Boud.
[*Rutstroemia bolaris* (Batsch) Rehm]
(=*Phialea bolaris* (Batsch) Boud.)
calopus (Fr.) Rehm
(=*Helotium gramineum* W. Phillips)
Sclerotinia curreyana (Berk. ex Currey) P. Karst.
duriaeana (Tul. & C. Tul.) Rehm

Tapesia evilescens (P. Karst.) Sacc.
  fusca (Pers. ex Mérat) Fuckel
  knieffii (Wallr.) J. Kunze
  (=*retincola* (Rabenh.) P. Karst.)
Unguicularia millepunctata (Lib.) Dennis (on *Filipendula ulmaria*)
  scrupulosa (P. Karst.) Höhnel
  (=*Urceolella scrupulosa* (P. Karst.) Boud.)
Urceolella carestiana (Rabenh.) Dennis
  (=*Trichopeziza carinata* Cooke & Massee)

OSTROPALES

Cryptodiscus rhopaloides Sacc.

PEZIZALES

Ascobolus furfuraceus Pers.
  immersus Pers.
Cheilymenia vitellina (Pers.) Dennis
  (=*dalmeniensis* (Cooke) Boud.)
Coprobia granulata (Bull.) Boud.
Coprotus ochraceus (H. Crouan & P. Crouan) Larsen
Fimaria cervaria (Phill. ex Stevenson) Brumm. (from deer droppings)
Geopora arenicola (Lév.) Kers
  (=*Sepultaria arenicola* (Lév.) Massee)
Humaria hemisphaerica (F. H. Wigg.) Fuckel
  (=*Lachnea hemisphaerica* (F. H. Wigg.) Gillet)
Iodophanus carneus (Pers.) Boud.
  (=*Ascophanus carneus* (Pers.) Korf)
Lasiobolus ciliatus (J. C. Schmidt) Boud.
  equinus (O. F. Müll.) P. Karst.
Mitrophora semilibera (DC.) Lév.
Peziza badia Pers.
  succosa Berk.
  varia (Hedw.) Fr. (on *Salix*)
  vesiculosa Bull.
Pulvinula constellatio (Berk. & Broome) Boud.
Pyronema omphalodes (Bull.) Fuckel
  (=*confluens* (Pers.) Tul.)
Ramsbottomia asperior (Nyl.) Benkert & T. Schumach.
  (=*Scutellinia asperior* (Nyl.) Dennis)
Scutellinia crinita (Bull.) Lamb (on *Salix caprea*)
  hirta (Schumach.) Kuntze
  scutellata (L.) Lambotte
Thelobolus stercoreus Tode (from deer droppings)

RHYTISMATALES

Propolomyces versicolor (Fr.) Dennis (on *Quercus*)

PROTOMYCETALES

Taphridium umbelliferarum (Rostr.) Lagerh. & Juel (on *Peucedanum palustre*)
'Pyrenomycetes' (flask fungi)

DIATRYPALES

Diatrypella quercina (Pers.) Cooke (on *Quercus*)
Eutypa lata (Pers.) Tul. & C. Tul.

DOTHIDEALES

Coleroa chaetomium (Kunze) Fr.
Didymella commanipula (Berk. & Broome) Sacc.
  (=*Didymosphaeria commanipula* (Berk. & Broome) Niessl)
Leptosphaeria acuta (Hoffm.) P. Karst.
  arundinacea (Sowerby) Sacc.
  doliolum (Fr.) Ces. & de Not. (on *Urtica dioica*)

Lophiostoma angustilabrum (Berk. & Broome) Cooke (on *Rubus* sect. *Corylifolii*)
  (='*L. microstomum* Niessl.' auctt.)
  caulium (Fr.) Ces. & de Not. (on *Urtica dioica*)
  fuckelii Sacc.
  semiliberum (Desm.) Ces. & de Not.
  vagabundum (Sacc.) Chesters & Bell (on *Viburnum opulus*)
Massarina eburnea (Tul. & C. Tul.) Sacc.
Mycosphaerella punctiformis (Pers.) Starb. (on *Quercus robur*)
Ophiosphaerella herpotricha (Fr.) J. Walker
Pleospora herbarum (Fr.) Rabenh.
Preussia vulgaris (Corda) Cain
Scirrhia aspidiorum (Lib.) Bubák (on *Thelpyteris palustris*)
Trematosphaeria britzelmayriana (Rehm) Sacc.
Venturia chlorospora (Ces.) P. Karst.
  rumicis (Desm.) G. Winter

ERYSIPHALES (powdery mildews)

Arthrocladiella mougeotii (Lév.) Vassilkov (on *Lycium barbarum*)
  (=*Microsphaera mougeotii* Lév.)
Erysiphe aquilegiae DC. var. *ranunculi* (Grev.) R. Y. Zheng & G. Q. Chen (on *Ranunculus repens*)
  cichoracearum DC.
  convolvuli DC. (on *Calystegia sepium*)
  cruciferarum Opiz ex Junell
  cynoglossi (Wallr.) U. Braun
  galeopsidis DC.
  graminis DC.
  heraclei Schleich. ex DC.
  knautiae Duby (on *Succisa pratensis*)
  urticae (Wallr.) S. Blumer (on *Urtica dioica*)
Sawadaea bicornis (Wallr.) Homma (on *Acer campestre*)
  (=*Uncinula bicornis* (Wallr.) Lév.)
Sphaerotheca aphanis (Wallr.) U. Braun
  fusca (Fr.) S. Blumer
  pannosa (Wall.) Lév.
  spiraeae Sawada
Uncinula adunca (Wallr.) Lév. (on *Salix cinerea*)

HYPOCREALES

Claviceps nigricans Tul. (on *Eleocharis palustris*)
  purpurea (Fr.) Tul.
  (=*microcephala* (Wallr.) Tul.)
Hypomyces aurantius (Pers.) Tul. (as anamorph *Cladobotryum varium* Nees) (on *Polyporus badius*)
Nectria cinnabarina (Tode) Fr.
  coccinea (Pers.) Fr.

PHYLLACHORALES

Phyllachora graminis (Pers.) Fuckel

SORDARIALES

Chaetomium cochliodes Pall.
  elatum J. C. Schmidt & Kunze (on *Phragmites australis*)
  spinosum Chivers

TAPHRINALES

Taphrina pruni Tul. (on *Prunus spinosus*)

XYLARIALES

Anthostomella tomicum (Lév.) Sacc.
Hypoxylon multiforme (Fr.) Fr. (on *Salix*)
Xylaria hypoxylon (L.) Grev.

BASIDIOMYCOTA

BASIDIOMYCETES

'Hymenomycetes' (mushrooms, toadstools, bracket fungi)

AGARICALES

Bolbitius vitellinus (Pers.) Fr.
Calocybe gambosa (Fr.) Donk.
   (=*Tricholoma gambosum* (Fr.) P. Kumm.)
Calyptella capula (Holmsk.) Quél.
Cellypha goldbachii (Weinm.) Donk.
   (=*Cyphella lactea* Bres.)
Claudopus byssisedus (Pers.) Gillet
Clitocybe cerussata (Fr.) P. Kumm.
Conocybe tenera (Schaeff.) Fayod sensu lato
Coprinus cordisporus Gibbs
   (=*patouillardii* auctt.)
  curtus Kalchbr. (from deer droppings)
  disseminatus (Pers.) Gray
  ephemerus (Bull.) Fr.
  friesii Quél.
  niveus (Pers.) Fr.
  plicatilis (Fr.) Fr. sensu lato
  stercoreus Fr. (from deer droppings)
Crinipellis stipitarius (Fr.) Pat. [as '*Naucoria graminicola*
  (Nees) Fr.']
Delicatula integrella (Pers.) Fayod
Hemimycena candida (Bres.) Singer
  cucullata (Pers.) Singer
    (=*Mycena gypsea* (Fr.) Quél.)
  cyphelloides (Orton) Maas Geest.
  delectabilis (Peck) Singer
  [*gracilis* (Quél.) Singer]
Hohenbuehelia cyphelliformis (Berk.) O. K. Mill.
Hygrocybe conica (Schaeff.) P. Kumm.
   (=*Hygrophorus conicus* (Schaeff.) Fr.)
Kuehneromyces mutabilis ((Schaeff.) Singer & A. H. Sm.)
Lachnella villosa (Pers.) Gillet (on *Urtica* sp.)
Leptonia [*asprella* (Fr.) P. Kumm.]
  griseorubida (Kühner) Orton
    (= *L. griseorubella* (Lasch) Orton)
  sericella (Fr.) Barbier
  serrulata (Fr.) P. Kumm.
Marasmiellus ramealis (Bull.) Singer
Marasmius cornelii Laessøe & Noordel.
  (as '*M. menieri* Boud.')
  curreyi Berk. & Broome (as '*M. graminum* (Lib.) Berk. &
    Broome')
  limosus Quél.
  rotula (Scop.) Fr.
[*Melanoleuca melaleuca* (Pers.) Murrill]
Merismodes anomalus (Pers.) Singer
   (=*Solenia anomala* (Pers.) Fuckel)
Mycena acicula (Schaeff.) P. Kumm.
  adscendens (Lasch) Maas Geest.
  arcangeliana Bres. (on *Quercus robur*)
  [*capillaris* (Schum.) P. Kumm.]
  cinerella P. Karst.
  clavularis (Batsch) Sacc.
  [*corticola* (Pers.) Gray]
  filopes (Bull.) P. Kumm.
  flavoalba (Fr.) Quél.
  galericulata (Scop.) Gray
  galopus (Pers.) P. Kumm. (on *Quercus robur*)
  hiemalis (Retz.) Quél.
  metata (Fr.) P. Kumm.
  mucor (Batsch) Gillet (on *Quercus robur*)

  niveipes (Murrill) Murrill (on *Salix*)
  polyadelpha (Lasch) Kühner (on *Quercus robur*)
  speirea (Fr.) Gillet (on 'bog oak'; *Rhamnus catharticus*)
  vitilis (Fr.) Quél. (on *Quercus robor*)
Nolanea papillatua Bres. (in grass)
Omphalina pyxidata (Bull.) Quél.
Panaeolina foenisecii (Pers.) Maire
Panaeolus campanulatus (Bull.) Quél.
  papilionaceus (Bull.) Quél.)
  semiovatus (Sowerby) S. Lundell & Nannfeldt
    (=*Anellaria separata* (L.) P. Karst.)
  sphinctrinus (Fr.) Quél.
Pluteus [*hispidulus* (Fr.) Gillet]
  lutescens (Fr.) Gillet
  nanus (Pers.) P. Kumm.
Psathyrella [*bifrons* (Berk.) A. H. Sm.]
  candolleana (Fr.) Maire
    (=*Hypholoma appendiculatum* (Bull.) Quél.)
  gossypina (Bull.) A. Pearson & Dennis
  gracilis (Fr.) Quél.
  prona (Fr.) Gillet
    (=*atomata* (Fr.) Quél.)
  spadiceogrisea (Schaeff.) Maire
  typhae (Kalchbr.) A. Pearson & Dennis
Psilocybe bullacea (Bull.) P. Kumm.
    (=*Deconica bullacea* Bull.)
  inquilina (Fr.) Bres.
    (=*D. inquilina* (Fr.) Lange)
  physaloides (Bull.) Quél.
Stropharia caerulea Kreisel (in grass)

AURICULARIALES

Auricularia auricula-judae (Bull.) Wettst. (on *Sambucus nigra*)
  (=*Hirneola auricula-judae* (Bull.) Berk.)

BOLETALES

Paxillus involutus (Batsch) Fr.

CANTHARELLALES

Ceratellopsis aculeata (Pat.) Corner
  (=*Pistillaria aculeata* Pat.)
Clavaria tenuipes Berk. & Broome
Pistillaria subuncialis Corner
Pistillina hyalina Quél.
    (=*Typhula subhyalina* Courtec.)
  patouillardii Quél.
    (=*Pistillina capitata* (Pat.) Sacc.)
Pterula gracilis (Berk. & Desm.) Corner
    (=*Pistillaria aculina* Quél.)
Typhula erythropus (Pers.) Fr.
  micans (Fr.) Berthier
    (=*Pistillaria micans* Fr.)
  phacorrhiza (Reichard) Fr.
  pusilla (Fr.) J. Schröt.
    (=*Pistillaria pusilla* Fr.)
  [*sclerotioides* (Pers.) Fr. sensu Corner]
  setipes (Grev.) Berthier
    (=*candida* Fr.)
    (=*grevillei* Fr.)
  [*uncialis* (Grev.) Berthier]
    (=*Pistillaria uncialis* (Grev.) Costantin & Dufour)

CERATOBASIDIALES

Thanatephorus fusisporus (J. Schröt.) Hauerslev & P. Roberts)
  (=*Corticium flavescens* (Bonord.) Massee)

CORTINARIALES

[*Cortinarius flexipes* (Pers.) Fr.]
Crepidotus variabilis (Pers.) P. Kumm. (on *Rosa canina,Salix cinerea, Phragmites australis*)
Galerina clavata (Velen.) Kühner
 hypnorum (Schrank) Kühner
Gymnopilus hybridus (Fr.) Singer
Inocybe geophylla (Sowerby) P. Kumm.
 rimosa (Bull.) Kumm.
 virgatula Kühner
Naucoria 'cerodes Fr.'
 escharoides (Fr.) P. Kumm. (under *Alnus glutinosa*)
Ramicola rubi (Berk.) Watling
Tubaria furfuracea (Pers.) Gillet

DACRYMYCETALES

Calocera cornea (Batsch.) Fr. (on 'bog oak')
Dacrymyces stillatus Nees

GANODERMATALES

Ganoderma lucidum (Curtis) P. Karst. (on *Betula pubescens*)

HYMENOCHAETALES

Phellinus ferreus (Pers.) Bourd. & Galz. (on *Quercus robur*)

PORIALES

Daedaleopsis confragosa (Bolton) J. Schröt.
Laetiporus sulphureus (Bull.) Murrill (on *Salix*)
Piptoporus betulinus (Bull.) P. Karst. (on *Betula pubescens*)
Polyporus badius (Pers.) Schwein.
 squamosus Huds. (on *Salix*)
 nummularius Bull.
 varius Fr.
'Poria vulgaris Fr.'
Trametes versicolor (L.)
 (=*Coriolus versicolor* (L.) Quél.)

RUSSULALES

Lactarius tabidus Fr.
Russula violacea Quél.

STEREALES

Athelia epiphylla Pers. (on *Salix*)
Cerocorticium confluens (Fr.) Jülich & Stalpers
 (=*Corticium confluens* Fr.)
Chondrostereum purpureum (Pers.) Pouzar
Epithele typhae (Pers.) Pat.
Fibulomyces mutabilis (Bres.) Jülich
 (=*Grandinia mutabilis* (Bres.) Bourd. & Galz.)
Hyphoderma sambuci (Pers.) Jülich (on *Sambucus nigra*)
 (=*Corticium sambuci* (Pers.) Fr.)
Lagarobasidium detriticum (Bourd. & Galz.) Jülich
 (=*Peniophora detritica* Bourd. & Galz.)
 (=*Hypochnicium detriticum* (Bourd. & Galz.) Erikss. & Ryvarden)
Lindtneria trachyspora (Bourd. & Galz.) Pilat
Mycoacia uda (Fr.) Donk
Peniophora cinerea (Fr.) Cooke
 incarnata (Pers.) P. Karst.
Schizopora paradoxa (Schrad.) Donk (as *Irpex obliquus* auctt.)
Sistotrema brinkmannii (Bres.) Erikss.
Steccherinum ochraceum (Pers.) Gray
 (=*Acia denticulata* (Pers.) Bourd. & Galz.)
Stereum hirsutum (Willd.) Gray

Subulicystidium longisporum (Pat.) Parmasto
 (=*Peniophora longispora* (Pat.) Höhn. & Litsch.)

THELEPHORALES

Pseudotomentella mucidula (P. Karst.) Höhn. & Litsch.
 (=*Hypochnus roseogriseus* Wakef. & A. Pearson)
Tomentella cladii Wakef.
 fusca (Pers.) Schröt.
 punicea (Alb. & Schwein.) J. Schröt.
 (=*granulosus* (Peck) Burt)

TREMELLALES

Microsebacina fugacissima (Bourd. & Galz.) P. Roberts
 (=*Sebacina fugacissima* Bourd. & Galz.)
Myxarium nucleatum Wallr.
 (=*Exidia nucleata* (Schwein.) Rea)
Tremella mesenterica Retz. ex Fr.

TELIOMYCETES

UREDINALES (rust fungi)

Coleosporium tussilaginis (Pers.) Lév.
 (=*rhinanthacearum* Lév.)
 (=*senecionis* Fr.)
 (=*sonchi* Lév.)
Melampsora capraearum Thüm.
Melampsorella symphyti Bubák (on *Symphytum officinale*)
Phragmidium mucronatum (Pers.) Schldtl.
 (=*disciflorum* J. James)
 violaceum (Schultz) G. Winter (on *Rubus ulmifolius*)
Puccinia angelicae (Schum.) Fuckel (on *Peucedanum palustre*)
 (=*P. bullata* (Pers.) Schröt.)
calcitrapae DC.
 (=*centaureae* DC.)
 (=*cirsii* Lasch)
 caricina DC. (on *Ribes nigrum*)
 cnici-oleracei Pers.
 coronata Corda (on *Dactylis glomerata*)
 (=*lolii* Nielsen)
 glechomatis DC.
 graminis Pers. (on *Dactylis glomerata*)
 hieracii H. Mart.
 (=*taraxaci* Plowr.)
 var. *hypochaeridis* (Oudem.) Jørst.
 (=*hypochaeridis* Oudem.)
 magnusiana Körn.
 malvacearum Mont. (on *Malva sylvestris*)
 menthae Pers.
 phragmitis (Schumach.) Körn.
 poarum Nielsen
 pulverulenta Grev.
 punctiformis (F. Strauss) Röhl.
 (=*obtegens* Tul.)
 recondita Roberge & Desm.
 (=*bromina* Erikss.)
 (=*holcina* Erikss.)
 (=*persistens* Plowr.)
 scirpi DC. (on *Schoenoplectus lacustris*)
 sessilis J. Schröt.
 (=*orchidearum-phalaridis* Kleb.)
Triphragmium ulmariae (DC.) Link
Uromyces junci (Desm.) Tul.
 polygoni-aviculariae (Pers.) P. Karst.
 (=*polygoni* (Rabenh.) Fuckel)
 rumicis (Schumach.) G. Winter
 viciae-fabae (Pers.) J. Schröt.
 (=*fabae* (Grev.) de Bary)

USTOMYCETES

USTILAGINALES (smut fungi)

Doassansia sagittariae (Westend.) C. Fisch.
Tilletia menieri Har. & Patt. (on *Phalaris arundinacea*)
Urocystis anemones (Pers.) G. Winter
Ustilago avenae (Pers.) Rostr.
  longissima (Sowerby) Meyen

'Gasteromycetes' (puff balls, earth stars, stinkhorns)

HYMENOGASTERALES

Hymenogaster tener Berk. & Broome

ZYGOMYCOTA
(includes fungi parasitic on arthropods)

ZYGOMYCETES

KICKXELLALES

[*Coemansia pectinata* Bainier]

MUCORALES

Absidia cylindrospora Hagem
  glauca Hagem
Mortierella isabellina Oudem. & Koning
  minutissima Tiegh.
  ramanniana (Möll.) Linnemann
    (=*Mucor ramannianus* (Möll.)
  silvaticus Hagem
  spinosus Tiegh.
Phycomyces nitens Kunze
Pilobolus crystallinus (F. H. Wigg.) Tode (from deer droppings)
Rhizopus nigricans Ehrenb.

DEUTEROMYCOTA
(Deuteromycetes, mitosporic, or conidial fungi)

Actinothyrium graminis Kunze (on *Molinia caerulea*)
Alternaria alternata (Fr.) Keissl. (on *Dactylis glomerata*)
  tenuissuma (Kunze) Wiltshire (on *D. glomerata*)
Aspergillus amstelodami (L. Mangin) Thom & Church
  fischeri Wehmer
  nidulans (Eidam) G. Winter
  sydowi (Bainier & Sart.) Thom & Church
  terreus Thom
  versicolor (Vuill.) Tirab.
Botryosporium longibrachiatum (Oudem.) Maire
  pulchrum Corda
Botrytis cinerea Pers.
  rosea Link
[*Cephalosporium acremonium* Corda]
Cladosporium herbarum (Pers.) Link
Codinaea britannica M. B. Ellis (on *Filipendula ulmaria* and *Rubus*)
  fertilis Hughes & Kendrick (on *Viburnum opulus*)
Cylindrocarpon destructans (Zinssm.) Scholten
    (=*radicicola* Wollenw.)
Deightoniella arundinaceum (Corda) Sacc.
    (=*Napicladium arundinaceum* (Corda) S. Hughes)
Dendryphion comosum Wallr. (on *Urtica*)
Doratomyces stemonitis (Pers). F. J. Morton & G. Sm.
    (=*Cephalotrichum* (=*Stysanus*) *stemonites*)

Fusarium culmorum (W. G. Sm.) Sacc.
Fusidium griseum Link (on *Quercus robur*)
Geomyces cretaceus Traaen
Gliocladium catenulatum J. C. Gilman & E. V. Abbott
  roseum (Link) Bainier
Gliomastix murorum var. *felina* (Marchal) S. Hughes
Haplariopsis fagicola Oudem. (on *Quercus robur*)
Helicomyces roseus Link (on *Filipendula ulmaria* and *Rubus*)
Menispora ciliata Corda (on *Quercus robur*)
Paecilomyces marquandii (Massee) S. Hughes
    (=*Spicaria violacea* E. V. Abbott)
  varioti Bainier
Papularia arundinis (Corda) Fr.
Penicillium albidum Sopp
  claviforme Bainier
  expansum Link
  frequentans Westling
  funiculosum Thom
  nigricans Bainier
  phoeniceum T. H. Beyma
  spinulosum Thom
  thomii Maire
  variabile Wehmer
  wortmanni Klöcker
Periconia cookei E. W. Mason & M. B. Ellis
Phaeosaria clematidis (Fuckel) S. Hughes
Phoma complanata (Tode) Desm.
Pleurophragmium parvisporum (Preuss.) Hol.-Jech. (on *Filipendula ulmaria*)
Polyscytalum berkeleyi M. B. Ellis (on *Urtica*)
Ramularia rubella (Bon.) Nannf.
  succisae Sacc. (on *Succisa pratensis*)
Scopulariopsis brevicaulis (Sacc.) Bainier
Sepedonium sepedonioides (Harz) A. L. Sm.
Stachybotrys atra Corda
Torula herbarum (Pers.) Link
Trichoderma viride Pers.
Trisporium elegans Corda
Verticillium (=*Acrostalagmus*) *cinnabarinus* (Corda) Reinke & Berthold
Volutella ciliata (Alb. & Schwein.) Fr.

MYCOPHYCOPHYTA
(lichens)

Lichens are a self-supporting association of a fungus and an alga or cyanobacterium, a biological but not a systematic group. The scientific names are considered to refer to the fungal partner alone. The classification of lichens is therefore within the Fungi kingdom. However, although most authorities would not regard them as a separate phylum, this is retained here for ease of reference.

Lists: Laundon (1973, 1991) Check list: Purvis, Coppins & James (1993)
Conservation status: Church *et. al.* (1996)

Buellia punctata (Hoffm.) A. Massal.
Caloplaca citrina (Hoffm.) Th.Fr.
  decipiens (Arnold) Blomb. & Forssel
  saxicola (Hoffm.) Nordin
Candelariella aurella (Hoffm.) Zahlbr.
  xanthostigma (Ach.) Lett.
Cladonia fimbriata (L.) Fr.
Diploicia canescens (Dicks.) A. Massal.
    (=*Buellia canescens* (Dicks.) De Not.)
Evernia prunastri (L.) Ach.
Hypogymnia physodes (L.) Nyl.
Lecanora campestris (Schaer.) Hue
  chlarotera Nyl.
    (=*chlarona* (Ach.) Nyl.)

9

conizaeoides Nyl. ex Cromb.
dispersa (Pers.) Sommerf.
expallens Ach.
muralis (Schreb.) Rabenh.
Lecidella stigmatea (Ach.) Hertel & Leuckert
Lepraria incana (L.) Ach.
Parmelia caperata (L.) Ach.
  glabratula (Lamy) Nyl.
  revoluta Flörke
  subaurifera Nyl.
  subrudecta Nyl.
  sulcata Taylor
Phaeophyscia orbicularis (Neck.) Poetsch
    (=*Physcia orbicularis* (Neck.) Poetsch)
Phlyctis argena (Spreng.) Flot.
Physcia adscendens (Th.Fr.) H. Olivier
  caesia (Hoffm.) Fürnr.
  tenella (Scop.) DC.
Physconia grisea (Lam.) Poelt
Placynthiella icmalea (Ach.) Coppins & P. James
Ramalina farinacea (L.) Ach.
Rinodina exigua Gray
  gennarii Bagl.
    (=*subexigua* (Nyl.) H. Olivier)
Trapeliopsis granulosa (Hoffm.) Lumbsch
    (=*Lecidea granulosa* (Hoffm.) Ach.)
Usnea subfloridana Stirt.
Xanthoria calcicola Oxner
  candelaria (L.) Th.Fr.
  parietina (L.) Th.Fr.
  polycarpa (Hoffm.) Th.Fr. ex Rieber

PLANTAE

BRYOPHYTA
(bryophytes)

List: J. M. Lock
Classification and nomenclature: Smith (1978, 1990); revised after Hill *et al.* (1991-94); Conservation status; Palmer *et al.* (1997); Hodgetts *et al.* (1996); Stewart & Church (in press)

* Not seen since 1975

HEPATICOPSIDA
(Hepaticae; liverworts)

CALYPOGEIACEAE
Calypogeia fissa (L.) Raddi

CEPHALOZIACEAE
Cephalozia bicuspidata (L.) Dumort

CEPHALOZIELLACEAE
Cephaloziella sp.*

GEOCALYCACEAE
Lophocolea bidentata (L.) Dumort
  heterophylla (Schrad.) Dumort
Chiloscyphus polyanthos (L.) Corda var. *pallescens* (Ehrh. ex Hoffm.) Hartm.

PLAGIOCHILACEAE
Plagiochila asplenioides (L. emend. Taylor) Dumort*

RADULACEAE
Radula complanata (L.) Dumort

FRULLANIACEAE
Frullania dilatata (L.) Dumort

PELLIACEAE
Pellia epiphylla (L.) Corda*
  endiviifolia (Dicks.) Dumort*

ANEURACEAE
Aneura pinguis (L.) Dumort
Riccardia multifida (L.) Gray*
  chamedryfolia (With.) Grolle

METZGERIACEAE
Metzgeria furcata (L.) Dumort
  fruticulosa (Dicks.) A. Evans

MARCHANTIACEAE
Marchantia polymorpha L.*

RICCIACEAE
Ricciocarpos natans (L.) Corda (N)
Riccia fluitans L. emend. Lorb.

SPHAGNOPSIDA
(sphagnum mosses)

SPHAGNACEAE
Sphagnum palustre L.
  squarrosum Crome
  fimbriatum Wilson
  subnitens Russow & Warnst.
  recurvum P. Beauv.

BRYOPSIDA
(mosses)

TETRAPHIDACEAE
Tetraphis pellucida Hedw.*

POLYTRICHACEAE
Polytrichum longisetum Sw. ex Brid.
  formosum Hedw.
  commune Hedw.
  juniperinum Hedw.*
Atrichum undulatum (Hedw.) P. Beauv.

DICRANACEAE
Ceratodon purpureus (Hedw.) Brid.
Dicranella heteromalla (Hedw.) Schimp.
Dicranoweisia cirrata (Hedw.) Lindb. ex Milde
Dicranum scoparium Hedw.
Campylopus pyriformis (Schultz) Brid.
  paradoxus Wilson
  introflexus (Hedw.) Brid.
  brevipilus Bruch, Schimp. & W. Gumbel*

LEUCOBRYACEAE
Leucobryum glaucum (Hedw.) Ångstr.

FISSIDENTACEAE
Fissidens incurvus Starke ex Röhl.
  taxifolius Hedw.
  adianthoides Hedw.

POTTIACEAE
Tortula virescens (De Not.) De Not. (N)
  laevipila (Brid.) Schwägr.
  muralis Hedw.
Barbula convoluta Hedw.
  tophacea (Brid.) Mitt.

FUNARIACEAE
Funaria hygrometrica Hedw.
Physcomitrium pyriforme (Hedw.) Brid.

BRYACEAE
Orthodontium lineare Schwägr.
Leptobryum pyriforme (Hedw.) Wilson*
Pohlia nutans (Hedw.) Lindb.
Bryum capillare Hedw.
  subelegans Kindb.
    (=*flaccidum*)
  pseudotriquetrum (Hedw.) Schwägr. var. *bimum* (Brid.) Lilj. (N)
  caespiticium Hedw. var. *caespiticium*
  bicolor Dicks.
  argenteum Hedw.
  klinggraeffi Schimp.
  rubens Mitt.

MNIACEAE

Mnium hornum Hedw.
Rhizomnium punctatum (Hedw.) T. J. Kop.
Plagiomnium affine T. J. Kop.
  elatum (Bruch, Schimp. & W. Gumbel) T. J. Kop.
  ellipticum (Brid.) T. J. Kop.
  undulatum(Hedw.) T. J. Kop.

AULACOMNIACEAE

Aulacomnium palustre (Hedw.) Schwägr.
  androgynum (Hedw.) Schwägr.

ORTHOTRICHACEAE

Orthotrichum lyelli Hook & Taylor
  affine Brid.
  diaphanum Brid.
  pulchellum Brunt.
Ulota crispa (Hedw.) Brid. var. *norvegica* (Gronvall) A. J. E.
  Sm. & M. O. Hill

FONTINALACEAE

Fontinalis antipyretica Hedw.*

CLIMACIACEAE

Climacium dendroides (Hedw.) F. Weber & D. Mohr

CRYPHAEACEAE

Cryphaea heteromalla (Hedw.) D. Mohr

HOOKERIACEAE

Hookeria lucens (Hedw.) Sm.*

LESKEACEAE

Leskea polycarpa Hedw.

THUIDIACEAE

Thuidium tamariscinum (Hedw.) Bruch, Schimp. & W.
  Gumbel

AMBLYSTEGIACEAE

Cratoneuron filicinum (Hedw.) Spruce
  commutatum (Hedw.) Roth*
Campylium stellatum (Hedw.) Lange & C. E. O. Jensen var.
  stellatum
  var. *protensum* (Brid.) Bryhn
  polygamum (Bruch, Schimp. & W. Gumbel) Lange & C. E.
  O. Jensen (N)
  elodes (Lindb.) Kindb. (N)
Amblystegium serpens (Hedw.) Bruch, Schimp. & W. Gumbel
  varium (Hedw.) Lindb.*
  riparium (Hedw.) Bruch, Schimp. & W. Gumbel
Drepanocladus aduncus (Hedw.) Warnst.
Calliergon cuspidatum (Hedw.) Kindb.

BRACHYTHECIACEAE

Isothecium myurum Brid.*
Homalothecium sericeum (Hedw.) Bruch, Schimp. & W.
  Gumbel
Brachythecium salebrosum (F. Weber & D. Mohr) Bruch,
  Schimp. & W. Gumbel (N)
  rutabulum (Hedw.) Bruch, Schimp. & W. Gumbel
  rivulare Bruch, Schimp. & W. Gumbel
  velutinum (Hedw.) Bruch, Schimp. & W. Gumbel
Pseudoscleropodium purum (Hedw.) Fleisch.
Cirriphyllum piliferum (Hedw.) Grout
Rhynchostegium confertum (Dicks.) Bruch, Schimp. & W.
  Gumbel

Eurhynchium striatum (Hedw.) Schimp.
  praelongum (Hedw.) Bruch, Schimp. & W. Gumbel
  swartzii (Turner) Curn.
  speciosum (Brid.) Jur.

PLAGIOTHECIACEAE

Plagiothecium denticulatum (Hedw.) Bruch, Schimp. & W.
  Gumbel var. *denticulatum*
  curvifolium Schlieph.
  nemorale (Mitt.) A. Jaeger
  undulatum (Hedw.) Bruch, Schimp. & W. Gumbel

HYPNACEAE

Hypnum cupressiforme Hedw. var. *cupressiforme*
  var. *resupinatum* (Taylor) Schimp.
  jutlandicum Holmen & E. Warncke
Ctenidium molluscum (Hedw.) Mitt.
Rhytidiadelphus squarrosus (Hedw.) Warnst.
  loreus (Hedw.) Warnst.
Pleurozium schreberi (Brid.) Mitt.
Hylocomium brevirostre (Brid.) Bruch, Schimp. & W. Gumbel
  splendens (Hedw.) Bruch, Schimp. & W. Gumbel

VASCULAR PLANTS

List: J. O. Mountford, J. M. Lock, S. M. Walters and T. J. Bennett (1994)

Classification and nomenclature: Stace (1991)

Key:
I Introduced or planted at Wicken Fen
A Other species not native at Wicken Fen
F Recorded only on fallow arable land
* Not recorded since 1980, presumed extinct
† Not recorded since 1980, possibly overlooked

Conservation status: Perring & Farrell (1983); Wigginton (1999)

PTERIDOPHYTA

EQUISETOPSIDA
(horsetails)

EQUISETACEAE
Equisetum fluviatile L. (Water Horsetail)†
  arvense L. (Field Horsetail)†
  palustre L. (Marsh Horsetail)†

PTEROPSIDA
(ferns)

OPHIOGLOSSACEAE
Ophioglossum vulgatum L. (Adder's-tongue)

THELYPTERIDACEAE
Thelypteris palustris Schott (Marsh Fern) (**N**)

WOODSIACEAE
Athyrium filix-femina (L.) Roth (Lady-fern)

DRYOPTERIDACEAE
Dryopteris filix-mas (L.) Schott (Male-fern)
  affinis ssp. *borreri* (Newman) Fraser-Jenk. (Scaly Male-fern)
  carthusiana (Vill.) H. P. Fuchs (Narrow Buckler-fern)
  dilatata (Hoffm.) A. Gray (Broad Buckler-fern)

AZOLLACEAE
Azolla filiculoides Lam. (Water Fern) **A**†

SPERMATOPHYTA
(seed plants)

PINOPSIDA
(Gymnospermae; conifers)

PINACEAE
Pinus sylvestris L. (Scots Pine) **I**

MAGNOLIOPSIDA
(Angiospermae)

Magnoliidae
(dicotyledons)

NYMPHAEACEAE
Nymphaea alba L. (White Water-lily)
Nuphar lutea (L.) Sm. (Yellow Water-lily)

CERATOPHYLLACEAE
Ceratophyllum demersum L. (Rigid Hornwort)

RANUNCULACEAE
Caltha palustris L. (Marsh-marigold)
Ranunculus acris L. (Meadow Buttercup)
  bulbosus (Bulbous Buttercup)†
  repens L. (Creeping Buttercup)
  sceleratus L. (Celery-leaved Buttercup)
  lingua L. (Greater Spearwort)
  flammula L. (Lesser Spearwort)
  ficaria L. (Lesser Celandine)
  trichophyllus Chaix (Thread-leaved Water-crowfoot)
  fluitans Lam. (River Water-crowfoot)†
  circinatus Sibth. (Fan-leaved Water-crowfoot)
Thalictrum flavum L. (Common Meadow-rue)

PAPAVERACEAE
Papaver somniferum L. (Opium Poppy) **I**
  rhoeas L. (Common Poppy)

FUMARIACEAE
Fumaria officinalis ssp. *wirtgenii* (Koch) Arcang. (Common Fumitory)

ULMACEAE
Ulmus procera Salisb. (English Elm)
  minor Mill. Anglianae group (East Anglian Small-leaved Elm)
  minor Mill. Coritanae group (Coritanian Elm)

URTICACEAE
Urtica dioica L. (Common Nettle)
  ssp. *galeopsifolia* (Wierzb. ex Opiz) Chrtek ('Fen Nettle')
  urens L. (Small Nettle) **F**

MYRICACEAE
Myrica gale L. (Bog-myrtle)

FAGACEAE
Quercus robur L. (Pedunculate Oak)

BETULACEAE (=*CORYLACEAE*)
Betula pendula Roth (Silver Birch)
  pubescens Ehrh. (Downy Birch)
Alnus glutinosa (L.) Gaertn. (Alder) **I**

CHENOPODIACEAE
Chenopodium bonus-henricus L. (Good-King-Henry) **A***
  rubrum L. (Red Goosefoot)
  polyspermum L. (Many-seeded Goosefoot)
  hybridum L. (Maple-leaved Goosefoot) **AF**
  ficifolium Smith (Fig-leaved Goosefoot)
  album L. (Fat-hen)

CARYOPHYLLACEAE

Stellaria media (L.) Vill. (Common Chickweed)
  palustris Retz. (Marsh Stitchwort)†
Cerastium fontanum Baumg. ssp. *vulgare* (Hartm.) Greuter & Burdet (Common Mouse-ear)
Myosoton aquaticum (L.) Moench (Water Chickweed)
Sagina nodosa (L.) Fenzl (Knotted Pearlwort)†
Lychnis flos-cuculi L. (Ragged-Robin)
Silene noctiflora L. (Night-flowering Catchfly) **F**
  latifolia Poir. (White Campion)

POLYGONACEAE

Persicaria amphibia (L.) Gray (Amphibious Bistort)
  maculosa Gray (Redshank)
  lapathifolia (L.) Gray (Pale Persicaria)
  hydropiper (L). Spach (Water-pepper)*
Polygonum aviculare L. (Knotgrass)
Fallopia convolvulus (L.) A. Love (Black-bindweed)
Fagopyrum esculentum Moench (Buckwheat) **A***
Rumex acetosa L. (Common Sorrel)
  hydrolapathum Huds. (Water Dock)
  crispus L. (Curled Dock)
  obtusifolius L. (Broad-leaved Dock)†
  palustris Sm. (Marsh Dock)
  maritimus L. (Golden Dock)*

CLUSIACEAE (=*HYPERICACEAE*)

Hypericum tetrapterum Fr. (Square-stalked St John's-wort)

MALVACEAE

Malva sylvestris L. (Common Mallow)

DROSERACEAE

Drosera rotundifolia L. (Round-leaved Sundew)*

VIOLACEAE

Viola hirta L. (Hairy Violet)
  riviniana Rchb. (Common Dog-violet)
  canina L. ssp. *montana* (L.) Hartm. (Heath Dog-violet) (**EN**)
  persicifolia Schreb. (Fen Violet) (**EN**)

CUCURBITACEAE

Bryonia dioica Jacq. (White Bryony)

SALICACEAE

Populus × *canescens* (Aiton) Sm. (*P. alba* L. × *P. tremula* L.) (Grey Poplar) **A**
  tremula L. (Aspen)
    var. *villosa* (Láng) Syme†
  × *canadensis* Moench (*P. deltoides* Marsh. × *P. nigra* L.) (Hybrid Black-poplar) **A**
Salix pentandra L. (Bay Willow) **I**
  fragilis L. (Crack Willow)
  alba L. (White Willow)
  purpurea L. (Purple Willow)
  viminalis L. (Osier)
  ×*calodendron* Wimm. (*S. caprea* × *S. cinerea* × *S. viminalis*) (Holme Willow)*
  caprea L. (Goat Willow)
  cinerea L. ssp. *cinerea* (Grey Willow)
  repens var. *fusca* Wimm. & Grab. (Creeping Willow)
  × *subsericea* Doell (*S. cinerea* × *S. repens*)†

BRASSICACEAE (=*CRUCIFERACEAE*)

Sisymbrium altissimum L. (Tall Rocket) **A**
  officinale (L.) Scop. (Hedge Mustard)

Descurainia sophia (L.) Webb ex Prantl (Flixweed) **F**
Alliaria petiolata (M. Bieb.) Cavara & Grande (Garlic Mustard)
Erysimum cheiranthoides L. (Treacle Mustard)
Barbarea vulgaris R. Br. (Winter-cress)
Rorippa nasturtium-aquaticum (L.) Hayek (Water-cress)†
  microphylla (Boenn.) Hyl. ex A. Löve & D. Löve (Narrow-fruited Water-cress)
  palustris (L.) Besser (Marsh Yellow-cress)
  amphibia ((L.) Besser (Great Yellow-cress)*
Cardamine pratensis L. (Cuckooflower)
Arabis hirsuta (L.) Scop. (Hairy Rock-cress)*
Capsella bursa-pastoris (L.) Medik. (Shepherd's-purse)
Lepidium campestre (L.) R. Br. (Field Pepperwort)*
Coronopus squamatus (Forssk.) Asch. (Swine-cress)
Diplotaxis muralis (L.) DC. (Annual Wall-rocket)
Brassica nigra (L.) W. D. J. Koch (Black Mustard)
Sinapis arvensis L. (Charlock)
  alba L. (White Mustard) **A***

RESEDACEAE

Reseda luteola L. (Weld)
  lutea L. (Wild Mignonette)

PRIMULACEAE

Primula veris L. (Cowslip)
Hottonia palustris L. (Water-violet)
Lysimachia nummularia L. (Creeping-Jenny)†
  vulgaris L. (Yellow Loosestrife)
Anagallis tenella (L.) L. (Bog Pimpernel)*
  arvensis L. (Scarlet Pimpernel)
Samolus valerandi L. (Brookweed)

GROSSULARIACEAE

Ribes rubrum L. (Red Currant)
  nigrum L. (Black Currant)

ROSACEAE

Filipendula ulmaria (L.) Maxim. (Meadowsweet)
Rubus idaeus L. (Raspberry)
  fruticosus L. agg. (Bramble)
  conjungens (Bab.) W. M. Rogers (Bramble)†
  warrenii Sudre (Bramble)†
  caesius L. (Dewberry)
Potentilla palustris (L.) Scop. (Marsh Cinquefoil)*
  anserina L. (Silverweed)
  norvegica L. (Ternate-leaved Cinquefoil)*
  erecta (L.) Raeusch. (Tormentil)
  reptans L. (Creeping Cinquefoil)
Fragaria vesca L. (Wild Strawberry)†
Geum urbanum L. (Wood Avens; Herb-Bennet)
Agrimonia eupatoria L. (Agrimony)
Rosa canina L. (Common Dog-rose)
  × *dumalis* Bechst. (*R. canina* × *R. caesia* Sm.)
Prunus spinosa L. (Blackthorn)
Sorbus aucuparia L. (Rowan)
Crataegus monogyna Jacq. (Hawthorn)
  × *macrocarpa* Hegetschw. (*C. monogyna* × *C. laevigata* (Poir.) DC.)†

FABACEAE (=*LEGUMINOSAE*)

Lotus corniculatus L. (Common Bird's-foot-trefoil)
  pedunculatus Cav. (Greater Bird's-foot-trefoil)†
Vicia cracca L. (Tufted Vetch)
Lathyrus palustris L. (Marsh Pea) (**N**)
  pratensis L. (Meadow Vetchling)
Medicago lupulina L. (Black Medick)
Trifolium repens L. (White Clover)
  fragiferum L. (Strawberry Clover)

pratense L. (Red Clover)†
ochroleucon Huds. (Sulphur Clover)* (N)

HALORAGACEAE

Myriophyllum verticillatum L. (Whorled Water-milfoil) (N)
spicatum L. (Spiked Water-milfoil)

LYTHRACEAE

Lythrum salicaria L. (Purple-loosestrife)

THYMELAEACEAE

Daphne mezereum L. (Mezereon) A

ONAGRACEAE

Epilobium hirsutum L. (Great Willowherb)
parviflorum Schreb. (Hoary Willowherb)
montanum L. (Broadleaved Willowherb)
tetragonum L. (Squarestalked Willowherb)
ciliatum Raf. (American Willowherb) A
ciliatum × E. *parviflorum*†
Chamerion angustifolium (L.) Holub (Rosebay Willowherb)
Circaea lutetiana L. (Enchanter's-nightshade)†

CORNACEAE

Cornus sanguinea L. (Dogwood)

EUPHORBIACEAE

Euphorbia helioscopia L. (Sun Spurge)

RHAMNACEAE

Rhamnus cathartica L. (Buckthorn)
Frangula alnus Mill. (Alder Buckthorn)

LINACEAE

Linum usitatissimum L. (Flax) F
catharticum L. (Fairy Flax)

POLYGALACEAE

Polygala vulgaris L. (Common Milkwort)

GERANIACEAE

Geranium dissectum L. (Cut-leaved Crane's-bill)
robertianum L. (Herb-Robert)

ARALIACEAE

Hedera helix L. (Ivy)

APIACEAE (=*UMBELLIFERAE*)

Hydrocotyle vulgaris L. (Marsh Pennywort)
Anthriscus sylvestris (L.) Hoffm. (Cow Parsley)
Sium latifolium L. (Greater Water-parsnip)* (N)
Berula erecta (Huds.) Coville (Lesser Water-parsnip)
Oenanthe fistulosa L. (Tubular Water-dropwort)
lachenalii C. C. Gmel. (Parsley Water-dropwort)
fluviatilis (Bab.) Coleman (River Water-dropwort)
aquatica (L.) Poiret (Fineleaved Water-dropwort)
Aethusa cynapium L. (Fool's Parsley)
Conium maculatum L. (Hemlock)
Apium graveolens L. (Wild Celery)*
nodiflorum (L.) Lag. (Fool's Water-cress)
inundatum (L.) Rchb. fil. (Lesser Marshwort)*
Angelica sylvestris L. (Wild Angelica)
Peucedanum palustre (L.) Moench (Milk-parsley) (N)
Pastinaca sativa L. (Wild Parsnip)
Heracleum sphondylium L. (Hogweed)
Torilis japonica (Houtt.) DC. (Upright Hedge-parsley)

SOLANACEAE

Solanum nigrum L. (Black Nightshade)
dulcamara L. (Bittersweet)
tuberosum L. (Potato) FA

CONVOLVULACEAE

Calystegia sepium (L.) R. Br. (Hedge Bindweed)

MENYANTHACEAE

Menyanthes trifoliata L. (Bogbean)*

BORAGINACEAE

Symphytum officinale L. (Common Comfrey)
Myosotis scorpioides L. (Water Forget-me-not)
laxa Lehm. (Tufted Forget-me-not))
arvensis (L.) Hill (Field Forget-me-not)

VERBENACEAE

Verbena officinalis L. (Vervain)*

LAMIACEAE (=*LABIATAE*)

Stachys sylvatica L. (Hedge Woundwort)
palustris L. (Marsh Woundwort)
Lamium album L. (White Dead-nettle)
purpureum L. (Red Dead-nettle)
Galeopsis speciosa Mill. (Large-flowered Hemp-nettle)†
tetrahit L. (Common Hemp-nettle)†
bifida Boenn. (Bifid or Lesser Hemp-nettle) F
Scutellaria galericulata L. (Skullcap)
Ajuga reptans L. (Bugle)
Glechoma hederacea L. (Ground-ivy)
Prunella vulgaris L. (Selfheal)
Lycopus europaeus L. (Gypsywort)
Mentha arvensis L. (Corn Mint)
× *verticillata* L. (M. *arvensis* × M. *aquatica*) (Whorled Mint)†
aquatica L. (Water Mint)

HIPPURIDACEAE

Hippuris vulgaris L. (Mare's-tail)

CALLITRICHACEAE

Callitriche stagnalis Scop. (Common Water-starwort)
platycarpa Kütz. (Various-leaved Water-starwort)
obtusangula Le Gall (Blunt-fruited Water-starwort)

PLANTAGINACEAE

Plantago major L. (Greater Ribwort)
lanceolata L. (Ribwort Plantain)

OLEACEAE

Fraxinus excelsior L. (Ash)
Ligustrum vulgare L. (Privet)

SCROPHULARIACEAE

Scrophularia auriculata L. (Water Figwort)
Chaenorhinum minus (L.) Lange (Small Toadflax) F
Kickxia elatine (L.) Dumort. (Sharp-leaved Fluellen)
spuria (L.) Dumort. (Round-leaved Fluellen)
Linaria vulgaris Mill. (Common Toadflax)†
Veronica beccabunga L. (Brooklime)
anagallis-aquatica L. (Blue Water-speedwell)*
catenata Pennell (Pink Water-speedwell)
arvensis L. (Wall Speedwell) F
agrestis L. (Green Field-speedwell) F
persica Poir. (Common Field-speedwell)

15

Flowering plants

Odontites vernus (Bellardi) Dumort. (Red Bartsia)
Rhinanthus minor L. ssp. *stenophyllus* (Schur) O. Schwarz (Yellow-rattle)
Pedicularis palustris L. (Marsh Lousewort)*

LENTIBULARIACEAE

Utricularia vulgaris L. (Greater Bladderwort)
  minor L. (Lesser Bladderwort)*

CAMPANULACEAE

Legousia hybrida (L.) Delarbre (Venus's-looking-glass)†

RUBIACEAE

Galium uliginosum L. (Fen Bedstraw)
  palustre L. (Common Marsh-bedstraw)
  verum L. (Lady's Bedstraw)†
  × *pomeranicum* Retz. (*G. verum* × *G. mollugo*)†
  mollugo L. (Hedge-bedstraw)
  aparine L. (Cleavers)

CAPRIFOLIACEAE

Sambucus nigra L. (Elder)
Viburnum opulus L. (Guelder-rose)
  lantana L. (Wayfaring-tree)*

VALERIANACEAE

Valeriana officinalis L. (Common Valerian)
  dioica L. (Marsh Valerian)

DIPSACACEAE

Dipsacus fullonum L. (Wild Teasel)
  pilosus L. (Small Teasel)†
Knautia arvensis (L.) Coult. (Field Scabious)†
Succisa pratensis Moench (Devil's-bit Scabious)

ASTERACEAE (=COMPOSITAE)

Arctium lappa L. (Greater Burdock)
  minus (Hill) Bernh. ssp. *pubens* (Bab.) Arenes (Lesser Burdock)
  × *nothum* (Ruhmer) J. Weiss (*A. lappa* × *A. minus*)†
Carduus crispus L. (Welted Thistle)
  nutans L. (Musk Thistle)
Cirsium vulgare (Savi) Ten. (Spear Thistle)
  dissectum (L.) Hill (Meadow Thistle)
  palustre (L.) Scop. (Marsh Thistle)
  arvense (L.) Scop. (Creeping Thistle)
Centaurea nigra L. (Common Knapweed)
Lapsana communis L. (Nipplewort)
Hypochoeris radicata L. (Cat's-ear)†
Leontodon autumnalis L. (Autumn Hawkbit)
  hispidus L. (Rough Hawkbit)†
  saxatilis Lam. (Lesser Hawkbit)†
Picris echioides L. (Bristly Oxtongue)
Tragopogon pratensis L. (Goat's-beard)
Sonchus arvensis L. (Perennial Sow-thistle)
  oleraceus L. (Smooth Sow-thistle)
  asper (L.) Hill (Prickly Sow-thistle)
Lactuca serriola L. (Prickly Lettuce)†
Taraxacum officinale Wigg. agg. (Dandelion)
  canoviride H. Lindb. ex Puolanne†
  ekmanii Dahlst.†
  haematicum G. E. Haglund†
  hamatum Raunk.†
  laciniosum Dahlst.†
  landmarkii Dahlst.†
  litorale Raunk.†
  longisquameum H. Lindb.†
  marklundii Palmgr.†

  naevosum Dahlst.†
  palustre (Lyons) Symons (Marsh Dandelion)
  pannucium Dahlst.†
  sublaeticolor Dahlst.†
Crepis capillaris (L.) Wallr. (Smooth Hawk's-beard)
  vesicaria L. (Beaked Hawk's-beard) A
Gnaphalium uliginosum L. (Marsh Cudweed)†
Pulicaria dysenterica (L.) Bernh. (Common Fleabane)
Aster novi-belgii L. (Confused Michaelmas-daisy) A
Conyza canadensis (L.) Cronquist (Canadian Fleabane) A
Bellis perennis L. (Daisy)
Artemisia vulgaris L. (Mugwort)
Achillea millefolium L. (Yarrow)
Leucanthemum vulgare Lam. (Oxeye Daisy)
Matricaria discoidea DC. (Pineappleweed) A
Tripleurospermum inodorum (L.) Sch.-Bip. (Scentless Mayweed)
Senecio paludosus L. (Fen Ragwort) [I], 1992* (CR)
  jacobaea L. (Common Ragwort)
  aquaticus Hill (Marsh Ragwort)
  erucifolius L. (Hoary Ragwort)
  squalidus L. (Oxford Ragwort) A†
  vulgaris L. (Groundsel)
  viscosus L. (Sticky Groundsel)†
Tussilago farfara L. (Colt's-foot)
Petasites hybridus (L.) P. Gaertn., B. Mey. & Scherb. (Butterbur)*
Bidens cernua L. (Nodding Bur-marigold)*
  tripartita L. (Trifid Bur-marigold)*
Eupatorium cannabinum L. (Hemp-agrimony)

Liliidae
(Monocotyledons)

BUTOMACEAE

Butomus umbellatus L. (Flowering-rush)

ALISMATACEAE

Sagittaria sagittifolia L. (Arrowhead)
Baldellia ranunculoides (L.) Parl. (Lesser Water-plantain)
Alisma plantago-aquatica L. (Water-plantain)
  lanceolatum With. (Narrow-leaved Water-plantain)

HYDROCHARITACEAE

Hydrocharis morsus-ranae L. (Frogbit)*
Stratiotes aloides L. (Water-soldier)* (N)
Elodea canadensis Michx. (Canadian Waterweed) A
  nuttallii (Planch.) H. St John (Nuttall's Waterweed) A

JUNCAGINACEAE

Triglochin palustre L. (Marsh Arrowgrass)

POTAMOGETONACEAE

Potamogeton natans L. (Broad-leaved Pondweed)
  coloratus Hornem. (Fen Pondweed) (N)
  lucens L. (Shining Pondweed)
  gramineus L. (Various-leaved Pondweed)*
  × *salicifolius* Wolfg. (*P. lucens* × *P. perfoliatus*) (Willow-leaved Pondweed)
  praelongus Wulfen (Long-stalked Pondweed)
  perfoliatus L. (Perfoliate Pondweed)
  friesii Rupr. (Flat-stalked Pondweed)
  pusillus L. (Lesser Pondweed)
  berchtoldii Fieber (Small Pondweed)
  crispus L. (Curled Pondweed)
  pectinatus L. (Fennel Pondweed)
Groenlandia densa (L.) Fourr. (Opposite-leaved Pondweed)*

ZANNICHELLIACEAE
Zannichellia palustris L. (Horned Pondweed)

ARACEAE
Arum maculatum L. (Lords-and-Ladies)

LEMNACEAE
Spirodela polyrhiza (L.) Schleid. (Greater Duckweed)*
Lemna gibba L. (Fat Duckweed)†
  minor L. (Common Duckweed)
  trisulca L. (Ivy-leaved Duckweed)
  minuta Kunth (Least Duckweed) A

JUNCACEAE
Juncus tenuis Willd. (Slender Rush) A
  compressus Jacq. (Round-fruited Rush)
  bufonius L. (Toad Rush)
  subnodulosus Schrank (Blunt-flowered Rush)
  articulatus L. (Jointed Rush)
  bulbosus L. (Bulbous Rush)*
  inflexus L. (Hard Rush)
  effusus L. (Soft-rush)
Luzula multiflora (Ehrh.) Lej. (Heath Wood-rush)*

CYPERACEAE
Eriophorum angustifolium Honck. (Common Cottongrass)*
Eleocharis palustris (L.) Roem. & Schult. (Common Spike-rush)
  uniglumis (Link) Schult. (Slender Spike-rush)
  quinqueflora (Hartmann) O. Schwarz (Fewflowered Spike-rush)
  acicularis (L.) Roem. & Schult. (Needle Spike-rush)
Schoenoplectus lacustris (L.) Palla (Common Club-rush)
Isolepis setacea (L.) (Bristle Club-rush)
Schoenus nigricans L. (Black Bog-rush)*
Cladium mariscus (L.) Pohl (Great Fen-sedge)
Carex appropinquata Schum. (Fibrous Tussock-sedge) (N)
  otrubae Podp. (False Fox-sedge)
  disticha Huds. (Brown Sedge)
  hirta L. (Hairy Sedge)
  lasiocarpa Ehrh. (Slender Sedge)
  acutiformis Ehrh. (Lesser Pond-sedge)
  riparia Curtis (Greater Pond-sedge)
  pseudocyperus L. (Cyperus Sedge)
  rostrata Stokes (Bottle Sedge)*
  vesicaria L. (Bladder-sedge)*
  flacca Schreb. (Glaucous Sedge)
  panicea L. (Carnation Sedge)
  distans L. (Distant Sedge)
  hostiana DC. (Tawny Sedge)
  viridula Michx. ssp. *brachyrrhyncha* (Celak.) B. Schmid (Yellow-sedge)
  ssp. *viridula* (Yellow-sedge)
  pallescens L. (Pale Sedge)*
  elata All. (Tufted-sedge)

POACEAE (=GRAMINEAE)
Festuca pratensis Huds. (Meadow Fescue)
  arundinacea Schreb. (Tall Fescue)
  rubra L. (Red Fescue)
  × *Festulolium loliaceum* (Huds.) P. Fourn. (*Festuca pratensis* × *Lolium perenne*) (Hybrid Fescue)†
Lolium perenne L. (Perennial Rye-grass)
Briza media L. (Quaking-grass)
Poa annua L. (Annual Meadow-grass)
  trivialis L. (Rough Meadow-grass)
  pratensis L. (Smooth Meadow-grass)†
  palustris L. (Swamp Meadow-grass) A*

Dactylis glomerata L. (Cock's-foot)
Glyceria maxima (Hartm.) Holmb. (Reed Sweet-grass)
  fluitans (L.) R. Br. (Floating Sweet-grass)
  × *pedicellata* F. Towns. (*G. fluitans* × *G. notata*) (Hybrid Sweet-grass)†
  notata Chevall. (Plicate Sweet-grass)
Helictotrichon pubescens (Huds.) Pilg. (Downy Oat-grass)
Arrhenatherum elatius (L.) P. Beauv. ex J. Presl & C. Presl (False Oat-grass)
Avena fatua L. (Wild-oat) F
Trisetum flavescens (L.) P. Beauv. (Yellow Oat-grass)
Deschampsia cespitosa (L.) P. Beauv. (Tufted Hair-grass)
Holcus lanatus L. (Yorkshire-fog)
Anthoxanthum odoratum L. (Sweet Vernal-grass)
Phalaris arundinacea L. (Reed Canary-grass)
  canariensis L. (Canary-grass) F
Agrostis stolonifera L. (Creeping Bent)
Calamagrostis epigejos (L.) Roth (Wood Small-reed)
  canescens (F. H. Wigg.) Roth (Purple Small-reed)
Alopecurus pratensis L. (Meadow Foxtail)†
  geniculatus L. (Marsh Foxtail)†
  myosuroides Huds. (Black-grass)
Phleum pratense L. (Timothy)
  bertolonii DC. (Smaller Cat's-tail)
Bromus commutatus Schrad. (Meadow Brome)
  hordeaceus L. (Soft-brome)
  pseudosecalinus P. M. Sm. (Smith's Brome) A†
Bromopsis erecta (Huds.) Fourr. (Upright Brome)
Anisantha sterilis (L.) Nevski (Barren Brome)
Elytrigia repens (L.) Desv. ex Nevski (Common Couch)
Hordeum murinum L. (Wall Barley)
  secalinum Schreb. (Meadow Barley)
Danthonia decumbens (L.) DC. (Heath-grass)*
Molinia caerulea (L.) Moench (Purple Moor-grass)
Phragmites australis (Cav.) Trin. ex Steud. (Common Reed)

SPARGANIACEAE
Sparganium erectum L. (Branched Bur-reed)
  emersum Rehmann (Unbranched Bur-reed)
  natans L. (Least Bur-reed)

TYPHACEAE
Typha latifolia L. (Great Reedmace or Bulrush)
  angustifolia (Lesser Reedmace or Lesser Bulrush)

LILIACEAE
Allium vineale L. (Wild Onion)
Galanthus nivalis L. (Snowdrop) A
Asparagus officinalis L. (Garden Asparagus) A

IRIDACEAE
Iris pseudacorus L. (Yellow Iris)

DIOSCOREACEAE
Tamus communis L. (Black Bryony)†

ORCHIDACEAE
Epipactis palustris (L.) Crantz (Marsh Helleborine)*
Listera ovata (L.) R. Br. (Common Twayblade) (EN)
Liparis loeselii (L.) Rich. (Fen Orchid)*
Dactylorhiza fuchsii (Druce) Soó (Common Spotted-orchid)
  maculata (L.) Soó ssp. *ericetorum* (E. F. Linton) P. F. Hunt & Summerh. (Heath Spotted-orchid)
  incarnata (L.) Soó ssp. *incarnata* (Early Marsh-orchid)
  incarnata (Druce) Soó ssp. *pulchella* (Early Marsh-orchid)
  praetermissa (Druce) Soó (Southern Marsh-orchid)
Orchis morio L. (Green-winged Orchid)*
Ophrys apifera Huds. (Bee Orchid)

ANIMALIA
(Metazoa)

PORIFERA
(sponges)

DEMOSPONGIAE

SPONGILLIDAE
Ephydatia fluviatilis (Lamour.)

CNIDARIA
(coelenterates)

HYDROZOA

HYDRIDAE
Hydra oligactis Pall.

PLATYHELMINTHES
(freshwater triclads, flatworms)

TURBELLARIA
List: Perkins (1928)

TRICLADIDA
(planarians)
Classification & Checklist: Reynoldson (1978)

PLANARIIDAE
Planaria torva (O. F. Müll.)
 (=*vruticiana* Vejd. var. *torfrida* nov.)
Polycelis nigra (O. F. Müll.)

DUGESIIDAE
Dugesia ?lugubris (Schmidt)
 tigrina (Girard)

DENDROCOELIDAE
Dendrocoelum lacteum (O. F. Müll.)
 (=*alba* (L.))

RHABDOCOELA

MESOSTOMIDAE
Bothromesostoma personatum (Schmidt)
Mesostoma platycephalum Braum
 ehrenbergii (Focke)

ROTIFERA
(wheel animalcules)
Lists: Griffiths (1925)*; Pontin (1995)
Classification: Pontin (1978)

MONOGONONTA

BRACHIONIDAE
Brachionus quadridentatus Herm.
Keratella cochlearis (Gosse)
 quadrata (O. F. Müll.)
 testudo (Ehrb.)
Argonotholca foliacea (Ehrb.)
Notholca acuminata (Ehrb.)
 labis Gosse
 squamula (O. F. Müll.)
Squatinella leydigii (Zach.)*
Euchlanis dilatata Ehrb. f. *lucksiana* Hauer
Mytilina ventralis (Ehrb.)
Lophocharis salpina (Ehrb.)
Trichotria pocillum (O. F. Müll.)
 tetractis (Ehrb.)
Lepadella ovalis (O. F. Müll.)

LECANIDAE
Lecane bulla (Gosse)
 lunaris (Ehrb.)

NOTOMMATIDAE
Cephalodella gibba (Ehrb.)
 obvia Donner
 ventripes Dixon-Nutt.

GASTROPODIDAE
Ascomorpha ecaudis Perty

ASPLANCHNIDAE
Asplanchna brightwelli Gosse

SYNCHAETIDAE
Synchaeta oblonga Ehrb.
 pectinata Ehrb.
Polyarthra delichoptera Idelson
 remata Skorikov

TESTUDINELLIDAE
Testudinella patina (Herm.)
Filinia longiseta (Ehrb.)

COLLOTHECIDAE
Collotheca ornata (Ehrb.)

ECTOPROCTA
(bryozoans, 'moss animals')

PHYLACTOLAEMATA
(freshwater ectoprocts)
Classification: Mundy (1980)

PLUMATELLIDA

LOPHOPODIDAE
Lophopus crystallinus (Pall.) (RDB3)

MOLLUSCA
(molluscs)

Lists: M. J. Bishop, R. C. Preece
Checklists: Ellis (1978); Kerney & Cameron (1979); Kerney (1999)
Conservation status: Bratton (1991)

* dead shells

GASTROPODA
(snails and slugs)

Prosobranchia

MONOTOCARDIA

VIVIPARIDAE
Viviparus contectus (Millet) (Lister's River-snail)

VALVATIDAE
Valvata cristata O. F. Müll. (Flat Valve-snail)
  macrostoma Mörch (**RDB2**)
  piscinalis (O. F. Müll.) (Common Valve-snail)

HYDROBIIDAE
Potamopyrgus antipodarum (Gray) (Jenkins's Spire-snail)
  (*jenkinsi* (E. A. Smith))

BITHYNIIDAE
Bithynia leachii (Shepp.) (Leach's Bithynia)
  tentaculata (L.) (Common Bithynia)

Pulmonata

BASOMMATOPHORA

ELLOBIIDAE
Carychium minimum O. F. Müll. (Herald (or Sedge) Snail)
  tridentatum (Risso) (Slender Herald-snail)

PHYSIDAE
Aplexa hypnorum (L.) (Moss Bladder-snail)
Physa fontinalis (L.) (Common Bladder-snail)

LYMNAEIDAE
Lymnaea auricularia (L.) (Ear Pond-snail)
  palustris (O. F. Müll.) (Marsh Pond-snail)
  peregra (O. F. Müll.) (Common (or Wandering) Pond-snail)
  stagnalis (L.) (Great Pond-snail)
  truncatula (O. F. Müll.) (Dwarf Pond-snail)

PLANORBIDAE
Planorbarius corneus (L.) (Great Ram's-horn)
Planorbis carinatus O. F. Müll. (Keeled Ram's-horn)
  planorbis (L.) (Margined Ram's-horn)
Anisus leucostoma (Millet) (Button (or White-lipped) Ram's-horn)
  vortex (L.) (Whirlpool Ram's-horn)
Gyraulus albus (O. F. Müll.) (White Ram's-horn)
  crista (L.) (Nautilus Ram's-horn)
Bathyomphalus contortus (L.) (Twisted Ram's-horn)
Hippeutis complanatus (L.) (Flat Ram's-horn)

ANCYLIDAE
Ancylus fluviatilis O. F. Müll. (River Limpet)

ACROLOXIDAE
Acroloxus lacustris (L.) (Lake Limpet)

STYLOMMATOPHORA

SUCCINEIDAE
Succinea putris (L.) (Large Amber-snail)
Oxyloma pfeifferi (Rossm.) (Pfeiffer's Amber-snail)
  cf. *sarsi* (Esmark) (1953–4) (Slender Amber-snail)*
  (**RDB2**)

COCHLICOPIDAE
Cochlicopa lubrica (O. F. Müll.) (Slippery Moss-snail)

VERTIGINIDAE
Vertigo antivertigo (Drap.) (Marsh Whorl-snail)
  moulinsiana (Dupuy) (Des Moulins' Whorl-snail) (**RDB3**)
  pygmaea (Drap.) (Common Whorl-snail)

PUPILLIDAE
Pupilla muscorum (L.) (Moss Chrysalis Snail)

VALLONIIDAE
Vallonia costata (O. F. Müll.) (Ribbed Grass-snail)
  pulchella (O. F. Müll.) (Smooth (or Beautiful) Grass-snail)

ENIDAE
Ena obscura (O. F. Müll.) (Lesser Bulin)

PUNCTIDAE
Punctum pygmaeum (Drap.) (Dwarf Snail)

DISCIDAE
Discus rotundatus (O. F. Müll.) (Rounded (or Radiated) Snail)

ARIONIDAE
Arion ater (L.) (Large Black Slug)
  circumscriptus Johnst.
  hortensis Fér. seg. (Garden Slug)
  intermedius Norm. (Hedgehog Slug)

VITRINIDAE
Vitrina pellucida (O. F. Müll.) (Pellucid Glass-snail)

ZONITIDAE
Vitrea contracta (Westerl.) (Milky Crystal-snail)
  crystallina (O. F. Müll.) (Crystal Snail)
Oxychilus cellarius (O. F. Müll.) (Cellar Snail)
Aegopinella nitidula (Drap.) (Smooth (or Dull) Glass-snail)
Zonitoides nitidus (O. F. Müll.) (Shiny Glass-snail)
Nesovitrea hammonis (Ström) (Rayed Glass-snail)

LIMACIDAE
Lehmannia marginata (O. F. Müll.) (Tree Slug)
Limax maximus L. (Great Grey Slug)

AGRIOLIMACIDAE
Deroceras laeve (O. F. Müll.) (Marsh Slug)
  reticulatum (O. F. Müll.) (Field (or Milky) Slug)

EUCONULIDAE
Euconulus fulvus (O. F. Müll.) (Tawny Glass-snail)

CLAUSILIIDAE
Balea perversa (L.) (Tree Snail)

HELICIDAE
Arianta arbustorum (L.) (Copse Snail)
Cepaea hortensis (O. F. Müll.) (White-lipped Snail)
   nemoralis (L.) (Grove (or Brown-lipped) Snail)
Helix aspersa O. F. Müll. (Garden (or Common) Snail)
Trichia hispida (L.) (Hairy Snail)
   striolata (C. Pfeiff.) (Strawberry Snail)
Monacha cantiana (Mont.) (Kentish Snail)
Cernuella virgata (da Costa) (Striped (or Zoned) Snail)
Helicella itala (L.) (Heath Snail)

BIVALVIA
(Pelecypoda, bivalves)

UNIONOIDA

UNIONIDAE
Unio pictorum (L.) (Painter's Mussel)
   tumidus Philipss. (Swollen River-mussel)
Anodonta anatina (L.) (Duck Mussel)
   cygnea (L.) (Swan Mussel)
Pseudanodonta complanata (Rossm.) (Compressed River-
   mussel)

CYRENODONTA

SPHAERIIDAE
Sphaerium corneum (L.) (Horny Orb-mussel)
   lacustre (O. F. Müll.) (Lake (or Capped) Mussel)
Pisidium amnicum (O. F. Müll.) (River (or Giant) Pea-shell)
   casertanum (Poli)
   henslowanum (Shepp.)
   hibernicum Westerl.
   milium Held (Rosy Pea-shell)
   moitessierianum Palad.
   nitidum Jenyns
   obtusale (Lam.)
   personatum Malm
   pseudosphaerium Schl. (RDB3)
   pulchellum Jenyns
   subtruncatum Malm
   supinum A. Schmidt

DREISSENIDAE
Dreissena polymorpha (Pall.) (Zebra Mussel) [1994]*

ANNELIDA
(annelid worms)

OLIGOCHAETA
(freshwater worms, earthworms)

Lists: Pickford (1926a); Gardiner (1932a)
Checklists: Brinkhurst (1971); Sims & Gerard (1985)

TUBIFICIDA

NAIDIDAE
Ophidonais serpentina (O. F. Müll.)
Specaria josinae (Vejd.)
Stylaria lacustris (L.)

TUBIFICIDAE
Psammoryctes barbata (Grube)

LUMBRICULIDA

LUMBRICULIDAE
Lumbriculus variegatus (O. F. Müll.)

HAPLOTAXIDA

LUMBRICIDAE

Lumbricinae

Allolobophora chlorotica (Savig.)
Aporrectodea caliginosa (Savig.)
  longa (Ude)
  rosea (Savig.)
Dendrodrilus rubidus (Savig.)
Eiseniella tetraedra (Savig.)
Lumbricus castaneus (Savig.)
  rubellus Hoffm.
  terrestris L.
Murchieona minuscula (Rosa)
Octolasion tyrtaeum (Savig.)

HIRUDINEA
(leeches)

List: Harding (1925)
Checklist & Classification: Elliott & Mann (1979)
Conservation status: Bratton (1991)

* extinct at Wicken Fen

RHYNCHOBDELLAE

PISCICOLIDAE
Piscicola geometra (L.)

GLOSSIPHONIIDAE
Glossiphonia complanata (L.)
  heteroclita (L.)
Helobdella stagnalis (L.)
Theromyzon tessulatum (O. F. Müll.)
  (=*Protoclepis tessellata* O. F. Müll.)
Hemiclepsis marginata (O. F. Müll.)

GNATHOBDELLIDA

HIRUDINIDAE
Hirudo medicinalis L. (the Medicinal Leech)* (RDB3)
Haemopsis sanguisuga (L.) (Horse Leech)

PHARYNGOBDELLIDA

ERPOBDELLIDAE
Erpobdella octoculata (L.)
  (=*Herpobdella atomaria* sensu Harding nec Carena)
  testacea (Savig.)
  (=*Herpobdella octoculata* sensu Harding nec (L.))

TARDIGRADA
(tardigrades, water bears)

List: L. Friday
Checklist: Morgan & King (1976)

EUTARDIGRADA

MACROBIOTIDAE
Hypsibius cf. *novemcinctus* Marcus

MILNESIIDAE
Milnesium tardigradum Doyère

Spiders

ARTHROPODA

Chelicerata

ARACHNIDA

ARANEAE
(spiders)

Lists: Bristowe (1925), Duffey (1970), E. Duffey (pers.comm.),
D. R. Nellist (2000, and pers.comm.)
Checklist: Roberts (1987, 1993)
Conservation status: Bratton (1991); see Duffey (1971)

* extinct at Wicken Fen; date gives last record

AMAUROBIIDAE

Amaurobius fenestralis (Stroem)
  ferox (Walck.)
  similis (Blackw.)

DICTYNIDAE

Dictyna arundinacea (L.)
  uncinata Thor.
Lathys humilis (Blackw.)

DYSDERIDAE

Dysdera erythrina (Walck.)
Harpactea hombergi (Scop.)

SEGESTRIIDAE

Segestria senoculata (L.)

GNAPHOSIDAE

Drassodes lapidosus (Walck.)
  pubescens (Thor.)
Haplodrassus signifer (C. L. Koch)
Scotophaeus blackwalli (Thor.)
Zelotes latreillei (Simon)
  lutetianus (L. Koch)
  praeficus (L. Koch)
  pusillus (C. L. Koch)
Micaria pulicaria (Sund.)

CLUBIONIDAE

Clubioninae

Clubiona brevipes Blackw.
  comta C. L. Koch
  diversa O. P.-Cambr.
  lutescens Westr.
  neglecta O. P.-Cambr.
  pallidula (Cl.)
  phragmitis C. L. Koch
  reclusa O. P.-Cambr.
  stagnatilis Kulcz.
  subtilis L. Koch
  terrestris Westr.

Liocraninae

Agroeca proxima (O. P.-Cambr.)
Agraecina striata (Kulcz.) **Nb**
Phrurolithus festivus (C. L. Koch)

ORIDAE

Zora armillata Simon (RDB3)
  spinimana (Sund.)

THOMISIDAE

Misumeninae

Xysticus cristatus (Cl.)
  erraticus (Blackw.)
  ulmi (Hahn)
Ozyptila atomaria (Panz.)
  brevipes (Hahn)
  praticola (C. L. Koch)
  simplex (O. P.-Cambr.)
  trux (Blackw.)

Philodrominae

Philodromus albidus Kulcz.
  aureolus (Cl.)
  cespitum (Walck.)
  dispar Walck.
Thanatus striatus C. L. Koch
Tibellus maritimus (Menge)
  oblongus (Walck.)

SALTICIDAE

Salticus cingulatus (Panz.)
  scenicus (Cl.)
Heliophanus flavipes (Hahn)
Marpissa nivoyi (Lucas)
  radiata (Grube) **Na**
Neon valentulus Falc. (RDB2)
Euophrys frontalis (Walck.)
Sitticus caricis (Westr.)
Evarcha arcuata (Cl.)

LYCOSIDAE

Pardosa amentata (Cl.)
  lugubris (Walck.)
  monticola (Cl.)
  palustris (L.)
  prativaga (L. Koch)
  pullata (Cl.)
Hygrolycosa rubrofasciata (Ohl.)
Alopecosa pulverulenta (Cl.)
Trochosa ruricola (DeGeer)
  spinipalpis (F. O. P.-Cambr.)
  terricola Thor.
Arctosa leopardus (Sund.)
Pirata hygrophilus Thor.
  latitans (Blackw.)
  piraticus (Cl.)
  piscatorius (Cl.)?*

PISAURIDAE

Pisaura mirabilis (Cl.)
Dolomedes fimbriatus (Cl.)*

ARGYRONETIDAE

Argyroneta aquatica (Cl.)

AGELENIDAE

Agelena labyrinthica (Cl.)
Textrix denticulata (Olivier)
Tegenaria domestica (Cl.)
Cicurina cicur (F.)

HAHNIIDAE

Hahnia nava (Blackw.)
Antistea elegans (Blackw.)

MIMETIDAE

Ero cambridgei Kulcz.
　furcata (Villers)
　tuberculata (DeGeer)

THERIDIIDAE

Episinus angulatus (Blackw.)
　truncatus Latr.
Crustulina sticta (O. P.-Cambr.)
Steatoda bipunctata (L.)
Anelosimus vittatus (C. L. Koch)
Theridion bimaculatum (L.)
　blackwalli O. P.-Cambr.
　impressum L. Koch
　instabile O. P.-Cambr.
　melanurum Hahn
　mystaceum L. Koch
　　(=*neglectum* Wiehle)
　pallens Blackw.
　sisyphium (Cl.)
　varians Hahn
Enoplognatha ovata (Cl.)
　thoracica (Hahn)
Robertus arundineti (O. P.-Cambr.)
　lividus (Blackw.)
Pholcomma gibbum (Westr.)

TETRAGNATHIDAE

Tetragnatha extensa (L.)
　montana Simon
　nigrita Lendl
　obtusa C. L. Koch
Pachygnatha clercki Sund.
　degeeri Sund.
Meta segmentata (Cl.)

ARANEIDAE

Araneus diadematus Cl.
　marmoreus Cl.
　quadratus Cl.
Larinioides cornutus (Cl.)
Nuctenea umbratica (Cl.)
Neoscona adianta (Walck.)
Araniella cucurbitina (Cl.)
　opistographa (Kulcz.)
Hyposinga heri (Hahn)* (**RDB1**)
Zygiella atrica (C. L. Koch)
　x-notata (Cl.)

LINYPHIIDAE

Ceratinella brevipes (Westr.)
　scabrosa (O. P.-Cambr.)
Walckenaeria acuminata Blackw.
　antica (Wider)
　atrotibialis (O. P.-Cambr.)
　cucullata (C. L. Koch)
　nudipalpis (Westr.)
　unicornis O. P.-Cambr.
　vigilax (Blackw.)
Dicymbium nigrum (Blackw.)
Entelecara acuminata (Wider)
　erythropus (Westr.)
　omissa O. P.-Cambr.
Moebelia penicillata (Westr.)
Hylyphantes graminicola (Sund.)
Gnathonarium dentatum (Wider)
Gongylidium rufipes (L.)
Dismodicus bifrons (Blackw.)
Hypomma bituberculatum (Wider)

　cornutum (Blackw.)
　fulvum (Bösenb.) **Na**
Baryphyma pratense (Blackw.)
　trifrons (O. P.-Cambr.)
Gonatium rubens (Blackw.)
Maso gallicus Simon **Na**
　sundevalli (Westr.)
Pocadicnemis juncea Locket & Millidge
　pumila (Blackw.)
Oedothorax agrestis (Blackw.)
　apicatus (Blackw.)
　fuscus (Blackw.)
　gibbosus (Blackw.)
　　(=*tuberosus* (Blackw.))
　retusus (Westr.)
Pelecopsis nemoralis (Blackw.)
Silometopus elegans (O. P.-Cambr.)
Tiso vagans (Blackw.)
Minyriolus pusillus (Wider)
Tapinocyba insecta (L. Koch)
Microctenonyx subitaneus (O. P.-Cambr.)
Lophomma punctatum (Blackw.)
Saloca diceros (O. P.-Cambr.)
Gongylidiellum murcidum Simon **Nb**
　vivum (O. P.-Cambr.)
Micrargus subaequalis (Westr.)
Glyphesis servulus (Simon) **RDBK**
Erigonella hiemalis (Blackw.)
Savignia frontata (Blackw.)
Diplocephalus picinus (Blackw.)
Araeoncus crassiceps (Westr.)
　humilis (Blackw.)
Typhochrestus digitatus (O. P.-Cambr.)
Erigone atra Blackw.
　dentipalpis (Wider)
Donacochara speciosa (Thor.)
Leptothrix hardyi (Blackw.)
Halorates distinctus (Simon)
Aphileta misera (O. P.-Cambr.)
Porrhomma microphthalmum (O. P.-Cambr.)
　oblitum (O. P.-Cambr.)
　pallidum Jackson
　pygmaeum (Blackw.)
Agyneta cauta (O. P.-Cambr.)
　conigera (O. P.-Cambr.)
　ramosa Jackson
　subtilis (O. P.-Cambr.)
Meioneta mollis (O. P.-Cambr.)
　rurestris (C. L. Koch)
　saxatilis (Blackw.)
Microneta viaria (Blackw.)
Maro sublestus Falc.
Centromerus dilutus (O. P.-Cambr.)
　incultus Falc. (**RDB2**) [1913]
　prudens (O. P.-Cambr.)
　sylvaticus (Blackw.)
Tallusia experta (O. P.-Cambr.)
Centromerita bicolor (Blackw.)
Saaristoa abnormis (Blackw.)
Bathyphantes gracilis (Blackw.)
　parvulus (Westr.)
　setiger F. O. P.-Cambr.
Kaestneria dorsalis (Wider)
　pullata (O. P.-Cambr.)
Diplostyla concolor (Wider)
Tapinopa longidens (Wider)
Floronia bucculenta (Cl.)
Taranucnus setosus (O. P.-Cambr.)
Stemonyphantes lineatus (L.)
Lepthyphantes ericaeus (Blackw.)
　flavipes (Blackw.)

leprosus (Ohl.)
mengei Kulcz.
minutus (Blackw.)
nebulosus (Sund.)
obscurus (Blackw.)
pallidus (O. P.-Cambr.)
tenebricola (Wider)
tenuis (Blackw.)
zimmermanni Bertkau
Helophora insignis (Blackw.)
Linyphia triangularis (Cl.)
Neriene clathrata (Sund.)
montana (Cl.)
Microlinyphia pusilla (Sund.)
Allomengea vidua (L. Koch)

OPILIONES

(harvestmen)

List: Bristowe (1925)
Checklist: Hillyard & Sankey (1989)

NEMASTOMATIDAE

Nemastoma bimaculatum (F.)

PHALANGIIDAE

Oligolophinae

Lacinius ephippiatus (C. L. Koch)
Mitopus morio (F.)
Paroligolophus agrestis (Meade)
    (=*Oligolophus agrestis* (Meade))
Odiellus spinosus (Bosc)
    (=*Oligolophus spinosus* (Bosc.))

Phalangiinae

Opilio parietinus (DeGeer)
saxatilis C. L. Koch
Rilaena triangularis (Herbst)
    (=*Platybunus triangularis* (Herbst))

LEIOBUNIDAE

Leiobuninae

Leiobunum rotundum (Latr.)

PSEUDOSCORPIONES

(pseudoscorpions)

Classification: Legg & Jones (1988)

Cheliferinea

CHERNETIDAE

Chernes cimicoides (F.)

ACARIDIDA

(Astigmata, Acarina, mites)

Records (mites and ticks): Thorne (1971), Barnett & Green (1972)

KNEMIDODOPTIDAE (skin parasites)

Knemidokoptes jamaicensis Turk Host at Wicken:
    Acrocephalus schoenobaenus (Reed Warbler)

IXODIDA

(Metastigmata, ticks)

IXODIDAE (hard ticks)

Ixodes frontalis (Panz.) Hosts at Wicken: *Pyrrhula pyrrhula* (Bullfinch), *Phylloscopus trochilus* (Willow Warbler), *Turdus merula* (Blackbird)

Crustacea

'ENTOMOSTRACA' (branchiopods, copepods, ostracods)

BRANCHIOPODA

CLADOCERA
(water fleas)

Nomenclature: Scourfield & Harding (1966)
Lists: Jenkin (1928), Lowndes (1932b), J. Hearn, J. H. Bratton

Calyptomera

BOSMINIDAE

Bosmina longirostris (O. F. Müll.)

CHYDORIDAE

Acroperus angustatus Sars
  harpae Baird
Alona affinis Leyd.
  costata Sars
  guttata Sars
  quadrangularis (O. F. Müll.)
  rectangula Sars
Alonella excisa (Fisch.)
Anchistropus emarginatus Sars
Camptocerus rectirostris (Schöd.)
Chydorus sphaericus (O. F. Müll.)
Eurycercus lamellatus (O. F. Müll.)
Graptoleberis testudinaria (Fisch.)
Leydigia acanthocercoides (Fisch.)
Oxyurella tenuicaudis (Sars)
  (=*Alona tenuicaudis* Sars)
Peracantha truncata (O. F. Müll.)
  (=*Peratacantha truncata* Lillj.)
Pleuroxus laevis Sars
  trigonellus (O. F. Müll.)
  uncinatus Baird
Pseudochydorus globosus (Baird)
  (=*Chydorus globosus* Baird)

DAPHNIIDAE

Ceriodaphnia laticaudata P. E. Müll.
  megalops Sars
  (=*megops* Sars)
  pulchella Sars
  quadrangula (O. F. Müll.)
  reticulata (Jur.)
    var. *serrata* (Sars)
  setosa Matile
Daphnia cucullata Sars
  curvirostris Eylmann
  hyalina Leydig
  longispina O. F. Müll.
  obtusa Kurz
  pulex (DeGeer)
  ?*rosea* Sars emend. Richard
Scapholeberis mucronata (O. F. Müll.)
Simocephalus exspinosus (Koch)
  vetulus (O. F. Müll.)

MACROTHRICIDAE

Ilyocryptus agilis Kurz
Lathonura rectirostris (O. F. Müll.)

SIDIDAE

Diaphanosoma brachyurum (Liéven)
Sida crystallina (O. F. Müll.)

Gymnomera

POLYPHEMIDAE

Polyphemus pediculus (L.)

COPEPODA
(copepods)

Lists: Lowndes (1928, 1932b)
Nomenclature: (calanoids and cyclopids): Harding & Smith (1974); (harpacticoids): Dussart & Defaye (1990)

CALANOIDA

DIAPTOMIDAE

Diaptomus castor (Jur.)
  gracilis (Sars)
  vulgaris (Schmeil)

CYCLOPOIDA

CYCLOPIDAE

Cyclops (*Macrocyclops*) *fuscus* (Jur.)
  (=*Pachycyclops signatus* Koch)
  albidus (Jur.)
  (=*Pachycyclops annulicornis* Koch)
  distinctus (Richard)
  (=*Pachycyclops bistriatus* Koch)
Cyclops (*Tropocyclops*) *prasinus* (Fisch. ex Schmeil)
  (=*Leptocyclops prasinus* Fisch.)
Cyclops (*Eucyclops*) *agilis* (s. str.) (Koch ex Sars)
  (=*Leptocyclops agilis* Koch)
  agilis speratus (Lillj.)
  macruroides (s. str.) (Lillj.)
  macrurus (Sars)
Cyclops (*Paracyclops*) *fimbriatus* (s. str.) (Fisch.)
  affinis (Sars)
Cyclops (*Ectocyclops*) *phaleratus* (Koch)
Cyclops (*Cyclops*) *strenuus* (Fisch.)
Cyclops (*Acanthocyclops*) *viridis* (Jur.)
  (=*Cyclops vulgaris* Fisch.)
  gigas (s. str.) (Claus)
  gigas latipes (Lowndes)
  vernalis (Fisch.)
  (=*Cyclops lucidulus* Koch)
  (=*C. robustus* Sars)
  bicuspidatus (Claus)
  (=*Cyclops pulchellus* Koch)
  bisetosus (Rehberg)
  languidoides hypnicola (Gurney)
Cyclops (*Microcyclops*) *varicans* (s. str.) (Sars)
  varicans rubellus (Lillj.)
  (=*Cryptocyclops rubellus* Lillj.)
  bicolor (Sars)
  (=*Cryptocyclops bicolor* Sars)
Cyclops (*Mesocyclops*) *leuckarti* (Claus)
  (=*Mesocyclops obsoletus* Koch)
  hyalinus (Rehberg)
  (=*Mesocyclops crassus* Fisch.)

HARPACTICOIDA

CANTHOCAMPTIDAE

Attheyella crassa (Sars)
  trispinosus (Brady)
Bryocamptus minutus (Claus)
    (=*Canthocamptus minutus* Claus)
  pygmaeus (Sars)
    (=*Attheyella pygmaea* Sars)
Canthocamptus microstaphylinus Wolf
  staphylinus (Jur.)
Elaphoidella gracilis (Sars)
    (=*Attheyella gracilis* (Sars))

AMEIRIDAE

Nitocra hibernica (Brady)

OSTRACODA

(ostracods)

Lists: Lowndes (1932a, 1938), revised H. I. Griffiths
Classification & Checklist: Henderson (1990), updated by
Griffiths & Evans (1995)

PODOCOPIDA

DARWINULIDAE

Darwinula stevensoni (Brady & Norman)

LIMNOCYTHERIDAE

Limnocythere inopinata (Baird)

CANDONIDAE

Candona candida (O. F. Müll.)
Fabaeformiscandona fabaeformis (Fisch.)
Pseudocandona albicans (Brady)
    (=*Candona albicans* (Brady))
  compressa (Koch)
    (=*Candona pubescens* (Koch))
  lobipes (Hartwig)
    (=*brevis* (Brady))
Candonopsis kingsleii (Brady & Rob.)
Cyclocypris globosa (Sars)
  laevis (O. F. Müll.)
  ovum (Jur.)
    (=*pygmaea* (Cronen.))
  serena (Koch)
Cypria exsculpta (Fisch.)
  ophthalmica (Jur.)

NOTODROMATIDAE

Notodromas monacha (O. F. Müll.)

CYPRIDIDAE

Bradleystrandesia reticulata (Zadd.)
    (=*Cypricercus affinis* (Fisch.))
Strandesia obliqua (Brady)
Herpetocypris reptans (Baird)
    (=*Siphlocandona similis* Baird (syn. of last instar))
Cypridopsis vidua (O. F. Müll.)
    (=*Pioncypris helvetica* Kaufm.)
Potamocypris villosa (Jur.)

BRANCHIURA

(fish-lice)

ARGULIDAE

Argulus foliaceus (L.)

MALACOSTRACA

Classification: (freshwater crustacea) Gledhill, Sutcliffe &
Williams (1993); (terrestrial isopods) Oliver & Meechan
(1993)

ISOPODA

(woodlice and water hog-lice)

Lists: Omer Cooper (1925); S. J. Gregory
Checklist: (woodlice) Oliver & Meechan (1993)

Asellota

(water-lice, water hog-lice)

ASELLIDAE

Asellus aquaticus (L.)
  meridianus Racov.

Oniscidea

(woodlice)

ARMADILLIDIIDAE

Armadillidium vulgare (Latr.)

ONISCIDAE

Oniscus asellus L.

PHILOSCIIDAE

Philoscia muscorum (Scop.)

PORCELLIONIDAE

Porcellio scaber Latr.
Porcellionides pruinosus (Brandt)

TRICHONISCIDAE

Androniscus dentiger Verhoeff
    (=*Trichoniscus roseus* (auctt. nec C. L. Koch))
Haplophthalmus danicus Budde-Lund
  mengei (Ladd.)
Trichoniscoides albidus (Budde-Lund)
Trichoniscus pusillus Brandt
  pygmaeus Sars

AMPHIPODA

(freshwater shrimps)

Gammaridea

CRANGONYCTIDAE

Crangonyx pseudogracilis Bousfield

GAMMARIDAE

Gammarus pulex (L.)

DECAPODA

Pleocymata (=Reptantia)
(crayfish)
Record: Omer Cooper (1925)

ASTACIDAE

Austropotamobius pallipes (Lereb.)
    (=*Potamobius pallipes* Lereb.)

Uniramia

MYRIAPODA (group of classes: *DIPLOPODA* and *CHILOPODA*)

DIPLOPODA
(millipedes)
Lists: Worthington (1928); S. J. Gregory
Checklist: Blower (1985)

Penicillata

POLYXENIDA

POLYXENIDAE
Polyxenus lagurus (L.)

Helminthomorpha

CHORDEUMATIDA

CRASPEDOSOMATIDAE
Nanogona polydesmoides (Leach)
  (=*Polymicrodon polydesmoides* (Leach))

JULIDA

JULIDAE
Tachypodoiulus niger (Leach)
Cylindroiulus latestriatus (Curt.)
  punctatus (Leach)
Brachyiulus pusillus (Leach)

POLYDESMIDA

POLYDESMIDAE
Polydesmus angustus Latz.
  denticulatus C. L. Koch
  inconstans Latz.
    (=*coriaeceus* auctt. nec Porat)
Brachydesmus superus Latz.

CHILOPODA
(centipedes)
Lists: Worthington (1928); S. J. Gregory
Checklist: Eason (1964); nomenclature, Barber & Keay (1988)

GEOPHILOMORPHA

GEOPHILIDAE
Dignathodontinae
Strigamia acuminata (Leach)
  (=*Scolioplanes acuminatus* (Leach))

Geophilinae
Geophilus insculptus Attems
Necrophloeophagus flavus DeGeer
  (=*Geophilus longicornis* (Leach))
Brachygeophilus truncorum (Bergs. & Mein.)

SCOLOPENDROMORPHA

CRYPTOPSIDAE
Cryptops hortensis Leach

LITHOBIOMORPHA

LITHOBIIDAE
Lithobiinae
Lithobius crassipes L. Koch
  (=*Monotarsobius crassipes* (L. Koch))
  forficatus (L.)

DIPLURA
(two-pronged bristle-tails)
Records: Pickford (1926b)

CAMPODEIDAE
Campodea lubbocki Silv.
  staphylinus Westw.

COLLEMBOLA
(springtails)
Lists: Jackson (1928, 1938)
Checklist: Kloet & Hincks (1964); nomenclature: Hopkin (1997)

ARTHROPLEONA

PODUROIDEA

PODURIDAE
Podura aquatica L.

HYPOGASTRURIDAE
Hypogastrurinae
Ceratophysella armata (Nic.)
  (=*Hypogastrura armata* (Nic.))
  bengtssoni (Ågren)
  (=*Hypogastrura bengtssoni* (Ågren))
Hypogastrura purpurescens (Lubb.)
  (=*purpurascens* auctt.)
Xenylla brevicauda Tullb.
  maritima Tullb.

NEANURIDAE
Frieseinae
Friesia claviseta Axels.
Brachystomella parvula (Schäff.)
  (=*Chondrachorutes wahlgreni* Dénis)

Pseudachorutinae
Anurida granaria (Nic.)

Neanurinae
Neanura muscorum (Templ.)
  (=*Achorutes muscorum* Templ.)

ONYCHIURIDAE

Onychiurinae

Protaphorura armata Tullb.
  (=*Onychiurus armatus* (Tullb.))

ENTOMOBRYOIDEA

ISOTOMIDAE

Anurophorus laricis Nic.
Folsomia quadrioculata (Tullb.)
Vertagopus arboreus (L.)
  (=*Isotoma arborea* (L.))
  cinerea (Nic.)
  (=*Isotoma cinerea* (Nic.))
Isotoma notabilis Schäff.
  olivacea Tullb.
  viridis Bourl.
Isotomurus palustris (O. F. Müll.)

ENTOMOBRYIDAE

Entomobryinae

Entomobrya albocincta (Templ.)
  nicoleti (Lubb.)
  nivalis (L.)
Lepidocyrtus cyaneus Tullb.
  ruber Schött

Orchesellinae

Orchesella cincta (L.)
  villosa (Geoff.)

TOMOCERIDAE

Tomocerus minor (Lubb.)

NEELIPLEONA

NEELIDAE

Megalothorax minimus Willem
  (=*Neelus minimus* (Willem))

SYMPHYPLEONA

MINTHURIDAE

Sminthuridinae

Sminthurides aquaticus (Bourl.)
  cruciatus Axels.
  malmgreni (Tullb.)
  schoetti (Axels.)
Stenacidia violacea (Reuter)
  (=*Sminthurides violaceus* (Reuter))

Katianninae

Sminthurinus albifrons (Tullb.)
  aureus (Lubb.)

Bourletiellinae

Deuterosminthurus bicinctus (C. L. Koch)
Bourletiella hortensis (Fitch)
  (=*signata* (Nic.))
Heterosminthurus insignis (Reuter)

Sminthurinae

Lipothrix lubbocki (Tullb.)
  (=*Sminthurus lubbocki* Tullb.)
  (=*Sphyrotheca lubbocki* (Tullb.))

Sminthurus viridis (L.)

Dicyrtominae

Dicyrtomina minuta (F.)

INSECTA
(insects)

EPHEMEROPTERA
(mayflies)

Lists: Allen & Gambles (1932); Imms (1938d); J. E. Harker
Checklist: Harker (1989)

EPHEMEROIDEA

EPHEMERIDAE

Ephemera vulgata L.

BAETOIDEA

LEPTOPHLEBIIDAE

Leptophlebia vespertina (L.)
  marginata (L.)
Paraleptophlebia submarginata (Steph.)

CAENIDAE

Caenis horaria (L.)
  luctuosa (Burmeist.)
  robusta Eaton

BAETIDAE

Baetis vernus Curt.
   (=*Baetis tenax* Eaton)
Centroptilum luteolum (O. F. Müll.)
Cloeon dipterum (L.)
  simile Eaton
Procloeon bifidum (Bengts.)

ODONATA
(dragonflies)

Lists: Lucas (1925); Imms (1938a); N. W. Moore, T. J. Bennett
Checklist: Askew (1988)

* extinct at Wicken Fen

Zygoptera
(damselflies)

CALOPTERYGIDAE

Calyopteryx splendens (Harris) (Banded Demoiselle)
   (=*Agrion splendens* (Harris))

LESTIDAE

Lestes sponsa (Hansem.) (Emerald Damselfly)
  dryas Kirby (Scarce Emerald Damselfly)* (RDB2)

COENAGRIONIDAE

Pyrrhosoma nymphula (Sulz.) (Large Red Damselfly)
Erythromma najas (Hansem.) (Red-eyed Damselfly)
Coenagrion puella (L.) (Azure Damselfly)
   (=*Agrion puella* L.)
  pulchellum (Vander Lind.) (Variable Damselfly)
   (=*Agrion pulchellum* Vander Lind.)
Enallagma cyathigerum (Charp.) (Common Blue Damselfly)
Ischnura elegans (Vander Lind.) (Blue-tailed Damselfly)
Ceriagrion tenellum (Vill.) (Small Red Damselfly)*
   (=*Palaeobasis tenella* (Vill.))
   (=*Pyrrhosoma tenellum* (Vill.))

Anisoptera
(dragonflies)

AESHNIDAE

Aeshna juncea (L.) (Common Hawker)*
  mixta Latr. (Migrant Hawker)
  cyanea (O. F. Müll.) (Southern Hawker)
  grandis (L.) (Brown Hawker)
Anax imperator Leach (Emperor Dragonfly)
Brachytron pratense (O. F. Müll.) (Hairy Dragonfly)

LIBELLULIDAE

Libellula quadrimaculata L. (Four-spotted Chaser)
  depressa L. (Broad-bodied Chaser)
Orthetrum cancellatum (L.) (Black-tailed Skimmer)
  coerulescens (F.) (Keeled Skimmer)*
Sympetrum striolatum (Charp.) (Common Darter)
  flaveolum (L.) (Yellow-winged Darter)
  sanguineum (O. F. Müll.) (Ruddy Darter)
  danae (Sulz.) (Black Darter)*

ORTHOPTERA
(crickets and grasshoppers)

List: Lucas (1925); Worthington (1938); J. H. Bratton; A. Colston
Checklist: Marshall & Haes (1988)

* extinct at Wicken; date refers to new record at Wicken

Ensifera
(crickets)

TETTIGONIDAE

Meconematinae
Meconema thalassinum (DeGeer) (Oak Bush-cricket)

Dectinae
Metrioptera roeselii (Hagenb.) (Roesel's Bush-cricket) [1998]

Conocephalinae
Conocephalus dorsalis (Latr.) (Short-winged Cone-head)

Phaneropterinae
Leptophyes punctatissima (Bosc) (Speckled Bush-cricket)

Caelifera
(grasshoppers)

TETRIGIDAE

Tetrix subulata (L.) (Slender Ground-hopper)
   (=*Acrydium subulatum* (L.))
  undulata (Sowerby) (Common Ground-hopper)
   (=*A. keifferi* (Saulay))

ACRIDIDAE

Oedipodinae
Stethophyma grossum (L.) (Large Marsh Grasshopper)†
  (RDB2)

Gomphocerinae
Omocestus viridulus (L.) (Common Green Grasshopper)
  rufipes (Zett.) (Woodland Grasshopper)
   (=*ventralis* (Zett.))

Chorthippus brunneus (Thunb.) (Field Grasshopper)
   (=*bicolor* (Charp.))
  parallelus (Zett.) (Meadow Grasshopper)
  albomarginatus (DeGeer) (Lesser Marsh Grasshopper)
   (=*elegans* (Charp.))
Myrmeleotettix maculatus (Thunb.) (Mottled Grasshopper)†

DERMAPTERA

(earwigs)
Records: Lucas (1928); Worthington (1938)
Checklist: Marshall & Haes (1988)

LABIIDAE

Labia minor (L.) (Lesser Earwig)

FORFICULIDAE

Forficula auricularia L. (Common Earwig)

PSOCOPTERA

(book lice and allies)
Lists: Gambles (1932, 1938)
Checklist and nomenclature: Kloet & Hincks (1964); updated
New (1974)

Trogiomorpha

LEPIDOPSOCIDAE

Pteroxanium kelloggi (Ribaga)
  (=*squamosum* (Enderl.))

TROGIIDAE

Cerobasis guestfalica (Kolbe)
   (=*Hyperetes guestfalicus* (Kolbe))
Trogium pulsatorium (L.)

Troctomorpha

LIPOSCELIDAE

Liposcelis terricolis Badon.
  (=*divinatorius* O. F. Müll.)

Psocomorpha

CAECILIIDAE

Kolbea quisquiliarum (Bertkau)
Caecilius atricornis McLach.
  flavidus (Steph.)
  kolbei Tetens
   (as *piceus* Kolbe f. *brevipennis* Enderl.)
  piceus Kolbe

STENOPSOCIDAE

Graphopsocus cruciatus (L.)
Stenopsocus immaculatus (Steph.)

LACHESILLIDAE

Lachesilla pedicularia (L.)
  (=*Pterodela pedicularia* (L.))

ECTOPSOCIDAE

Ectopsocus briggsi McLach.

PERIPSOCIDAE

Peripsocus phaeopterus (Steph.)

ELIPSOCIDAE

Elipsocus westwoodi McLach
  (=*hyalinus* misident.)

PHILOTARSIDAE

Philotarsus picicornis (F.)
  (=*flaviceps* (Steph.))

MESOPSOCIDAE

Mesopsocus unipunctatus (O. F. Müll.)
  laticeps (Kolbe)

PSOCIDAE

Metylophorus nebulosus (Steph.)
  (=*Psocus nebulosus* (Steph.))
Trichadenotecnum majus (Kolbe)
  variegatum (Latr.)
   (=*Amphigerontia variegata* (Latr.))
   (=*Loensia variegata* (Latr.))
Psococerastis gibbosa (Sulz)

PHTHIRAPTERA

(Mallophaga and Anoplura) (bird lice and sucking
lice)
Records: M. Brooke
Checklist: Kloet & Hincks (1964)

Amblycera

MENOPONIDAE

Cuculiphilus fasciatus (Scop.) Host at Wicken: *Cuculus
canorus* (cuckoo)

Ischnocera

PHILOPTERIDAE

Cuculicola latirostris (Burmeist.)   Host at Wicken: *C.
canorus*

HEMIPTERA

Heteroptera
(bugs, water boatmen, and allies)

Lists: Hutchinson (1925, 1926); Harris (1928); N. A. Straw, T. Huxley
Checklist: Kloet & Hincks (1964), amended by N. A. Straw
Classification: Dolling (1991)

PENTATOMOIDEA

ACANTHOSOMATIDAE

Acanthosoma haemorrhoidale (L.)
Elasmucha grisea (L.)

CYDNIDAE

Legnotus limbosus (Geoff.)
Sehirus bicolor (L.)
Thyreocoris scarabaeoides (L.)

SCUTELLERIDAE

Eurygaster testudinaria (Geoff.)

PENTATOMIDAE

Podops inuncta (F.)
Aelia acuminata (L.)
Eysarcoris fabricii (Kirk.)
Pentatoma rufipes (L.)
Picromerus bidens (L.)
Troilus luridus (F.)
Zicrona caerulea (L.)

COREOIDEA

RHOPALIDAE

Myrmus miriformis (Fall.)

LYGAEOIDEA

LYGAEIDAE

Heterogaster urticae (F.)
Ischnodemus sabuleti (Fall.)
Kleidocerys resedae (Panz.)
Pachybrachius fracticollis (Schill.)
  (=*Pamera fracticollis* (Schill.))
Peritrechus geniculatus (Hahn)
  lundi (Gmel.)
Acompus rufipes (J. F. Wolff)
Stygnocoris fuligineus (Geoff. in Fourc.)
  rusticus (Fall.)
Drymus brunneus (Sahlb.)
  pilicornis (Mulsart) (**Nb**)
  ryei Dougl. & Scott
  sylvaticus (F.)
Scolopostethus affinis (Schill.)
  puberulus Horváth
  thomsoni Reuter
Eremocoris plebejus (Fall.) (**Nb**)
Taphropeltus contractus (H.-S.)

BERYTINIDAE

Cymus glandicolor Hahn
  melanocephalus Fieb.
Berytinus montivagus (Meyer)

TINGOIDEA

TINGIDAE

Acalypta parvula (Fall.)
Tingis ampliata (H.-S.)
  cardui (L.)
Physatocheila dumetorum (H.-S.)
Dictyla convergens (H.-S.)
  (=*Monanthia humuli* auctt. nec (F.))
Agramma laeta (Fall.)
  (=*Serenthia laeta* (Fall.))

REDUVIOIDEA

REDUVIIDAE

Empicoris culiciformis (DeGeer)

CIMICOIDEA

NABIDAE

Nabis ferus (L.)
Himacerus apterus (F.)
Nabicula flavomarginatus (Scholtz)
  (=*Nabis flavomarginatus* (Scholtz))
  limbatus (Dahlb.)
  lineatus (Dahlb.)

CIMICIDAE

Temnostethus pusillus (H.-S.)
Anthocoris confusus Reuter
  gallarum-ulmi (DeGeer)
  limbatus Fieb.
  nemoralis (F.)
  nemorum (L.)
Orius majusculus (Reuter)
  (=*Triphleps majuscula* Reuter)
  niger (J. F. Wolff)
Xylocoris galactinus (Fall.)

MIROIDEA

MICROPHYSIDAE

Loricula elegantula (Bärenspr.)
Myrmedobia tenella (Zett.)

MIRIDAE

Deraeocoris lutescens (Schill.)
  ruber (L.)
  scutellaris (F.)
Amblytylus nasutus (Kirsch.)
Macrotylus solitarius (Meyer-Dür)
Orthonotus rufifrons (Fall.)
Tytthus geminus (Flor) (**Nb**)
  pygmaeus (Zett.)
Psallus falleni Reuter
  haematodes (Gmel.)
  (=*roseus* (F.))
  variabilis (Fall.)
  varians (H.-S.)
Atractotomus mali (Meyer-Dür)
Plagiognathus arbustorum (F.)
  chrysanthemi (J. F. Wolff)
Salicarus roseri (H.-S.)
Dicyphus epilobii Reuter
  stachydis Reuter
Campyloneura virgula (H.-S.)
Pilophorus perplexus Dougl. & Scott
Halticus apterus (L.)

Fieberocapsus flaveolus (Reuter)
Heterotoma planicornis (Pall.)
    (=*meriopterum* auctt. nec (Scop.))
Blepharidopterus angulatus (Fall.)
Orthotylus diaphanus (Kirsch.)
    marginalis Reuter
    nassatus (F.)
    ochrotrichus Fieb.
    prasinus (Fall.)
Mecomma ambulans (Fall.)
Lygus pratensis (L.) (**RDB3**)
    rugulipennis Poppius
Liocoris tripustulatus (F.)
Orthops campestris (L.)
    cervinus (H.-S.)
    kalmi (L.)
        (=*Lygus kalmi* (L.))
Lygocoris contaminatus (Fall.)
        (=*Lygus contaminatus* (Fall.))
    lucorum (Meyer-Dür)
    pabulinus (L.)
    spinolai (Meyer-Dür)
    viridis (Fall.)
Agnocoris reclairei (Wagner) (**Nb**)
Plesiocoris rugicollis (Fall.)
Polymerus nigritus (Fall.)
    unifasciatus (F.)
Calocoris norvegicus (Gmel.)
    roseomaculatus (DeGeer)
    sexguttatus (F.)
Adelphocoris lineolatus (Goeze)
    ticinensis (Meyer-Dür) (**Nb**)
Stenotus binotatus (F.)
Phytocoris dimidiatus Kirsch.
    longipennis Flor
    populi (L.)
    tiliae (F.)
    ulmi (L.)
    varipes Boh.
Capsus ater (L.)
    wagneri Remane (**Nb**)
Pantilius tunicatus (F.)
Stenodema calcaratum (Fall.)
    laevigatum (L.)
Notostira elongata (Geoff. in Fourc.)
        (=*erratica* auctt. nec (L.))
Megaloceraea recticornis (Geoff. in Fourc.)
        (=*linearis* (Füssl))
Teratocoris antennatus (Boh.)
    saundersi Dougl. & Scott
Leptopterna dolabrata (L.)
        (=*Miris dolabratus* L.)
    ferrugata (Fall.)
        (=*M. ferrugatus* Fall.)

DIPSOCORIDAE

Ceratomcombus coleoptratus (Zett.)

SALDIDAE

Saldula saltatoria (L.)
        (=*Acanthia saltatoria* L.)
Chartoscirta cincta (H.-S.)
    elegantula (Fall.)

HEBRIDAE

Hebrus pusillus (Fall.) (**Nb**)
    ruficeps (Thomson)

HYDROMETRIDAE

Hydrometra stagnorum (L.)

VELIIDAE

Microvelia reticulata (Burmeist.)
    umbricola Wroblewski (**RDB3**)

GERRIDAE

Gerris argentatus Schumm.
    gibbifer Schumm.
    lacustris (L.)
    lateralis Schumm.
    odontogaster (Zett.)

NEPIDAE

Nepa cinerea L.
Ranatra linearis (L.)

NAUCORIDAE

Ilyocoris cimicoides (L.)

NOTONECTIDAE

Notonecta glauca L.
    obliqua Gallen
        (=*furcata* F.)

PLEIDAE

Plea atomaria (Pall.)

CORIXIDAE

Micronecta poweri (Dougl. & Scott)
Cymatia bonsdorffi (C. Sahl.)
    coleoptrata (F.)
Callicorixa praeusta (Fieb.)
Corixa dentipes (Thomson)
    punctata (Ill.)
        (=*geoffroyi* Leach)
Hesperocorixa linnei (Fieb.)
        (=*Arctocorisa linnei* (Fieb.))
    sahlbergi (Fieb.)
Sigara dorsalis (Leach)
    falleni (Fieb.)
    fossarum (Leach)
    lateralis (Leach)
    limitata (Fieb.)
    nigrolineata (Fieb.)
    semistriata (Fieb.)
    striata (L.) (**Nb**)

'Homoptera'

Auchenorrhynca
(leaf-hoppers and allies)
Lists: N. A. Straw, W. A. Foster
Checklists: Hodkinson & White (1979); Le Quesne & Payne (1981)

CERCOPIDAE

Cercopis vulnerata Ill. in Rossi
Aphrophora alni (Fall.)
    alpina Melichar (**Nb**)
        (=*major* misident.)
    costalis Matsumura
        (=*forneri* Haupt)
    salicina (Goeze)
Philaenus spumarius (L.)
Neophilaenus lineatus (L.)

CICADELLIDAE

Megophthalmus scanicus (Fall.)
Cicadella viridis (L.)
Evacanthus interruptus (L.)
Idiocerus albicans Kirsch.
  confusus Flor
  elegans Flor
  lituratus (Fall.)
  populi (L.)
  rutilans Kirsch.
  similis Kirsch.
  stigmaticalis Lewis
  vitreus (F.)
Iassus lanio (L.)
Oncopsis flavicollis (L.)
  tristis (Zett.)
Macropsis albae Wagner
  cerea (Germar)
  fuscula (Zett.)
  impura (Boh.)
  infuscata (J. Sahl.)
  marginata (H.-S.)
  prasina (Boh.)
  scotti Edw.
Agallia brachyptera (Boh.) (**Nb**)
  consobrina Curt.
Aphrodes albifrons (L.)
  bifasciatus (L.)
  flavostriatus (Don.)
  makarovi Zachvat.
  serratulae (F.)
Stroggylocephalus agrestis (Fall.)
  livens (Zett.) (**Nb**)
Deltocephalus pulicaris (Fall.)
Recilia coronifera (Marshall)
Adarrus ocellaris (Fall.)
Mocuellus metrius (Flor)
Arthaldeus pascuellus (Fall.)
  striifrons (Kirsch.)
Psammotettix confinis (Dahlb.)
Paralimnus phragmitis (Boh.) (**Nb**)
Graphocraerus ventralis (Fall.)
Allygus mixtus (F.)
  modestus Scott
Euscelis incisus (Kirsch.)
    (=*plebejus* (Fall.)
  lineolatus Brullé
Conosanus obsoletus (Kirsch.)
Streptanus aemulans (Kirsch.)
  sordidus (Zett.)
Macustus grisescens (Zett.)
Mocydia crocea (H.-S.)
Thamnotettix confinis (Zett.)
Cicadula frontalis (H.-S.)
  persimilis (Edw.)
  quadrinotata (F.)
Macrosteles septemnotatus (Fall.)
  sexnotatus (Fall.)
  viridigriseus (Edw.)
Notus flavipennis (Zett.)
Forcipata citrinella (Zett.)
Kybos rufescens (Melichar)
  smaragdula (Fall.)
  virgator (Ribaut)
Empoasca decipiens Paoli
  vitis (Göthe)
Eurhadina pulchella (Fall.)
Eupteryx melissae Curt.
  signatipennis (Boh.)
  urticae (F.)

vittata (L.)
Ribautiana tenerrima (H.-S.)
Linnavuoriana sexmaculata (Hardy)
    (=*sexpunctata* (Fall.))
Typhlocyba quercus (F.)
Edwardsiana salicicola (Edw.)
Alnetoidia alneti (Dahlb.)
Arboridia parvula (Boh.)
Zyginidia scutellaris (H.-S.)
Zygina angusta Lethierry
  flammigera (Geoff. in Fourc.)

CIXIIDAE

Tachycixius pilosus (Olivier)
Cixius distinguendus Kirsch.
  nervosus (L.)

DELPHACIDAE

Asiraca clavicornis (F.) (**Nb**)
Kelisia pallidula (Boh.)
  punctulum (Kirch.)
Anakelisia fasciata (Kirsch.)
Stenocranus fuscovittatus (Stål) (**Nb**)
  major (Kirsch.)
  minutus (F.)
Chloriona smaragdula (Stål)
  unicolor (H.-S.)
Euconomelus lepidus (Boh.)
Conomelus anceps (Germar)
Delphax pulchellus (Curt.)
Euides speciosa (Boh.)
Eurysula lurida (Fieb.) (**Na**)
Dicranotropis hamata (Boh.)
Megamelus notula (Germar)
Megamelodes quadrimaculatus (Signoret)
Delphacodes venosus (Germar)
Javesella dubia (Kirsch.)
  pellucida (F.)
Paraliburnia adela (Flor)
  clypealis (J. Sahl.) (**RDBK**)
Florodelphax leptosoma (Flor)

Stenorrhyncha

(jumping plant lice and aphids)

PSYLLOIDEA

LIVIIDAE

Livia juncorum (Latr.)

PSYLLIDAE

Psylla alni (L.)
  ambigua Först.
  foersteri Flor
  mali Schmidb.
  peregrina Först.
  subferruginea Edw.
Trioza urticae (L.)

APHIDOIDEA

APHIDIDAE

List: Gardiner (1932a)
Checklist: Kloet & Hincks (1964); Stroyan (1984)

Pterocomma salicis (L.)
    (=*Melanoxanthus salicis* (L.))
Hyalopterus pruni (Geoff.)
Rhopalosiphum nymphaeae (L.)

Longicaudus trirhodus (Walk.)
 (=*Pergandeida trirhodus* (Walk.))
Cavariella pastinacae (L.)
 (=*capreae* (F.))
Ovatus crataegarius (Walk.)
 (=*Phorodon crataegarum* (Walk.))
Myzus lythri (Schr.)
Macrosiphum gei (C. L. Koch)
 rosae (L.)
Dactynotus cirsii (L.)
 (=*Macrosiphum olivatum* (Buckt.))
 jaceae (L.)
  (=*Macrosiphum jaceae* (L.))
 sonchi (L.)
Megoura viciae Buckt.
 (=*viciae* (Kalt.))

THYSANOPTERA

(thrips)

List: W. D. J. Kirk
Checklist: Mound *et al.* (1976)

THRIPIDAE

Chirothrips manicatus Halid.
Limothrips cerealium Halid.
 denticornis Halid.
Anaphothrips obscurus (O. F. Müll.)
Frankliniella tenuicornis (Uzel)
Odontothrips biuncus John
Rhaphidothrips longistylosus Uzel
Taeniothrips inconsequens (Uzel)
Thrips angusticeps Uzel
 atratus Halid.
 fuscipennis Halid.
 major Uzel
 pillichi Priesn.
 tabaci Lindem.
 validus Uzel
 vulgatissimus Halid.

PHLAEOTHRIPIDAE

Bolothrips dentipes (Reuter)
Megathrips nobilis Bagn.
Abiastothrips schaubergeri (Priesn.)
Haplothrips leucanthemi (Schr.)
Hoplothrips ulmi (F.)

RAPHIDIOPTERA

(snake flies)

Checklist: Plant (1994)

RAPHIDIIDAE

Xanthostigma xanthostigma (Schumm.)

MEGALOPTERA

(alder flies)

List: Lucas (1925)
Checklist: Plant (1994)

SIALIDAE

Sialis lutaria (L.)

NEUROPTERA

(lace-wings)

Lists: Lucas (1925, 1928); Gambles & Kerrich (1932); Imms
(1938b); C. W. Plant
Checklist: Plant (1994)

CONIOPTERYGOIDEA

CONIOPTERYGIDAE

Coniopteryginae
Semidalis aleyrodiformis (Steph.)

SISYRIDAE

Sisyra fuscata (F.)

HEMEROBIOIDEA

HEMEROBIIDAE

Psectra diptera (Burmeist.)

Micromus variegatus (F.)
Hemerobius humulinus L.
 lutescens F.
 micans (Olivier)

CHRYSOPIDAE

Chrysopinae

Chrysopa pallens (Rambur)
 (*septempunctata* Wesm.)
 perla (L.)
 phyllochroma Wesm. and/or *commata* Kis & Ujhelyi
Chrysoperla carnea (s. str.) (Steph.)
 carnea agg.
Cunctochrysa albolineata (Killington)
 (=*Chrysopa albolineata* Killington)
Dichochrysa flavifrons (Brauer)
 prasina (Burmeist.)
 (=*Chrysopa aspersa* Wesm.)

MECOPTERA

(scorpion flies)

Lists: Lucas (1928); Imms (1938b)
Checklist: Plant (1994)

PANORPIDAE

Panorpa communis L.
 germanica L.

TRICHOPTERA

(caddis-flies)

Lists: Wood (1929); Imms (1938c); D. J. Painter; I. Wallace
Checklist: Barnard (1985)

RHYACOPHILOIDEA

HYDROPTILIDAE

Agraylea sexmaculata (Curt.)
 =*pallidula* (McLach.)

HYDROPSYCHOIDEA

PSYCHOMYIIDAE

Tinodes waeneri (L.)
Lype reducta (Hagen)

POLYCENTROPODIDAE

Polycentropus flavomaculatus (F. J. Pict.)
Holocentropus dubius (Rambur)
 picicornis (Steph.)
Cyrnus flavidus McLach.
 trimaculatus (Curt.)

LIMNEPHILOIDEA

PHRYGANEIDAE

Phryganea bipunctata Retz.
 grandis L.
Trichostegia minor (Curt.)
Agrypnia pagetana Curt.
 varia (F.)
 (=*Phryganea varia*)

LIMNEPHILIDAE

Limnephilinae

Halesus radiatus (Curt.)
Anabolia nervosa (Curt.)
Glyphotaelius pellucidus (Retz.)
Grammotaulius nigropunctatus (Retz.)
    (=*atomarius* F.)
  nitidus (O. F. Müll.) (**RDB1**)
Limnephilus affinis Curt.
  centralis Curt.
  decipiens (Kolen.)
  flavicornis (F.)
  incisus Curt.
    (=*Colpotaulius incisus*)
  lunatus Curt.
  marmoratus Curt.
  politus McLach.
  rhombicus (L.)
  stigma Curt.

SERICOSTOMATIDAE

Notidobia ciliaris (L.)

MOLANNIDAE

Molanna angustata Curt.

LEPTOCERIDAE

Athripsodes aterrimus (Steph.)
    (=*Leptocerus aterrimus* (Steph.))
  cinereus (Curt.)
    (=*Leptocerus cinereus* (Curt.))
Ceraclea fulva (Rambur)
    (=*Leptocerus fulvus* (Rambur))
  senilis (Burmeist.)
    (=*Leptocerus senilis* (Burmeist.))
Mystacides azurea (L.)
  longicornis (L.)
  nigra (L.)
Erotesis baltica McLach. (**RDB2**)
Triaenodes bicolor (Curt.)
Oecetis furva (Rambur)
  lacustris (F. J. Pict.)
  ochracea (Curt.)

LEPIDOPTERA
(butterflies and moths)

'Microlepidoptera' list (smaller, primitive moths) by A. M. Emmet (1972), revised A. M. Emmet (pers.comm.)

'Macrolepidoptera' list (butterflies and larger moths, including Hepialidae (swift moths), Cossidae (goat and leopard moths), Zygaenidae (burnets) and Sesiidae (clear-wings)) by T. J. Bennett; C. C. Smith; D. E. Wilson Checklists and classification: Emmet (1991); Bradley (1998; edn 2, 2000)

* not recorded since Farren (1923, 1926a,b);
† not recorded since Fryer (1938);
§ possible misidentification, confirmation required
Dates refer to extinctions, last records, reintroductions or recent new records of rare or local species of special interest

MICROPTERIGOIDEA

MICROPTERIGIDAE
Micropterix mansuetella Zell.*
  aruncella (Scop.)
  calthella (L.)

ERIOCRANIOIDEA

ERIOCRANIIDAE
Eriocrania sparrmannella (Bosc)
  semipurpurella (Steph.)

HEPIALOIDEA

HEPIALIDAE
Hepialus humuli (L.) (Ghost Moth)
  sylvina (L.) (Orange Swift)
  hecta (L.) (Gold Swift)
  lupulinus (L.) (Common Swift)
  fusconebulosa (DeGeer) (Map-winged Swift)§

NEPTICULOIDEA

NEPTICULIDAE
Bohemannia pulverosella (Stt.)
Ectoedemia argyropeza (Zell.)
  turbidella (Zell.)
  intimella (Zell.)
  angulifasciella (Stt.)
  atricollis (Stt.)
  rubivora (Wocke)
  occultella (L.)
    (*argentipedella* (Zell.))
  albifasciella (Hein.)
  subbimaculella (Haw.)
  heringi (Toll)
    (*quercifoliae* (Toll))
Fomoria septembrella (Stt.)
Stigmella aurella (Fabr.)
    (*fragariella* (Hein.))
  splendidissimella (H.-S.)
  ulmariae (Wocke)
  lemniscella (Zell.)
    (*marginicolella* (Stt.))
  continuella (Stt.)
  plagicolella (Stt.)
  salicis (Stt.)
  obliquella (Hein.)
  trimaculella (Haw.)
  assimilella (Zell.)

perpygmaeella (Doubl.)
    (*pygmaeella* (Haw.))
  ulmivora (Fol.)
  paradoxa (Frey)
  atricapitella (Haw.)
  ruficapitella (Haw.)
  basiguttella (Hein.)
  anomalella (Goeze) (Rose Leaf Miner)
  centifoliella (Zell.)
  viscerella (Stt.)
  malella (Stt.) (Apple Pygmy)
  catharticella (Stt.)
  hybnerella (Hb.)
  oxyacanthella (Stt.)
  regiella (H.-S.)
  crataegella (Klim.)
  betulicola (Stt.)
  luteella (Stt.)
  alnetella (Stt.)
  lapponica (Wocke)
  confusella (Wood)

OPOSTEGIDAE
Opostega salaciella (Treit.)
Pseudopostega auritella (Hb.)*
  crepusculella (Zell.)

TISCHERIOIDEA

TISCHERIIDAE
Emmetia marginea (Haw.)

INCURVARIOIDEA

INCURVARIIDAE

Incurvariinae

Phylloporia bistrigella (Haw.)
Incurvaria masculella ([D. & S.])
  oehlmanniella (Hb.)

Prodoxinae

Lampronia corticella (L.) (Raspberry Moth)
  (*rubiella* (Bjerk.))

Nematopogoninae

Nematopogon schwarziellus (Zell.)*
    (*panzerella* auctt.)
  metaxella (Hb.)

Adelinae

Nemophora fasciella (Fabr.)§
  minimella ([D. & S.])
  cupriacella (Hb.)*
  degeerella (L.)
Adela reaumurella (L.)
  croesella (Scop.)
  rufimitrella (Scop.)*

HELIOZELIDAE
Heliozela sericiella (Haw.)
    (*stanneella* (F. v. R.))
  resplendella (Stt.)
  hammoniella (Sorh.)
    (*betulae* (Stt.))
Antispila metallella ([D. & S.])§
    (*pfeifferella* (Hb.))

COSSOIDEA

COSSIDAE

Zeuzerinae

Phragmataecia castaneae (Hb.) (Reed Leopard) (**RDB2**)
Zeuzera pyrina (L.) (Leopard Moth)

Cossinae

Cossus cossus (L.) (Goat Moth) [1997]

ZYGAENOIDEA

Zygaeninae

Zygaena filipendulae (L.) (Six-spot Burnet) [Verrall's Fen: 1999]

TINEOIDEA

PSYCHIDAE

Taleporiinae

Narycia monilifera (Geoff.)

Psychinae

Luffia ferchaultella (Steph.)
Psyche casta (Pall.)

TINEIDAE

Myrmecozelinae

Haplotinea insectella (Fabr.)*

Nemapogoninae

Nemapogon cloacella (Haw.) (Cork Moth)
Nemaxera betulinella (Payk.)
  (*corticella* (Curt.))

Tineinae

Monopis imella (Hb.)*
Trichophaga tapetzella (L.) (Tapestry Moth)*
Tineola bisselliella (Hum.) (Common Clothes Moth)*
Niditinea fuscella (L.) (Brown-dotted Clothes Moth)*
  (*fuscipunctella* (Haw.))
  striolella (Matsum.)
    piercella (Bent.)
Tinea pellionella L. (Case-bearing Clothes Moth)
  flavescentella Haw.*
  pallescentella Stt. (Large Pale Clothes Moth)*
  semifulvella Haw.
  trinotella Thunb.

BUCCULATRICIDAE

Bucculatrix cristatella Zell.*
  nigricomella Zell.
  frangutella (Goeze)
    (*frangulella* missp.)
  albedinella Zell.
  cidarella Zell.
  ulmella Zell.
  bechsteinella (Bech. & Scharf.)
    (*crataegi* Zell.)

GRACILLARIIDAE

Gracillariinae

Caloptilia elongella (L.)*
  robustella Jäckh
  stigmatella (Fabr.)

  syringella (Fabr.)
Aspilapterix tringipennella (Zell.)†
Calybites phasianipennella (Hb.)
Eucalybites auroguttella (Steph.)
Parornix betulae (Stt.)
  anglicella (Stt.)
  finitimella (Zell.)
Deltaornix torquillella (Zell.)
Callisto denticulella (Thunb.)
Dialectica imperialella (Zell.)
Acrocercops brongniardella (Fabr.)

Lithocolletinae

Phyllonorycter harrisella (L.)
  heegeriella (Zell.)
  quercifoliella (Zell.)
  messaniella (Zell.)
  oxyacanthae (Frey)
  blancardella (Fabr.)
  pomonella (Zell.)
    (*spinicolella* (Zell.))
    (*cerasicolella* (H.-S.))
  lantanella (Schr.)
  corylifoliella (Hb.)
  leucographella (Zell.) [1998]
  salictella (Zell.) ssp. *viminiella* (Sirc.)
  salicicolella (Sirc.)
  dubitella (H.-S.)
  hilarella (Zett.)*
    (*spinolella* (Dup.))
  rajella (L.)
    (*alnifoliella* (Hb.))
  quinqueguttella (Stt.)
  schreberella (Fabr.)
  ulmifoliella (Hb.)
  emberizaepenella (Bouché)
  tristrigella (Haw.)
  stettinensis (Nic.)

Phyllocnistinae

Phyllocnistis saligna (Zell.)
  unipunctella (Steph.)

SESIOIDEA

SESIIDAE

Sesiinae

Sesia apiformis (Cl.) (Hornet Moth) [1997]
  bembeciformis (Hb.) (Lunar Hornet Moth) [1997]

Paranthreninae

Synanthedon tipuliformis (Cl.) (Currant Clearwing)*
  vespiformis (L.) (Yellow-legged Clearwing) [1973]
  myopaeformis (Borkh.) (Red-belted Clearwing) [1948]
  formicaeformis (Esp.) (Red-tipped Clearwing)*

CHOREUTIDAE

Anthophila fabriciana (L.) (Nettle Tap)
Prochoreutis sehestediana (Fabr.)
  (*punctosa* (Haw.))
  myllerana (Fabr.)*
Choreutis pariana (Cl.) (Apple Leaf Skeletonizer)†

YPONOMEUTOIDEA

GLYPHIPTERIGIDAE

Glyphipteriginae

Glyphipterix simpliciella (Steph.) (Cocksfoot Moth)
  schoenicolella Boyd*
  forsterella (Fabr.)*
  fuscoviridella (Haw.)*
  thrasonella (Scop.)

Orthoteliinae

Orthotelia sparganella (Thunb.)*

YPONOMEUTIDAE

Argyresthiinae

Argyresthia brockeella (Hb.)
  goedartella (L.)
  pygmaeella ([D. & S.])
  curvella (L.)
    (*cornella* auctt.)
  retinella Zell.
  spinosella Stt.
    (*mendica* (Haw.))
  semifusca (Haw.)
  pruniella (Cl.) (Cherry Fruit Moth)
  bonnetella (L.)
    (*curvella* auctt.)
  albistria (Haw.)

Yponomeutinae

Yponomeuta evonymella (L.) (Bird-cherry Ermine)*
  padella (L.) (Orchard Ermine)
  malinellus Zell. (Apple Ermine)
  plumbella ([D. & S.])
  sedella Treit.
    (*vigintipunctata* (Retz.))
Swammerdamia caesiella (Hb.)
  pyrella (Vill.)
Paraswammerdamia albicapitella (Scharf.)*
  (*spiniella* (Hb.))
  lutarea (Haw.)
Prays fraxinella (Bjerk.) (Ash Bud Moth)*
Scythropia crataegella (L.) (Hawthorn Moth)*

Ypsolophinae

Ypsolopha dentella (Fabr.) (Honeysuckle Moth)
  scabrella (L.)
  horridella (Treit.)
  vittella (L.)*

Plutellinae

Plutella xylostella (L.) (Diamond-back Moth)

Acrolepiinae

Acrolepia autumnitella Curt.
  (*pygmeana* (Haw.))

LYONETIIDAE

Cemiostominae

Leucoptera laburnella (Stt.) (Laburnum Leaf Miner)*
  lathyrifoliella Stt. f. *orobi* Stt.§
  lotella (Stt.)*
  malifoliella (Costa) (Pear Leaf Blister Moth)
    (*scitella* (Zell.))

Lyonetiinae

Lyonetia clerkella (L.) (Apple Leaf Miner)

Bedelliinae

Bedellia somnulentella (Zell.)

GELECHIOIDEA

COLEOPHORIDAE

Coleophora lutipennella (Zell.)
  gryphipennella (Hb.)
  flavipennella (Dup.)
  serratella (L.)
  spinella (Schr.) (Apple & Plum Case-bearer)
    (*cerasivorella* Pack.)
  badiipennella (Dup.)
  siccifolia Stt.
  lusciniaepennella (Treit.)
    (*viminetella* Zell.)
  violacea (Ström)
    (*hornigi* Toll)
  binderella (Koll.)
  potentillae Elisha
  albitarsella Zell.
  trifolii (Curt.)
  mayrella (Hb.)
    (*spissicornis* (Haw.))
  lineolea (Haw.)
  albidella ([D. & S.])
  anatipennella (Hb.) (Pistol Case-bearer)
    (*bernoulliella* auctt.)
  betulella Hein. & Wocke
    (*ibipennella* auctt.)
  palliatella (Zinck.)*
    (*kuehnella* (Goeze))
  striatipennella Nyl.
  follicularis (Vall.)
    (*troglodytella* (Dup.))
  trochilella (Dup.)*
  peribenanderi Toll
  paripennella Zell.*
  therinella Tengst.§
  argentula (Steph.)
  saxicolella (Dup.)*
    (*laripennella* auctt.)
  otidipennella (Hb.)§
    (*murinipennella* (Dup.))
  taeniipennella H.-S.
  glaucicolella Wood
  alticolella Zell.

ELACHISTIDAE

Elachista atricomella Stt.
  alpinella Stt.
  luticomella Zell.*
  apicipunctella Stt.
  subnigrella Dougl.*
  pomerana Frey
  humilis Zell.
  canapennella (Hb.)
    (*pulchella* (Haw.))
  rufocinerea (Haw.)
  maculicerusella Bru.
    (*monosemiella* Rössler)
    (*cerusella* (Hb.))
  argentella (Cl.)
  triatomea (Haw.)*
  bedellella (Sirc.)*
  megerlella (Hb.)
  bisulcella (Dup.)
Biselachista cinereopunctella (Haw.)*
  eleochariella (Stt.)*

utonella (Frey)
   (*paludum* (Frey))
albidella (Nyl.)
Cosmiotes freyerella (Hb.)

OECOPHORIDAE

Oecophorinae

Denisia albimaculea (Haw.)
  (*augustella* auctt.)
Batia lunaris (Haw.)
  unitella (Hb.)
Borkhausenia fuscescens (Haw.)
  minutella (L.)*
Telechrysis tripuncta (Haw.)
Hofmannophila pseudospretella (Stt.) (Brown House-moth)
Endrosis sarcitrella (L.) (White-shouldered House-moth)
Esperia sulphurella (Fabr.)

Carcinae

Carcina quercana (Fabr.)

Chimabachinae

Diurnea fagella ([D. & S.])
Dasystoma salicella (Hb.)

Depressariinae

Luquetia lobella ([D. & S.])*
Depressaria ultimella Stt.*
  pastinacella (Dup.)
  sordidatella Tengst.
    (*weirella* Stt.)
  albipunctella ([D. & S.])
    (*aegopodiella* (Hb.))*
  chaerophylli Zell.*
Agonopterix heracliana (L.)
  ciliella (Stt.)
  purpurea (Haw.)*
  subpropinquella (Stt.)*
  alstromeriana (Cl.)
  propinquella (Treit.)*
  arenella ([D. & S.])
  kaekeritziana (L.)
    (*liturella* [D. & S.])
  pallorella (Zell.)§
  ocellana (Fabr.)
  carduella (Hb.)§
  liturosa (Haw.)
    (*huebneri* Bradley)
  conterminella (Zell.)
  anglicella (Hb.)
  yeatiana (Fabr.)

ETHMIIDAE

Ethmia quadrillella (Goeze) (**Na**)
  (*funerella* (Fabr.))

GELECHIIDAE

Anomologinae

Metzneria lappella (L.)*
  metzneriella (Stt.)*
Apodia bifractella (Dup.)
Eulamprotes atrella ([D. & S.])
Monochroa lucidella (Steph.)*
  palustrella (Dougl.)*
  conspersella (H.-S.) (**RDB1**)
    (*morosa* (Mühl.))
    (*quaestionella* (H.-S.))

suffusella (Dougl.)
lutulentella (Zell.) (**RDBK**)
arundinetella (Stt.)* (**RDB1**)
divisella (Dougl.)* (**RDB2**)
Chrysoesthia drurella (Fabr.)
  (*hermannella* auctt.)
  sexguttella (Thunb.)†
Ptocheuusa paupella (Zell.)
Aristotelia subdecurtella (Stt.)* (?**Extinct**)
Bryotropha basaltinella (Zell.)*
  umbrosella (Zell.)§
  affinis (Haw.)*
  senectella (Zell.)
  desertella (Dougl.)*
  terrella ([D. & S.])*
  politella (Stt.)*

Gelechiinae

Exoteleia dodecella (L.)*
Athrips tetrapunctella (Thunb.)* (**RDB1**)
Pseudotelphusa paripunctella (Thunb.)*
Altenia scriptella (Hb.) (**Nb**)
Teleiodes vulgella ([D.&S.])
Carpatolechia notatella (Hb.)
  proximella (Hb.)
  alburnella (Zell.)
Chionodes fumatella (Dougl.)*
  distinctella (Zell.)* (**Nb**)
Mirificarma mulinella (Zell.)*
Gelechia rhombella ([D. & S.])*
  sororculella (Hb.)
  muscosella Zell. (**RDB2**)
  turpella ([D. & S.])* (**RDBK**)
Scrobipalpa costella (Humph. & West.)
  acuminatella (Sirc.)
Caryocolum fraternella (Dougl.)*

Anacampsinae

Aproaerema anthyllidella (Hb.)*
Anacampsis populella (Cl.)

Dichomeridinae

Acompsia cinerella (Cl.)*
Brachmia blandella (Fabr.)
  (*gerronella* (Zell.))
  inornatella (Dougl.) (**Nb**)
Helcystogramma rufescens (Haw.)

Pexicopiinae

Thiotricha subocellea (Steph.)

AUTOSTICHIDAE

Oegoconiinae

Oegoconia deauratella (H.-S.)

BLASTOBASIDAE

Blastobasis decolorella (Woll.)

BATRACHEDRIDAE

Batrachedra praeangusta (Haw.)

MOMPHIDAE

Mompha raschkiella (Zell.)
  miscella ([D. & S.])§
  ochraceella (Curt.)
  lacteella (Steph.)*
  propinquella (Stt.)
  divisella H.-S.

epilobiella ([D. & S.])
  (*fulvescens* (Haw.))

COSMOPTERIGIDAE

Cosmopteriginae

Cosmopterix zieglerella (Hb.)§
  orichalcea Stt.
  lienigiella Lien. & Zell.
Limnaecia phragmitella Stt.

Blastodacninae

Spuleria flavicaput (Haw.)
Blastodacna hellerella (Dup.)

Chrysopeleiinae

Sorhagenia rhamniella (Zell.)
  lophyrella (Dougl.)

TORTRICOIDEA

TORTRICIDAE

Tortricinae

Phtheochroa inopiana (Haw.)
  rugosana (Hb.)
  schreibersiana (Fröl.)*
  sodaliana (Haw.)
Phalonidia manniana (F. v. R.)
Gynnidomorpha minimana (Carad.)*
  permixtana ([D. & S.])§
  vectisana (Humph. & Westw.)*
  alismana (Rag.)
Cochylimorpha straminea (Haw.)
Agapeta hamana (L.)
  zoegana (L.)
Aethes tesserana ([D. & S.])*
  hartmanniana (Cl.)*
  williana (Brahm)†
  cnicana (Westw.)
  rubigana (Treit.)
  smeathmanniana (Fabr.)*
  dilucidana (Steph.)*
Commophila aeneana (Hb.)
Eupoecilia angustana (Hb.)†
  ambiguella (Hb.) Vine Moth
Cochylidia rupicola (Curt.)
Falseuncaria ruficiliana (Haw.) [1930]
  degreyana (McLach.)*
Cochylis nana (Haw.)
Pandemis corylana (Fabr.) (Chequered Fruit-tree Tortrix)
  cerasana (Hb.) (Barred Fruit-tree Tortrix)
  heparana ([D. & S.]) (Dark Fruit-tree Tortrix)
  dumetana (Treit.)
Argyrotaenia ljungiana (Thunb.)*
  (*pulchellana* (Haw.))
Archips podana (Scop.) (Large Fruit-tree Tortrix)
  crataegana (Hb.) (Brown Oak Tortrix)*
  xylosteana (L.) (Variegated Golden Tortrix)
  rosana (L.) (Rose Tortrix)
Choristoneura diversana (Hb.)
Syndemis musculana (Hb.)
Aphelia paleana (Hb.) (Timothy Tortrix)
Clepsis senecionana (Hb.)
  spectrana (Treit.) (Cyclamen Tortrix)
  consimilana (Hb.)
Ptycholoma lecheana (L.)
Lozotaenia forsterana (Fabr.)
Ditula angustiorana (Haw.) (Red-barred Tortrix)
Pseudargyrotoza conwagana (Fabr.)
Eulia ministrana (L.)

Cnephasia longana (Haw.)
  communana (H.-S.)*
  conspersana Dougl.*
  stephensiana (Doubl.) (Grey Tortrix)
  asseclana ([D. & S.]) (Flax Tortrix)
    (*interjectana* (Haw.))
  pasiuana (Hb.)
  incertana (Treit.) (Light Grey Tortrix)
Neosphaleroptera nubilana (Hb.)*
Tortrix viridana L. (Green Oak Tortrix)
Acleris bergmanniana (L.)
  holmiana (L.)
  laterana (Fabr.)
    (*latifasciana* (Haw.))
  comariana (Lien. & Zell.) (Strawberry Tortrix)
  rhombana ([D. & S.]) (Rhomboid Tortrix)
  aspersana (Hb.)
  shepherdana (Steph.)
  schalleriana (L.)
  variegana ([D. & S.]) (Garden Rose Tortrix)
  kochiella (Goeze)
    (*boscana* (Fabr.))
  hastiana (L.)
  cristana ([D. & S.])
  lorquiniana (Dup.)
  emargana (Fabr.)

Chlidanotinae

Isotrias rectifasciana (Haw.)

Olethreutinae

Celypha striana ([D. & S.])
  rosaceana (Schläg.)
  lacunana ([D. & S.])
  doubledayana (Barr.)*
  rivulana (Scop.)*
Olethreutes olivana (Treit.)*
Hedya pruniana (Hb.) (Plum Tortrix)
  nubiferana (Haw.) (Marbled Orchard Tortrix)
    (*dimidioalba* (Retz.))
  ochroleucana (Fröl.)
  salicella (L.)
Orthotaenia undulana ([D. & S.])
Apotomis semifasciana (Haw.)
  lineana ([D. & S.])
  betuletana (Haw.)
  capreana (Hb.)
Endothenia gentianaeana (Hb.)*
  oblongana (Haw.)*
  marginana (Haw.)*
    (*sellana* (Fröl.))
  pullana (Haw.)
    (*fuligana* auctt.)
  ustulana (Haw.)
  nigricostana (Haw.)
  ericetana (Humph. & Westw.)
  quadrimaculana (Haw.)
Lobesia abscisana (Doubl.)
Bactra furfurana (Haw.)
  lancealana (Hb.)
Eudemis profundana ([D. & S.])*
Ancylis achatana ([D. & S.])
  unguicella (L.)*
  uncella ([D. & S.])*
  geminana (Don.)*
  diminutana (Haw.)
  subarcuana (Dougl.)*
  unculana (Haw.)*
  badiana ([D. & S.])
  paludana (Barr.)
  apicella ([D. & S.])

Epinotia subocellana (Don.)
　bilunana (Haw.)
　ramella (L.)
　immundana (F. v. R.)
　tetraquetrana (Haw.)
　nisella (Cl.)
　tenerana ([D. & S.]) (Nut Bud Moth)
　cruciana (L.) (Willow Tortrix)
　abbreviana (Fabr.)
　　(*trimaculana* (Don.))
　caprana (Fabr.)
　brunnichana (L.)
　solandriana (L.)*
Rhopobota naevana (Hb.) (Holly Tortrix)
　(*unipunctana* (Haw.))
Zeiraphera isertana (Fabr.)
Gypsonoma aceriana (Dup.)
　dealbana (Fröl.)
　oppressana (Treit.)
　minutana (Hb.)
Gibbifera simplana (F. v. R.)*
Epiblema cynosbatella (L.)
　uddmanniana (L.) (Bramble Shoot Moth)
　trimaculana (Haw.)
　rosaecolana (Doubl.)
　roborana ([D. & S.])
　foenella (L.)
　scutulana ([D. & S.])
　cirsiana (Zell.)
　costipunctana (Haw.)
Eucosma campoliliana ([D. & S.])
　hohenwartiana ([D. & S.])
　f. *fulvana* (Steph.)*
　cana (Haw.)
　obumbratana (Lien. & Zell.)
Spilonota ocellana ([D. & S.]) (Bud Moth)
Enarmonia formosana (Scop.) (Cherry Bark Moth)*
Pammene obscurana (Steph.)
　argyrana (Hb.)*
　populana (Fabr.)*
　regiana (Zell.)*
　rhediella (Cl.) (Fruitlet Mining Tortrix)
　gallicana (Guen.)*
　aurana (Fabr.)
Grapholita compositella (Fabr.)
　janthinana (Dup.)
　tenebrosana (Dup.)*
　funebrana (Treit.) (Plum Fruit Moth)
　jungiella (Cl.)*
　orobana (Treit.)
Cydia succedana ([D. & S.])*
　servillana (Dup.)
　nigricana (Fabr.) (Pea Moth)
　pomonella (L.) (Codling Moth)
　leguminana (Lien. & Zell.) [Extinct at Wicken, *c.* 1976]
　　(**RDB1**)
Dichrorampha petiverella (L.)*
　alpinana (Treit.)
　sequana (Hb.)*
　acuminatana (Lien. & Zell.)
　consortana Steph.*
　simpliciana (Haw.)*
　gueneeana Obraz.*
　plumbana (Scop.)
　sedatana Busck*

EPERMENIOIDEA

EPERMENIIDAE

Phaulernis dentella (Zell.)*
　fulviguttella (Zell.)

Epermenia falciformis (Haw.)
　(*illigerella* auctt.)
　chaerophyllella (Goeze)

SCHRECKENSTEINIOIDEA

SCHRECKENSTEINIIDAE

Schreckensteinia festaliella (Hb.)

ALUCITOIDEA

ALUCITIDAE

Alucita hexadactyla L. (Twenty-plume Moth)

PYRALOIDEA

PYRALIDAE

Crambinae

Chilo phragmitella (Hb.)
Calamotropha paludella (Hb.)* (**Nb**)
Chrysoteuchia culmella (L.)
Crambus pascuella (L.)
　silvella (Hb.)§ (**RDB3**)
　uliginosellus Zell.*
　lathoniellus (Zinck.)
　　(*nemorella* auctt.)
　perlella (Scop.)
Agriphila selasella (Hb.)
　straminella ([D. & S.])
　tristella ([D. & S.])
　inquinatella ([D. & S.])
　latistria (Haw.) [1998]
　geniculea (Haw.)
Catoptria pinella (L.)*
　falsella ([D. & S.])
Platytes cerussella ([D. & S.]) [1992]

Schoenobiinae

Schoenobius gigantella ([D. & S.]) (**Nb**)
Donacaula forficella (Thunb.)
　mucronellus ([D. & S.])

Scopariinae

Scoparia subfusca Haw.
　(*cembrella* auctt.)
　pyralella ([D. & S.])
　　(*arundinata* (Thunb.))
　ambigualis (Treit.)
Dipleurina lacustrata (Panz.)
　(*crataegella* auctt.)
Eudonia pallida (Curt.)
　truncicolella (Stt.)*
　lineola (Curt.)* (**Nb**)
　mercurella (L.)

Acentropinae

Acentria ephemerella ([D. & S.]) (Water Veneer)
　(*nivea* (Olivier))

Nymphulinae

Elophila nymphaeata (L.) (Brown China-mark)
Parapoynx stratiotata (L.) (Ringed China-mark)
Nymphula stagnata (Don.) (Beautiful China-mark)
Cataclysta lemnata (L.) (Small China-mark)

Evergestinae

Evergestis forficalis (L.) (Garden Pebble)
　extimalis (Scop.) [1981]
　pallidata (Hufn.)

Moths and butterflies

Pyraustinae

Pyrausta aurata (Scop.)
 purpuralis (L.)
 ostrinalis (Hb.)
 despicata (Scop.)
   (*cespitalis* ([D. & S.]))*
Loxostege sticticalis (L.) (**Extinct** as resident in Britain)
Sitochroa palealis ([D. & S.])
 verticalis (L.)
Ostrinia nubilalis (Hb.) [1998]
Eurrhypara hortulata (L.) (Small Magpie)
Perinephela lancealis ([D. & S.])
Phlyctaenia coronata (Hufn.)
 perlucidalis (Hb.)
Anania verbascalis ([D. & S.])§ (**Nb**)
Ebulea crocealis (Hb.)
Opsibotys fuscalis ([D. & S.])
Nascia cilialis (Hb.) (**Na**)
Udea lutealis (Hb.)
 prunalis ([D. & S.])
 olivalis ([D. & S.])
 ferrugalis (Hb.)
Nomophila noctuella ([D. & S.]) (Rush Veneer)
Pleuroptya ruralis (Scop.) (Mother of Pearl)

Pyralinae

Hypsopygia costalis (Fabr.) (Gold Triangle)
Orthopygia glaucinalis (L.)
Pyralis farinalis (L.) (Meal Moth)
Aglossa caprealis (Hb.) (Small Tabby)
 pinguinalis (L.) (Large Tabby)
Endotricha flammealis ([D. & S.]) [1977]

Galleriinae

Galleria mellonella (L.) (Wax Moth)
Achroia grisella (Fabr.) (Lesser Wax Moth)*
Aphomia sociella (L.) (Bee Moth)

Phycitinae

Cryptoblabes bistriga (Haw.)*
Acrobasis consociella (Hb.)
Trachycera suavella (Zinck.)*
 advenella (Zinck.)
 marmorea (Haw.)
Pempelia palumbella ([D. & S.])*
 formosa (Haw.)
Phycita roborella ([D. & S.]) [1973]
Dioryctria abietella ([D. & S.]) [1977]
Hypochalcia ahenella ([D. & S.])*
Myelois circumvoluta Fourc. (Thistle Ermine) [1992]
 (*cribrella* (Hb.))
Ephestia elutella (Hb.) (Cacao Moth)
Homeosoma nebulella ([D. & S.])* (**Nb**)
 sinuella (Fabr.) [1992]
Phycitodes binaevella (Hb.)

PTEROPHOROIDEA

PTEROPHORIDAE

Pterophorinae

Buckleria paludum (Zell.)*
Platyptilia gonodactyla ([D. & S.])
 ochrodactyla ([D. & S.])*
 pallidactyla (Haw.)*
Stenoptilia zophodactylus (Dup.)*
 bipunctidactyla (Scop.)
Pterophorus pentadactyla (L.) (White Plume Moth)
Adaina microdactyla (Hb.)
Oidaematophorus lithodactyla (Treit.)
Emmelina monodactyla (L.)

'Rhopalocera' (butterflies)

HESPERIOIDEA

HESPERIIDAE

Hesperiinae

Thymelicus sylvestris (Poda) (Small Skipper)
 lineola (Ochsen.) (Essex Skipper)
Ochlodes faunus (Turati) (Large Skipper)
 (*venatus* auctt.)

Pyrginae

Pyrgus malvae L. (Grizzled Skipper) [1940s]

PAPILIONOIDEA

PAPILIONIDAE

Papilioninae

Papilio machaon (L.) (Swallowtail) [extinct at Wicken, 1950s; reintroduced (unsuccessfully), 1960s and 1993] (**RDB2**)

PIERIDAE

Coliadinae

Colias hyale (L.) (Pale Clouded Yellow)*
 croceus (Geoff.) (Clouded Yellow)*
Gonepteryx rhamni (L.) (Brimstone)

Pierinae

Pieris brassicae (L.) (Large White)
 rapae (L.) (Small White)
 napi (L.) (Green-veined White)
Anthocharis cardamines (L.) (Orange-tip)

LYCAENIDAE

Theclinae

Callophrys rubi (L.) (Green Hairstreak)
Satyrium w-album (Knoch) (White-letter Hairstreak)†

Lycaeninae

Lycaena phlaeas (L.) (Small Copper)
 dispar dispar Haw. (Large Copper) (Burw.Fen, 'Wicken') [**Extinct, 1851**]
 dispar rutilus Werneb. (Large Copper, German race) [introduced 1909 (unsuccessfully)]
 dispar batavus (Ob.) (Large Copper, Dutch race) [introduced, bred 1927–42]

Polyommatinae

Aricia agestis ([D. & S.]) (Brown Argus)
Polyommatus icarus (Rott.) (Common Blue)
Celastrina argiolus (L.) (Holly Blue)

NYMPHALIDAE

Limenitinae

Limenitis camilla (L.) (White Admiral) [one, 1989]

Nymphalinae

Vanessa atalanta (L.) (Red Admiral)
 cardui (L.) (Painted Lady)
Aglais urticae (L.) (Small Tortoiseshell)
 polychloros (L.) (Large Tortoiseshell)* [Extinct nationally as breeding sp.] (**RDB1**)
Inachis io (L.) (Peacock)
Polygonia c-album (L.) (Comma)

Argynninae

Argynnis adippe ([D. & S.]) (High Brown Fritillary) [1882]*
   (**RDB2**)
   aglaja (L.) (Dark Green Fritillary) [1923]*
Eurodryas aurinia (Rott.) (Marsh Fritillary) [1922]*

Satyrinae

Pararge aegeria (L.) (Speckled Wood)
Lasiommata megera (L.) (Wall)
Melanargia galathea (L.) (Marbled White) [1946]
Pyronia tithonus (L.) (Gatekeeper)
Maniola jurtina (L.) (Meadow Brown)
Coenonympha pamphilus (L.) (Small Heath)
Aphantopus hyperantus (L.) (Ringlet)

Danainae

Danaus plexippus (L.) (Monarch) [one, 1992]

'Heterocera' (larger moths)

BOMBYCOIDEA

LASIOCAMPIDAE

Poecilocampa populi (L.) (December Moth)
Trichiura crataegi (L.) (Pale Eggar)
Eriogaster lanestris (L.) (Small Eggar) (**RDB2**)
Malacosoma neustria (L.) (Lackey)
Lasiocampa quercus (L.) (Oak Eggar)
Macrothylacia rubi (L.) (Fox Moth)
Euthrix potatoria (L.) (Drinker)
Gastropacha quercifolia (L.) (Lappet)

SATURNIIDAE

Saturnia pavonia (L.) (Emperor Moth)

DREPANOIDEA

DREPANIDAE

Falcaria lacertinaria (L.) (Scalloped Hook-tip)
Watsonalla binaria (Hufn.) (Oak Hook-tip)
Drepana falcataria (L.) (Pebble Hook-tip)
Cilix glaucata (Scop.) (Chinese Character)

Thyatirinae

Thyatira batis (L.) (Peach Blossom)
Habrosyne pyritoides (Hufn.) (Buff Arches)
Tethea ocularis (L.) (Figure of Eighty)
   or ([D. & S.]) (Poplar Lutestring) [1939]
Ochropacha duplaris (L.) (Common Lutestring)

GEOMETROIDEA

GEOMETRIDAE

Archiearinae

Archiearis parthenias (L.) (Orange Underwing)

Oenochrominae

Alsophila aescularia ([D. & S.]) (March Moth)

Geometrinae

Pseudoterpna pruinata (Hufn.) (Grass Emerald) [1980]
Geometra papilionaria (L.) (Large Emerald)
Hemithea aestivaria (Hb.) (Common Emerald)
Chlorissa viridata (L.) (Small Grass Emerald) †
Jodis lactearia (L.) (Little Emerald)

Sterrhinae

Cyclophora albipunctata (Hufn.) (Birch Mocha)†
   punctaria (L.) (Maiden's Blush) [1930s]
Timandra comae Schmidt (Blood-vein)
   (*griseata* auctt.)
Scopula rubiginata (Hufn.) (Tawny Wave) [1897]* (**RDB3**)
   marginepunctata (Goeze) (Mullein Wave) [1930s]†
   imitaria (Hb.) (Small Blood-vein)
   immutata (L.) (Lesser Cream Wave)
   floslactata (Haw.) (Cream Wave)
Idaea muricata (Hufn.) (Purple-bordered Gold)
   biselata (Hufn.) (Small Fan-footed Wave)
   fuscovenosa (Goeze) (Dwarf Cream Wave)
   seriata (Schr.) (Small Dusty Wave)†
   dimidiata (Hufn.) (Single-dotted Wave)
   trigeminata (Haw.) (Treble Brown Spot)
   emarginata (L.) (Small Scallop)
   aversata (L.) (Riband Wave)

Larentiinae

Orthonama vittata (Borkh.) (Oblique Carpet)
   obstipata (Fabr.) (Gem) [1930s]†
Xanthorhoe biriviata (Borkh.) (Balsam Carpet) [1970s]§
   (**RDB3**)
   spadicearia ([D. & S.]) (Red Twin-spot Carpet)
   ferrugata (Cl.) (Dark-barred Twin-spot Carpet)
   quadrifasiata (Cl.) (Large Twin-spot Carpet)
   montanata ([D. & S.]) (Silver-ground Carpet)
   fluctuata (L.) (Garden Carpet)
Scotopteryx bipunctaria ([D. & S.]) Chalk Carpet*
   chenopodiata (L.) (Shaded Broad-bar)
Catarhoe cuculata (Hufn.) (Royal Mantle) [1992]
Epirrhoe tristata (L.) (Small Argent & Sable) [1980s]
   alternata (Müll.) (Common Carpet)
   rivata (Hb.) (Wood Carpet)†
Costaconvexa polygrammata (Borkh.) (Many-lined)†
   [Extinct, 1850s]
Camptogramma bilineata (L.) (Yellow Shell)
Larentia clavaria (Haw.) (Mallow)
Anticlea badiata ([D. & S.]) (Shoulder Stripe)
   derivata ([D. & S.]) (Streamer)
Mesoleuca albicillata (L.) (Beautiful Carpet)
Pelurga comitata (L.) (Dark Spinach)
Cosmorhoe ocellata (L.) (Purple Bar)
Eulithis testata (L.) (Chevron)
   populata (L.) (Northern Spinach) [1920]†
   mellinata (Fabr.) (Spinach)
   pyraliata ([D. & S.]) (Barred Straw)
Ecliptoptera silaceata ([D. & S.]) (Small Phoenix)
Chloroclysta miata (L.) (Autumn Green Carpet)†§
   citrata (L.) (Dark Marbled Carpet)
   truncata (Hufn.) (Common Marbled Carpet)
Cidaria fulvata (Forst.) (Barred Yellow)
Plemyria rubiginata ([D. & S.]) (Blue-bordered Carpet)
Colostygia pectinataria (Knoch) (Green Carpet)
Hydriomena furcata (Thunb.) (July Highflyer)
   impluviata ([D. & S.]) (May Highflyer)†
   ruberata (Freyer) (Ruddy Highflyer)
Horisme vitalbata ([D. & S.]) (Small Waved Umber)
   tersata ([D. & S.]) (Fern)
Melanthia procellata ([D. & S.]) (Pretty Chalk Carpet)
Rheumaptera undulata (L.) (Scallop Shell)
Triphosa dubitata (L.) (Tissue) [1988]
Philereme vetulata ([D. & S.]) (Brown Scallop)
   transversata (Hufn.) (Dark Umber)
Euphyia unangulata (Haw.) (Sharp-angled Carpet) [1980s]
Epirrita dilutata ([D. & S.]) (November Moth)
Operophtera brumata (L.) (Winter Moth)
Perizoma affinitata (Steph.) (Rivulet)
   alchemillata (L.) (Small Rivulet)

bifaciata (Haw.) (Barred Rivulet)†
albulata ([D. & S.]) (Grass Rivulet)
flavofasciata (Thunb.) (Sandy Carpet)
didymata (L.) (Twin-spot Carpet)
sagittata (Fabr.) (Marsh Carpet) (**RDB2**)
Eupithecia tenuiata (Hb.) (Slender Pug)
plumbeolata (Haw.) (Lead-coloured Pug)
linariata ([D. & S.]) (Toadflax Pug)
pulchellata Steph. (Foxglove Pug)*
exiguata (Hufn.) (Mottled Pug)
valerianata (Hb.) (Valerian Pug)† [1936]
pygmaeata (Hb.) (Marsh Pug)
venosata (Fabr.) (Netted Pug)
centaureata ([D. & S.]) (Lime-speck Pug)
trisignaria H.-S. (Triple-spotted Pug)
satyrata (Hb.) (Satyr Pug)
absinthiata (Cl.) (Wormwood Pug)
   f. *goossensiata* Mab. (Ling Pug)*
assimilata Doubl. (Currant Pug)*
vulgata (Haw.) (Common Pug)
tripunctaria H.-S. (White-spotted Pug)
subfuscata (Haw.) (Grey Pug)
icterata (Vill.) (Tawny Speckled Pug)
succenturiata (L.) (Bordered Pug)
subumbrata ([D. & S.]) (Shaded Pug)
indigata (Hb.) (Ochreous Pug)*
pimpinellata (Hb.) (Pimpinel Pug)
nanata (Hb.) (Narrow-winged Pug)*
abbreviata Steph. (Brindled Pug) [1973]
dodoneata Guen. (Oak-tree Pug)
Chloroclystis v-ata (Haw.) (V-Pug)
Pasiphila chloerata Mab. (Sloe Pug)
   rectangulata (L.) (Green Pug)
Gymnoscelis rufifasciata (Haw.) (Double-striped Pug)
Anticollix sparsata (Treit.) (Dentated Pug)
Asthena albulata (Hufn.) (Small White Wave)*
Hydrelia flammeolaria (Hufn.) (Small Yellow Wave)
Lobophora halterata (Hufn.) (Seraphim)
Trichopteryx carpinata (Borkh.) (Early Tooth-striped)
Pterapherapteryx sexalata (Retz.) (Small Seraphim)
Acasis viretata (Hb.) (Yellow-barred Brindle)

Ennominae

Abraxas grossulariata (L.) (Magpie)
Lomaspilis marginata (L.) (Clouded Border)
Ligdia adustata ([D. & S.]) (Scorched Carpet)
Macaria alternata ([D. & S.]) (Sharp-angled Peacock)
   (*alternaria* (Hb.))
   liturata (Cl.) (Tawny-barred Angle)
   wauaria (L.) (V-Moth)
Chiasmia clathrata (L.) (Latticed Heath)
Itame brunneata (Thunb.) (Rannoch Looper) [1920]
Petrophora chlorosata (Scop.) (Brown Silver-line)
Plagodis dolabraria (L.) (Scorched Wing)
Opisthograptis luteolata (L.) (Brimstone Moth)
Epione repandaria (Hufn.) (Bordered Beauty)
Apeira syringaria (L.) (Lilac Beauty)
Ennomos autumnaria (Werneb.) (Large Thorn) [1998]
   quercinaria (Hufn.) (August Thorn)†
   alniaria (L.) (Canary-shouldered Thorn)
   fuscantaria (Haw.) (Dusky Thorn)
   erosaria ([D. & S.]) (September Thorn)
Selenia dentaria (Fabr.) (Early Thorn)
   tetralunaria (Hufn.) (Purple Thorn)
Odontoptera bidentata (Cl.) (Scalloped Hazel)
Crocallis elinguaria (L.) (Scalloped Oak)
Ourapteryx sambucaria (L.) (Swallow-tailed Moth)
Colotois pennaria (L.) (Feathered Thorn)
Angerona prunaria (L.) (Orange Moth)*
Phigalia pilosaria ([D. & S.]) (Pale Brindled Beauty)
Lycia hirtaria (Cl.) (Brindled Beauty)

Biston strataria (Hufn.) (Oak Beauty)
   betularia (L.) (Peppered Moth)
Agriopis marginaria (Fabr.) (Dotted Border)
Erannis defoliaria (Cl.) (Mottled Umber)
Menophra abruptaria (Thunb.) (Waved Umber)
Peribatodes rhomboidaria ([D. & S.]) (Willow Beauty)
Alcis repandata (L.) (Mottled Beauty)
Hypomecis punctinalis (Scop.) (Pale Oak Beauty)
Ectropis bistortata (Goeze) (Engrailed) §
   crepuscularia ([D. & S.]) (Small Engrailed)
Aethalura punctulata ([D. & S.]) (Grey Birch)
Ematurga atomaria (L.) (Common Heath)
Bupalus piniaria (L.) (Bordered White)
Cabera pusaria (L.) (Common White Wave)
   exanthemata (Scop.) (Common Wave)
Lomographa bimaculata (Fabr.) (White-pinion Spotted)
   temerata ([D. & S.]) (Clouded Silver)
Theria primaria (Haw.) (Early Moth)
Campaea margaritata (L.) (Light Emerald)
Semispilates ochrearia (Rossi) (Yellow Belle)

SPHINGOIDEA

SPHINGIDAE

Sphinginae

Agrius convolvuli (L.) (Convolvulus Hawk-moth)*
Acherontia atropos (L.) (Death's-head Hawk-moth)*
Sphinx ligustri L. (Privet Hawk-moth)
Hyloicus pinastri (L.) (Pine Hawk-moth) [1990s]
Mimas tiliae (L.) (Lime Hawk-moth)
Smerinthus ocellata (L.) (Eyed Hawk-moth)
Laothoe populi (L.) (Poplar Hawk-moth)

Macroglossinae

Hemaris tityus (L.) (Narrow-bordered Bee Hawk-moth)
   [extinct at Wicken, before mid-1920s]*
Macroglossum stellatarum (L.) (Humming-bird Hawk-moth)*
Deilephila elpenor (L.) (Elephant Hawk-moth)
   porcellus (L.) (Small Elephant Hawk-moth)

NOCTUOIDEA

NOTODONTIDAE

Notodontinae

Cerura vinula L. (Puss Moth)
Furcula furcula (Cl.) (Sallow Kitten)
   bifida (Brahm) (Poplar Kitten) [1992]
Notodonta dromedarius (L.) (Iron Prominent)
   ziczac (L.) (Pebble Prominent)
Pheosia gnoma (Fabr.) (Lesser Swallow Prominent)
   tremula (Cl.) (Swallow Prominent)
Ptilodon capucina L. (Coxcomb Prominent)
   cucullina ([D. & S.]) (Maple Prominent)
Pterostoma palpina (Cl.) (Pale Prominent)
Ptilophora plumigera ([D. & S.]) (Plumed Prominent)*
   [1870s]

Pygaerinae

Clostera pigra (Hufn.) (Small Chocolate-tip)
   curtula (L.) (Chocolate-tip)

Phalerinae

Phalera bucephala (L.) (Buff-tip)

Dilobinae

Diloba caeruleocephala (L.) (Figure of Eight)

LYMANTRIIDAE

Laelia coenosa (Hb.) (Reed Tussock) [1879] (**Extinct**)
Orgyia recens (Hb.) (Scarce Vapourer)* [not since 1829]
  (RDB2)
  antiqua (L.) (Vapourer)
Dicallomera fascelina (L.) (Dark Tussock)*
Calliteara pudibunda (L.) (Pale Tussock)
Euproctis chrysorrhoea (L.) (Brown-tail)
  similis (Fuessl.) (Yellow-tail)
Leucoma salicis (L.) (White Satin Moth)
Lymantria dispar (L.) (Gypsy Moth) [*c*.1870]* (**Extinct**)

ARCTIIDAE

Lithosiinae

Thumatha senex (Hb.) (Round-winged Muslin)
Nudaria mundana (L.) (Muslin Footman)
Cybosia mesomella (L.) (Four-dotted Footman)
Eilema griseola (Hb.) (Dingy Footman)
  complana (L.) (Scarce Footman)
  lurideola (Zinck.) (Common Footman)
Lithosia quadra (L.) (Four-spotted Footman)*

Arctiinae

Arctia caja (L.) (Garden Tiger)
Diacrisia sannio (L.) (Clouded Buff)*
Spilosoma lubricipeda (L.) (White Ermine)
  lutea (Hufn.) (Buff Ermine)
  urticae (Esp.) (Water Ermine)†
Diaphora mendica (Cl.) (Muslin Moth)
Phragmatobia fuliginosa (L.) (Ruby Tiger)
Callimorpha dominula (L.) (Scarlet Tiger) [extinct at Wicken,
  c.1879]*
Tyria jacobaeae (L.) (Cinnabar)

NOLIDAE

Nolinae

Nola cucullatella (L.) (Short-cloaked Moth)

NOCTUIDAE

Noctuinae

Euxoa tritici (L.) (White-line Dart)
  nigricans (L.) (Garden Dart)
Agrotis vestigialis (Hufn.) (Archer's Dart)
  segetum ([D. & S.]) (Turnip Moth)
  clavis (Hufn.) (Heart & Club)
  exclamationis (L.) (Heart & Dart)
  ipsilon (Hufn.) (Dark Sword-grass)
  puta (Hb.) (Shuttle-shaped Dart)
Axylia putris (L.) (Flame)
Ochropleura praecox (L.) (Portland Moth)* (Burw.Fen)
  plecta (L.) (Flame Shoulder)
Rhyacia simulans (Hufn.) (Dotted Rustic)
Noctua pronuba L. (Large Yellow Underwing)
  orbona (Hufn.) (Lunar Yellow Underwing) [1878]
  comes Hb. (Lesser Yellow Underwing)
  fimbriata (Schreb.) (Broad-bordered Yellow Underwing)
  janthe (Borkh.) (Lesser Broad-bordered Yellow Underwing)
    (*janthina* auctt.)
  interjecta Hb. (Least Yellow Underwing)
Spaelotis ravida ([D. & S.]) (Stout Dart)
Graphiphora augur (Fabr.) (Double Dart)
Lycophotia porphyrea ([D. & S.]) (True Lover's Knot)
Peridroma saucia (Hb.) (Pearly Underwing)
Diarsia mendica (Fabr.) (Ingrailed Clay)
  brunnea ([D. & S.]) (Purple Clay)
  rubi (View.) (Small Square-spot)
  florida (Schmidt) (Fen Square-spot)

Xestia c-nigrum (L.) (Setaceous Hebrew Character)
  triangulum (Hufn.) (Double Square-spot)
  baja ([D. & S.]) (Dotted Clay)
  sexstrigata (Haw.) (Six-striped Rustic)
  xanthographa ([D. & S.]) (Square-spot Rustic)
Naenia typica (L.) (Gothic)
Eurois occulta (L.) (Great Brocade)*
Cerastis rubricosa ([D. & S.]) (Red Chestnut)

Hadeninae

Discestra trifolii (Hufn.) (Nutmeg)
Hada plebeja (L.) (Shears)
  (*nana* Hufn.)
Polia bombycina (Hufn.) (Pale Shining Brown)
  nebulosa (Hufn.) (Grey Arches)
Heliophobus reticulata (Goeze) (Bordered Gothic)
Mamestra brassicae (L.) (Cabbage Moth)
Melanchra persicariae (L.) (Dot Moth)
  pisi (L.) (Broom Moth)
Lacanobia w-latinum (Hufn.) (Light Brocade) [1980s]
  thalassina (Hufn.) (Pale-shouldered Brocade)
  suasa ([D. & S.]) (Dog's Tooth)
  oleracea (L.) (Bright-line Brown-eye)
Hecatera bicolorata (Hufn.) (Broad-barred White)
  dysodea ([D. & S.]) (Small Ranunculus) [1900]*
Hadena rivularis (Fabr.) (Campion)
  perplexa ([D. & S.]) (Tawny Shears)
  compta ([D. & S.]) (Varied Coronet)
  confusa (Hufn.) (Marbled Coronet)
  bicruris (Hufn.) (Lychnis)
Cerapteryx graminis (L.) (Antler Moth)
Tholera decimalis (Poda) (Feathered Gothic)
Orthosia cruda ([D. & S.]) (Small Quaker)
  opima (Hb.) (Northern Drab)†
  populeti (Fabr.) (Lead-coloured Drab)*
  gracilis ([D. & S.]) (Powdered Quaker)
  cerasi (Fabr.) (Common Quaker)
  incerta (Hufn.) (Clouded Drab)
  munda ([D. & S.]) (Twin-spotted Quaker)
  gothica (L.) (Hebrew Character)
Mythimna conigera ([D. & S.]) (Brown-line Bright-eye)
  ferrago (Fabr.) (Clay)
  albipuncta ([D. & S.]) (White-point) [1990s]
  pudorina ([D. & S.]) (Striped Wainscot)
  straminea (Treit.) (Southern Wainscot)
  impura (Hb.) (Smoky Wainscot)
  pallens (L.) (Common Wainscot)
  obsoleta (Hb.) (Obscure Wainscot)
  comma (L.) (Shoulder-striped Wainscot)
  flammea (Curt.) (Flame Wainscot) (RDB3)

Cuculliinae

Cucullia absinthii (L.) (Wormwood) [1998]
  umbratica (L.) (Shark) [1981]
  asteris ([D. & S.]) (Star-wort)
Shargacucullia verbasci (L.) (Mullein)*
Brachylomia viminalis (Fabr.) (Minor Shoulder-knot)
Asteroscopus sphinx (Hufn.) (Sprawler)*
Aporophyla lutulenta lutulenta ([D. & S.]) (Deep-brown
  Dart)
  nigra (Haw.) (Black Rustic)
Lithophane semibrunnea (Haw.) (Tawny Pinion)†
  leautieri (Bois.) (Blair's Shoulder-Knot) [1998]
Xylena exsoleta (L.) (Sword-grass)†
Xylocampa areola (Esp.) (Early Grey)
Allophyes oxyacanthae (L.) (Green-brindled Crescent)
Blepharita satura ([D. & S.]) (Beautiful Arches)§
  adusta (Esp.) (Dark Brocade)
Polymixis flavicincta ([D. & S.]) (Large Ranunculus)*

Moths

Acronictinae

Eupsilia transversa (Hufn.) (Satellite)*
Conistra vaccinii (L.) (Chestnut)
  ligula (Esp.) (Dark Chestnut)
Agrochola circellaris (Hufn.) (Brick)†
  lota (Cl.) (Red-line Quaker)
  macilenta (Hb.) (Yellow-line Quaker)
  helvola (L.) (Flounced Chestnut)
  litura (L.) (Brown-spot Pinion)
  lychnidis ([D. & S.]) (Beaded Chestnut)
Atethmia centrago (Haw.) (Centre-barred Sallow)
Omphaloscelis lunosa (Haw.) (Lunar Underwing)
Xanthia aurago ([D. & S.]) (Barred Sallow)
  togata (Esp.) (Pink-barred Sallow)
  icteritia (Hufn.) (Sallow)
  gilvago ([D. & S.]) (Dusky-lemon Sallow)
  ocellaris (Borkh.) (Pale-lemon Sallow)
Acronicta megacephala ([D. & S.]) (Poplar Grey)
  aceris (L.) (Sycamore)
  leporina (L.) (Miller)
  alni (L.) (Alder Moth) [1983]
  tridens ([D. & S.]) (Dark Dagger)
  psi (L.) (Grey Dagger)
  strigosa ([D. & S.]) (Marsh Dagger) [?extinct at Wicken, 1907]* (**RDB1, ?Extinct**)
  rumicis (L.) (Knot Grass)
Simyra albovenosa (Goeze) (Reed Dagger)
Craniophora ligustri ([D. & S.]) (Coronet)

Bryophilinae

Cryphia domestica (Hufn.) (Marbled Beauty)

Amphipyrinae

Amphipyra pyramidea (L.) (Copper Underwing)
  berbera (Rungs) (Svensson's Copper Underwing)
  tragopoginis (Cl.) (Mouse Moth)
Mormo maura (L.) (Old Lady)
Dypterygia scabriuscula (L.) (Bird's Wing)
Rusina ferruginea (Esp.) (Brown Rustic)
Thalpophila matura (Hufn.) (Straw Underwing)
Trachea atriplicis (L.) (Orache Moth) [1895]* (**Extinct** as resident)
Euplexia lucipara (L.) (Small Angle Shades)
Phlogophora meticulosa (L.) (Angle Shades)
Ipimorpha subtusa ([D. & S.]) (Olive)
Parastichtis suspecta (Hb.) (Suspected)
  ypsillon ([D. & S.]) (Dingy Shears)
Cosmia affinis (L.) (Lesser-spotted Pinion) [1934]
  diffinis (L.) (White-spotted Pinion) [1950]
  trapezina (L.) (Dun-bar)
  pyralina ([D. & S.]) (Lunar-spotted Pinion)
Apamea monoglypha (Hufn.) (Dark Arches)
  lithoxylaea ([D. & S.]) (Light Arches)
  sublustris (Esp.) (Reddish Light Arches)
  oblonga (Haw.) (Crescent Striped)
  crenata (Hufn.) (Clouded-bordered Brindle)
  epomidion (Haw.) (Clouded Brindle)
  remissa (Hb.) (Dusky Brocade)
  unanimis (Hb.) (Small Clouded Brindle)
  anceps ([D. & S.]) (Large Nutmeg)
  sordens (Hufn.) (Rustic Shoulder-knot)
  scolopacina (Esp.) (Slender Brindle) [1981]
  ophiogramma (Esp.) (Double Lobed)
Oligia strigilis (L.) (Marbled Minor)
  versicolor (Borkh.) (Rufous Minor) [1988]§
  latruncula ([D. & S.]) (Tawny Marbled Minor)
  fasciuncula (Haw.) (Middle-barred Minor)
Mesoligia furuncula ([D. & S.]) (Cloaked Minor)
  literosa (Haw.) (Rosy Minor)
Mesapamea secalis (L.) (Common Rustic)

  didyma (Esp.) (Lesser Common Rustic) [1998]
Photedes minima (Haw.) (Small Dotted Buff)
Chortodes extrema (Hb.) (Concolorous) [1935]† (**RDB3**)
  fluxa (Hb.) (Mere Wainscot)
  pygmina (Haw.) (Small Wainscot)
Eremobia ochroleuca ([D. & S.]) (Dusky Sallow)
Luperina testacea ([D. & S.]) (Flounced Rustic)
Amphipoea oculea (L.) (Ear Moth)†
Hydraecia micacea (Esp.) (Rosy Rustic)
  petasitis Doubl. (Butterbur)*
Gortyna flavago ([D. & S.]) (Frosted Orange)
Celaena haworthii (Curt.) (Haworth's Minor) [1939]
  leucostigma (Hb.) (Crescent)
Nonagria typhae (Thunb.) (Bulrush Wainscot)
Archanara geminipuncta (Haw.) (Twin-spotted Wainscot)
  dissoluta (Treit.) (Brown-veined Wainscot)
  algae (Esp.) (Rush Wainscot) [1966]§ (**RDB3**)
Rhizedra lutosa (Hb.) (Large Wainscot)
Arenostola phragmitidis (Hb.) (Fen Wainscot)
Coenobia rufa (Haw.) (Small Rufous)
Charanyca trigrammica (Hufn.) (Treble Lines)
Hoplodrina alsines (Brahm) (Uncertain)
  blanda ([D. & S.]) (Rustic)
Spodoptera exigua (Hb.) (Small Mottled Willow)
Caradrina morpheus (Hufn.) (Mottled Rustic)
Paradrina clavipalpis (Scop.) (Pale Mottled Willow)
Chilodes maritimus (Tausch.) (Silky Wainscot)
Athetis pallustris (Hb.) (Marsh Moth) [?extinct at Wicken, 1955] (**RDB3**)

Stiriinae

Panemeria tenebrata (Scop.) (Small Yellow Underwing)†

Heliothinae

Pyrrhia umbra (Hufn.) (Bordered Sallow)
Heliothis viriplaca (Hufn.) (Marbled Clover) [1999] (**RDB3**)

Eustrotiinae

Protodeltote pygarga (Hufn.) (Marbled White Spot)
Deltote uncula (Cl.) (Silver Hook)
  bankiana (Fabr.) (Silver Barred) (**RDB2**)

Acontiinae

Emmelia trabealis (Scop.) (Spotted Sulphur) [extinct at Wicken, *c*.1860]† (**RDB1**)

Eariadinae

Earias chlorana (L.) (Cream-bordered Green Pea)

Chloephorinae

Bena bicolorana (Fuessly) (Scarce Silver-lines)
  (*prasinana* auctt.)
Pseudoips prasinana (L.) (Green Silver-lines) [from 1992]
  (*fagana* Fabr.)

Plusiinae

Diachrysia chrysitis (L.) (Burnished Brass)
Polychrysia moneta (Fabr.) (Golden Plusia)
Plusia festucae (L.) (Gold Spot)
  putnami gracilis (Lempke) (Lempke's Gold Spot)
Autographa gamma (L.) (Silver Y)
  pulchrina (Haw.) (Beautiful Golden Y)
  jota (L.) (Plain Golden Y)
Abrostola triplasia (L.) (Dark Spectacle)
  (*trigemina* Werneb.)
  tripartita (Hufn.) (Spectacle)
  (*triplasia* auctt.)

Catocalinae

Catocala nupta (L.) (Red Underwing)
Callistege mi (Cl.) (Mother Shipton)
Euclidia glyphica (L.) (Burnet Companion)*

Ophiderinae

Tyta luctuosa ([D. & S.]) (Four-spotted) [1935] (**RDB2**)
Lygephila pastinum (Treit.) (Blackneck)
Scoliopteryx libatrix (L.) (Herald)
Phytometra viridaria (Cl.) (Small Purple-barred)*

Rivulinae

Laspeyria flexula ([D. & S.]) (Beautiful Hook-tip)
Rivula sericealis (Scop.) (Straw Dot)

Hypeninae

Hypena proboscidalis (L.) (Snout)
   rostralis (L.) (Buttoned Snout)

Strepsimaninae

Schrankia taenialis (Hb.) (White-line Snout)
   costaestrigalis (Steph.) (Pinion-streaked Snout)

Herminiinae

Pechipogo strigilata (L.) (Common Fan-foot) [1960s]
Zanclognatha tarsipennalis (Treit.) (Fan-foot)
Herminia grisealis ([D. & S.]) (Small Fan-foot)
   (*nemoralis* (Fabr.))
Macrochilo cribrumalis (Hb.) (Dotted Fan-foot)

COLEOPTERA
(beetles)

Lists: Balfour-Browne (1926), Omer Cooper et al. (1928), Omer Cooper & Tottenham (1932), Donisthorpe (1938), A. B. Drane, L. E. Friday, I.S.R. (J.N.C.C.). Water beetle records checked by G. N. Foster.
Checklist: Kloet & Hincks, edn 2 (1977), updated by R. D. Pope and H. Mendel, except for water beetles (G. N. Foster, 1998, pers.comm.); Curculionoidea revised by Morris (1990, 1991, 1993a,b, 1997) and Morris & Booth (1997); Kateretidae and Nitidulidae follow Kirk-Spriggs (1996); and Elateroidea follow Mendel & Clarke (1996). Higher classification rearranged to conform with Hodge & Jones (1995).
Conservation status: Hyman (1992; 1994)

* records derived from Victoria County History list (Donisthorpe, 1938)
§ records requiring confirmation
NOTE. Some previously-recorded species have been split into two species. Where the original material has not been redetermined, both names are printed in this list, separated by 'and/or', pending further research. In one case, *Elodes* (p.56), two species have become part of a complex of five.

Adephaga

CARABOIDEA

CARABIDAE

Carabinae

Cychrus caraboides (L.)
Carabus granulatus L.
 monilis F.* (**Nb**)
Leistus ferrugineus (L.)
 fulvibarbis Dejean*
 rufescens (F.)
 spinibarbis (F.)*
Nebria brevicollis (F.)
Notiophilus aquaticus (L.)
 biguttatus (F.)
 palustris (Duft.)
 substriatus Waterh.
Blethisa multipunctata (L.) (**Nb**)
Elaphrus cupreus Duft.
 riparius (L.)
Loricera pilicornis (F.)
Dyschirius aeneus (Dejean)
 globosus (Herbst)
 luedersi Wagner
Clivina collaris (Herbst)*
 fossor (L.)
Trechus discus (F.)* (**Nb**)
 micros (Herbst)*
 obtusus Erichs.
 quadristriatus (Schr.)
 rivularis (Gyll.) (**RDB3**)
Asaphidion flavipes (L.)* and/or *curtum* (Heyd.) and/or
 stierlini (Heyd.)
Bembidion aeneum Germar*
 andreae (F.)*
 articulatum (Panz.)
 assimile Gyll.
 atrocoeruleum Stephens*
 biguttatum (F.)
 bruxellense Wesmael
 clarki (Dawson) (**Nb**)
 dentellum (Thunb.)
 fluviatile Dejean* (**Nb**)
 fumigatum (Duft.) (**Nb**)

 gilvipes Sturm (**Nb**)
 guttula (F.)
 harpaloides Serv.*
 lampros (Herbst)
 litorale (Olivier)* (**Nb**)
 lunulatum (Fourc.)*
 mannerheimi Sahlb.
 obliquum Sturm* (**Nb**)
 obtusum Serv.
 quadrimaculatum (L.)
 quadripustulatum Serv. (**Nb**)
 semipunctatum Don.* (**Na**)
 tetracolum Say
 varium (Olivier)*
Stomis pumicatus (Panz.)
Pterostichus anthracinus (Panz.) (**Nb**)
 aterrimus Payk.* (**RDB1**)
 cupreus (L.)
 diligens (Sturm)
 gracilis (Dejean) (**Nb**)
 macer (Marsh.)
 madidus (F.)
 melanarius (Ill.)
 minor (Gyll.)
 niger (Schall.)
 nigrita (Payk.) and/or *rhaeticus* Heer
 strenuus (Panz.)
 vernalis (Panz.)
 versicolor (Sturm)*
Abax parallelepipedus (Pill. & Mitterp.)*
Calathus fuscipes (Goeze)
 melanocephalus (L.) and/or *cinctus* Motsch.
Olisthopus rotundatus (Payk.)*
Agonum albipes (F.)
 assimile (Payk.
 dorsale (Pont.)
 fuliginosum (Panz.)
 gracile Sturm
 livens (Gyll.) (**Nb**)
 marginatum (L.)
 micans Nicolai*
 moestum (Duft.)
 muelleri (Herbst)
 obscurum (Herbst)
 piceum (L.)*
 thoreyi Dejean
 viduum (Panz.)
Amara aenea (DeGeer)
 apricaria (Payk.)
 anthobia Villa*
 aulica (Panz.)
 bifrons (Gyll.)*
 consularis (Duft.) (**Nb**)
 convexiuscula (Marsh.)*
 eurynota (Panz.)*
 familiaris (Duft.)
 lucida (Duft.)* (**Nb**)
 lunicollis Schiödte
 ovata (F.)
 plebeja (Gyll.)
 praetermissa (Sahlb.)* (**Nb**)
 similata (Gyll.)
Zabrus tenebrioides (Goeze)* (**Na**)
Harpalus ardosiacus Lutschn.* (**Nb**)
 azureus (F.) (**Nb**)
 latus (L.)*
 melleti Heer* (**Na**)
 monticola Dejean
 punctatulus (Duft.)* (**Na**)
 puncticollis (Payk.)* (**RDB3**)
 rubripes (Duft.)*

rufibarbis (F.)
rufipes (DeGeer)
rupicola Sturm* (Nb)
sabulicola (Panz.)* (RDB3)
smaragdinus (Duft.)* (Nb)
Anisodactylus binotatus (F.)*
Trichocellus placidus (Gyll.)
Bradycellus collaris (Payk.)*
harpalinus (Serv.)
verbasci (Duft.)
Stenolophus mixtus (Herbst)
skrimshiranus Steph.* (Na)
teutonus (Schr.)* (Nb)
Acupalpus consputus (Duft.)* (Nb)
dubius Schilsky
exiguus Dejean* (Nb)
meridianus (L.)*
parvulus (Sturm)
Badister bullatus (Schr.)
dilatatus Chaudoir (Nb)
peltatus (Panz.)* (Na)
sodalis (Duft.)
unipustulatus Bonelli (Nb)
Panagaeus cruxmajor (L.) (RDB1)
Chlaenius nigricornis (F.)* (Nb)
vestitus (Payk.)*
Oodes helopioides (F.) (Nb)
Odacantha melanura (L.) (Nb)
Lebia chlorocephala (Hoffmann.) (Nb)
Demetrias atricapillus (L.)
imperialis (Germar) (Nb)
monostigma Samouelle (Nb)
Dromius agilis (F.)
angustus Brullé*
linearis (Olivier)
longiceps Dejean (Na)
melanocephalus Dejean
meridionalis Dejean*
quadrimaculatus (L.)
spilotus (Ill.)
Metabletus obscuroguttatus (Duft.)*
truncatellus (L.)
Microlestes maurus (Sturm) and/or *minutulus* (Goeze)*

HALIPLIDAE

Brychius elevatus (Panz.)
Peltodytes caesus (Duft.)
Haliplus confinis Steph.
flavicollis Sturm
fluviatilis Aubé
fulvus (F.)
heydeni Wehn. (Nb)
immaculatus Gerh.
laminatus (Schall.) (Nb)
lineatocollis (Marsh.)
lineolatus Mann.
mucronatus Steph. (Na)
obliquus (F.)
ruficollis (DeGeer)
variegatus Sturm (RDB3)
wehnckei Gerh.

HYGROBIIDAE

Hygrobia hermanni (F.)

NOTERIDAE

Noterus clavicornis (DeGeer)
crassicornis (O. F. Müll.) (Nb)

DYTISCIDAE

Lacophilinae

Laccophilus hyalinus (DeGeer)
minutus (L.)

Hydroporinae

Hyphydrus ovatus (L.)
Hydroglyphus pusillus (F.)
Bidessus unistriatus (Schr.) (RDB1)
Hygrotus confluens (F.)
decoratus (Gyll.) (Nb)
impressopunctatus (Schall.)
inaequalis (F.)
parallelogrammus (Ahrens)
versicolor (Schall.)
Suphrodytes dorsalis (F.)
Hydroporus angustatus Sturm
discretus Fair. & Brisout
erythrocephalus (L.)
gyllenhalii Schiödte
incognitus Sharp
memnonius Nic.
neglectus Schaum (Nb)
nigrita (F.)
obscurus Sturm
palustris (L.)
planus (F.)
pubescens (Gyll.)
rufifrons (O. F. Müll.) (RDB2)
striola (Gyll.)
tessellatus Drap.
tristis (Payk.)
umbrosus (Gyll.)
Stictonectes lepidus (Olivier) (Nb)
Graptodytes flavipes (Olivier) (RDB2)
granularis (L.) (Nb)
pictus (F.)
Porhydrus lineatus (F.)
Nebrioporus (=*Potamonectes*) *assimilis* (Payk.)
depressus elegans (Panz.)
Stictotarsus duodecimpustulatus (F.)
Oreodytes sanmarkii (Sahlb.)
Scarodytes halensis (F.) (Nb)
Laccornis oblongus (Steph.) (RDB3)

Colymbetinae

Copelatus haemorrhoidalis (F.)
Platambus maculatus (L.)
Agabus bipustulatus (L.)
chalconatus (Panz.) (Nb)
congener (Thunb.)*
didymus (Olivier)
guttatus (Payk.)*
labiatus (Brahm) (Nb)
montanus Zimm.
nebulosus (Forst.)
paludosus (F.)
sturmii (Gyll.) (Nb)
uliginosus (L.) (Nb)
undulatus (Schr.) (RDB3)
unguicularis Thoms. (Nb)
Ilybius aenescens Thoms. (Nb)
ater (DeGeer)
fenestratus (F.) (Nb)
fuliginosus (F.)
guttiger (Gyll.) (Nb)
quadriguttatus (Lac. & Bois.)
subaeneus Erichs. (Nb)

Rhantus exsoletus (Forst.)
  frontalis (Marsh.) (**Nb**)
  grapii (Gyll.) (**Nb**)
  suturalis (MacL.) (**Nb**)
  suturellus (Harris)
Colymbetes fuscus (L.)
Graphoderus cinereus (L.)* (**RDB3**)

Dytiscinae

Hydaticus seminiger (DeGeer) (**Nb**)
  transversalis (Pont.) (**RDB3**)
Acilius sulcatus (L.)
Dytiscus circumcinctus Ahrens (**Na**)
  circumflexus F. (**Nb**)
  dimidiatus Bergstr. (**RDB3**)
  marginalis L.
  semisulcatus O. F. Müll.

GYRINIDAE

Gyrininae

Gyrinus aeratus Steph. (**Nb**)
  caspius Ménétr.
  marinus Gyll.
  paykulli Ochs (**Na**)
  substriatus Steph.
  suffriani Scriba (**RDB3**)

Orectochilinae

Orectochilus villosus (O. F. Müll.)

Myxophaga

HYDROSCAPHOIDEA

MICROSPORIDAE

Microsporus obsidianus Kolenati
  (=*Sphaerius acaroides* Waltl)*

Polyphaga

Staphyliniformia

HYDROPHILOIDEA

HELOPHORIDAE

Helophorus aequalis Thoms.
  brevipalpis Bedel
  dorsalis (Marsh.) (**Nb**)
  flavipes (F.)*
  grandis Ill.*
  griseus Herbst (**Nb**)
  minutus F.
  nanus Sturm (**Nb**)
  nubilus F.*
  obscurus Mulsant
  rufipes (Bosc)
  strigifrons Thoms. (**Nb**)

GEORISSIDAE

Georissus crenulatus (Rossi)* (**Na**)

HYDROCHIDAE

Hydrochus carinatus Germar (**RDB3**)
  elongatus (Schall.) (**RDB3**)
  ignicollis Motsch. (**RDB3**)

SPERCHEIDAE

Spercheus emarginatus (Schall.) (?Extinct at Wicken) (**RDB1**)

HYDROPHILIDAE

Hydrophilinae

Berosus affinis Brullé (**Nb**)
  luridus (L.) (**Nb**)
  signaticollis (Charp.) (**Nb**)
Chaetarthria seminulum (Herbst) (**Nb**)
Anacaena bipustulata (Marsh.) (**Nb**)
  globulus (Payk.)
  limbata (F.) sensu stricto
  lutescens (Steph.)
Laccobius biguttatus Gerh.
  bipunctatus (F.)
  minutus (L.)
  sinuatus Motsch. (**Nb**)
  striatulus (F.)
Helochares lividus (Forst.) (**Nb**)
  punctatus Sharp (**Nb**)
Enochrus coarctatus (Gredler)
  halophilus Bedel* (**Na**)
  melanocephalus (Olivier) (**Nb**)
  nigritus (Sharp)
  ochropterus (Marsh.) (**Nb**)
  quadripunctatus (Herbst) (**Nb**)
  testaceus (F.)
Cymbiodyta marginella (F.)
Hydrobius fuscipes (L.)
Limnoxenus niger (Zschach)* (**Nb**)
Hydrochara caraboides (L.)* (**RDB1**)
Hydrophilus piceus (L.) (**RDB3**)

Sphaeridiinae

Coelostoma orbiculare (F.)
Cercyon analis (Payk.)
  atricapillus (Marsh.) (**N**)
  bifenestratus Küster (**Na**)
  convexiusculus Steph. (**Nb**)
  haemorrhoidalis (F.)
  laminatus Sharp
  lateralis (Marsh.)
  littoralis (Gyll.)
  marinus Thoms.
  melanocephalus (L.)
  pygmaeus (Ill.)
  quisquilius (L.)
  sternalis Sharp (**Nb**)
  tristis (Ill.) (**Nb**)
  unipunctatus (L.)
  ustulatus (Preyss.) (**Nb**)
Cryptopleurum minutum (F.)
Megasternum obscurum (Marsh.)
Sphaeridium bipustulatum F.
  lunatum F.
  scarabaeoides (L.)

HISTERIDAE

Saprininae

Gnathoncus nannetensis (Marseul)*
  nanus (Scriba)*
Saprinus aeneus (F.)*
  semistriatus (Scriba)*
Dendrophilinae

Carcinops pumilio (Erichs.)
Onthophilus striatus (Forst.)

Histerinae

Hister carbonarius (J. Hoffm.)*
  impressus F.
  neglectus (Germar)*
  purpurascens (Herbst)*
  unicolor L.
Atholus 12-striatus (Schr.)

STAPHYLINOIDEA

HYDRAENIDAE

Hydraena palustris Erichs. (RDB2)
  riparia Kugel.
  testacea Curt. (Nb)
Limnebius aluta Bedel
  nitidus (Marsh.)
  papposus Muls.
  truncatellus (Thunb.)
Ochthebius bicolon Germar
  dilatatus Steph.
  minimus (F.)
  nanus Steph. (Nb)

PTILIIDAE

Ptenidium fuscicorne Erichs.
  intermedium Wankow.
  laevigatum Erichs.*
  nitidum (Heer)*
  pusillum (Gyll.)
Ptilium affine Erichs.* (RDBK)
Ptiliola fusca (Erichs.)
Microptilium palustre Kuntzen (RDBK)
Ptinella aptera (Guér.-Ménev.)*
  britannica Matth.* (RDBK)
Nephanes titan (Newman)
Acrotrichis atomaria (DeGeer)
  brevipennis (Erichs.) (N)
  fascicularis (Herbst)
  grandicollis (Mann.)*
  intermedia (Gillm.)*
  montandoni (Allib.)
  sericans (Heer)*
  sitkaensis (Motsch.)
  thoracica (Waltl)*

LEIODIDAE

Leiodinae

Leiodes badia (Sturm)*
  dubia Kugelann*
  ferruginea (F.)*
  gyllenhali Stephens* (RDBK)
  obesa (W.L.E. Schmidt)*
  polita (Marsh.)*
  rufipennis (Payk.)
Cyrtusa vittata (Curt.)*
Anisotoma humeralis (F.)
Amphicyllis globus (F.)
Agathidium atrum (Payk.)
  laevigatum Erichs.
  nigripenne (F.)
  varians Beck

Catopinae

Ptomaphagus subvillosus (Goeze)*
Nemadus colonoides (Kraatz)*
Nargus velox (Spence)
Choleva agilis (Ill.)
  angustata (F.)*

cisteloides (Frölich)* (RDBK)
  oblonga Latr.*
Sciodrepoides watsoni (Spence)*
Catops chrysomeloides (Panz.)*
  fuliginosus Erichs.
  fuscus (Panz.)*
  morio (F.)*
  nigricans (Spence)*
  nigrita Erichs.*
  tristis (Panz.)
Colon serripes (Sahlb.)

SCYDMAENIDAE

Eutheia schaumi Kiez.* (N)
  scydmaenoides Steph.* (N)
Neuraphes elongatulus (P. W. J. Müll. & Kunze)
  talparum Lokay
Scydmoraphes helvolus (Schaum)* (N)
  sparshalli (Denny)* (RDBK)
Stenichnus collaris (P. W. J. Müll. & Kunze)
  scutellaris (P. W. J. Müll. & Kunze)
Euconnus fimetarius (Chaudoir)*
  hirticollis (Ill.)
Scydmaenus tarsatus (P. W. J. Müll. & Kunze)

SILPHIDAE

Nicrophorus humator (Gledit.)*
  investigator Zett.
  vespillo (L.)*
  vespilloides Herbst
Necrodes littoralis (L.)*
Thanatophilus rugosus (L.)
  sinuatus (F.)*
Silpha atrata L.
  laevigata F.
  obscura L.
  tristis Ill.*
  tyrolensis Laich.* (Nb)

STAPHYLINIDAE

Scaphidiinae

Scaphisoma agaricum (L.)*
  boleti (Panz.) (Nb)

Micropeplinae

Micropeplus fulvus Erichs.
  staphylinoides (Marsh.)

Proteininae

Metopsia retusa (Steph.)
Megarthrus affinis Miller*
  denticollis (Beck)*
  depressus (Payk.)*
  sinuatocollis (Bois. & Lac.)
Proteinus brachypterus (F.)
  macropterus (Grav.)
  ovalis Steph.

Omaliinae

Anthobium atrocephalum (Gyll.)
  unicolor (Marsh.)
Olophrum fuscum (Grav.)
Lesteva heeri Fauvel
  longoelytrata (Goeze)*
  punctata Erichs.*
Eusphalerum minutum (F.)*
  torquatum (Marsh.)

Phyllodrepa floralis (Payk.)
  salicis (Gyll.)* (**RDBK**)
Dropephylla gracilicornis (Fair. & Lab.) (**N**)
  ioptera (Steph.)
Acrolocha minuta (Olivier)* (**N**)
Omalium caesum Grav.
  excavatum Steph.
  oxycanthae Grav.*
  rivulare (Payk.)
Xylodromus concinnus (Marsh.)
  depressus (Grav.)*
Coryphium angusticolle Steph.
Siagonium quadricorne Kirby*
Pseudopsis sulcata Newm.* (**N**)
Bledius occidentalis Bondr. (**RDBK**)
Aploderus caelatus (Grav.)*
Carpelimus bilineatus Steph.
  corticinus (Grav.)
  elongatulus (Erichs.)
  pusillus (Grav.)*
  rivularis (Motschulsky)*
Thinobius brevipennis Kiesenw.* (**RDBK**)
Platystethus arenarius (Fourc.)*
  cornutus (Grav.)*
  nitens (Sahlb.)
  nodifrons Mann. (**N**)
Anotylus complanatus (Erichs.)*
  *insecatus** (**N**)
  inustus (Grav.)*
  nitidulus (Grav.)*
  rugosus (F.)
  sculpturatus (Grav.)
  tetracarinatus (Block)
Oxytelus laqueatus (Marsh.)*
  sculptus Grav.*

Oxyporinae

Oxyporus rufus (L.)*

Steninae

Stenus argus Grav.* (**Nb**)
  ater Mann.* (**Nb**)
  atratulus Erichs.* (**Nb**)
  bifoveolatus Gyll.
  biguttatus (L.)*
  bimaculatus Gyll.
  binotatus Ljungh*
  boops Ljungh
  brunnipes Steph.
  canaliculatus Gyll.*
  carbonarius Gyll. (**Nb**)
  cicindeloides (Schall.)*
  circularis Grav.* (**Nb**)
  clavicornis (Scop.)
  comma LeConte*
  crassus Erichs.*
  exiguus Erichs.* (**Nb**)
  flavipes Steph.
  fulvicornis Steph.*
  fuscipes Grav.*
  guttula P. W. J. Müll.*
  impressus Germar
  incrassatus Erichs.*
  juno (Payk.)
  latifrons Erichs.
  lustrator Erichs.
  melanarius Steph.§
  melanopus (Marsh.)*
  nanus Steph.
  nigritulus Gyll.* (**Nb**)

nitens Steph.
  nitidiusculus Steph.*
  opticus Grav.* (**Na**)
  ossium Steph.*
  pallipes Grav.*
  pallitarsis Steph.*
  palustris Erichs. (**Nb**)
  picipennis Erichs.
  picipes Steph.*
  proditor Erichs.* (**RDB I**)
  providus Erichs.
  pubescens Steph.
  pusillus Steph.*
  rogeri Kraatz*
  similis (Herbst)*
  solutus Erichs.
  subaeneus Erichs.*
  vafellus Erichs.*

Euaesthelinae

Euaesthetus bipunctatus (Ljungh)
  laeviusculus Mann.*
  ruficapillus Bois. & Lac.

Paederinae

Paederus riparius (L.)
Lathrobium brunnipes (F.)
  elongatum (L.)
  fovulum Steph.
  fulvipenne (Grav.)
  geminum Kraatz
  impressum Heer
  longulum Grav.
  multipunctum Grav.*
  quadratum (Payk.)*
  terminatum Grav.*
Ochthephilum fracticorne (Payk.)
Medon apicalis (Kraatz)* (**N**)
Sunius bicolor (Olivier) (**RDBK**)
  melanocephalus (F.) (**N**)
  propinquus (Brisout)*
Lithocharis ochracea (Grav.)*
Astenus lyonessius (Joy)
  pulchellus (Heer)*
Rugilus erichsoni (Fauv.)
  fragilis (Grav.) (**N**)
  orbiculatus (Payk.)
  rufipes Germar
  similis (Erichs.) (**N**)

Staphylininae

Othius laeviusculus Steph.*
  myrmecophilus Kiesenw.
  punctulatus (Goeze)
Leptacinus pusillus (Steph.)
Phacophallus parumpunctatus (Gyll.)*
Gauropterus fulgidus (F.)*
Gyrohypnus angustatus Steph.
Xantholinus glabratus (Grav.)*
  jarrigei Coiffait (as *tricolor* (F.) misident.)*
  linearis (Olivier)
  longiventris Heer
Neobisnius villosulus (Steph.)*
Erichsonius cinerascens (Grav.)
Philonthus addendus Sharp*
  agilis (Grav.)*
  albipes (Grav.)*
  cognatus Steph.
  concinnus (Grav.)*
  cruentatus (Gmel. in L.)

debilis (Grav.)*
decorus (Grav.)
discoideus (Grav.)
fimetarius (Grav.)
fumarius (Grav.) (**Nb**)
immundus (Gyll.)
intermedius (Bois. & Lac.)*
laminatus (Creutz.)
longicornis Steph.*
mannerheimi Fauvel* (**Nb**)
marginatus (Ström)
micans (Grav.)*
nigrita (Grav.)*
politus (L.)
quisquiliarius (Gyll.)
sanguinolentus (Grav.)*
sordidus (Grav.)
splendens (F.)*
succicola Thoms.
tenuicornis Muls. & Rey*
umbratilis (Grav.)
varians (Payk.)
varius (Gyll.)
ventralis (Grav.)*
Gabrius bishopi Sharp* (**Nb**)
nigritulus (Grav.)
osseticus (Kolenati)* (**Nb**)
pennatus Sharp
trossulus (von Nord.)
Staphylinus aeneocephalus DeGeer
ater Grav.*
brunnipes F.*
caesareus Cederhjelm* (**RDB I**)
compressus Marsh.*
fuscatus Grav.*
olens O. F. Müll.
Ontholestes murinus (L.)*
Heterothops dissimilis (Grav.) (**RDBK**)
niger Kraatz*
praevius Erichs.*
Quedius balticus Korge (**RDB1**)
cinctus (Payk.)
cruentus (Olivier)
curtipennis Bernh.
fulgidus (F.) (**Nb**)
fuliginosus (Grav.)
fumatus (Steph.)
humeralis Steph.*
longicornis Kraatz* (**Nb**)
maurorufus (Grav.)
mesomelinus (Marsh.)
molochinus (Grav.)
nemoralis Baudi*
nigriceps Kraatz*
nigrocaeruleus Fauv.* (**Nb**)
nitipennis (Steph.)*
picipes (Mann.)
puncticollis (Thoms.)* (**Nb**)
scintillans Grav.*
semiaeneus (Steph.)*
semiobscurus (Marsh.)
tristis (Grav.)
ventralis (Arag.)* (**Nb**)

Habrocerinae

Habrocerus capillaricornis (Grav.)

Tachyporinae

Mycetoporus lepidus (Grav.)*
longicornis Maeklin (**N**)
nigricollis Steph.*
punctus (Grav.) (**N**)
rufescens (Steph.)
splendidus (Grav.)
Lordithon trinotatus (Erichs.)*
Bolitobius analis (F.)
cingulatus (Mann.)
Sepedophilus immaculatus (Steph.)*
littoreus (L.)
marshami (Steph.)
nigripennis (Steph.)
pedicularius (Grav.) (**N**)
testaceus (F.)* (**N**)
Tachyporus chrysomelinus (L.) and/or *dispar* (Payk.)
hypnorum (F.)
nitidulus (F.)
obtusus (L.)
pallidus Sharp*
solutus Erichs.*
tersus Erichs.
transversalis Grav.
Tachinus laticollis Grav.*
marginellus (F.)
signatus Grav.
Cilea silphoides (L.)*

Aleocharinae

Deinopsis erosa (Steph.)*
Gymnusa brevicollis (Payk.)*
Cypha discoidea (Erichs.)* (**Nb**)
longicornis (Payk.)
pulicarius (Erichs.)* (**N**)
seminulum (Erichs.)* (**RDBK**)
Oligota picipes (Steph.)
punctulata Heer*
Myllaena brevicornis (Matthews)*
dubia (Grav.)*
infuscata Kraatz
minuta (Grav.)*
Hygronoma dimidiata (Grav.)
Gyrophaena angustata (Steph.)* (**N**)
fasciata (Marsh.)
joyi Wendel. (**N**)
nana (Payk.)*
Bolitochara obliqua Erichs.
Autalia impressa (Olivier)
rivularis (Grav.)
Cordalia obscura (Grav.)
Falagria caesa Erichs.*
sulcatula (Grav.)* (**N**)
Tachyusa atra Grav.*
Gnypeta carbonaria (Mann.)*
Callicerus obscurus Grav.*
Schistoglossa viduata (Erichs.) (**RDBK**)
Dacrila fallax (Kraatz)* (**N**)
Aloconota gregaria (Erichs.)*
languida (Erichs.) (**N**)
longicollis (Muls. & Rey)* (**N**)
Amischa analis (Grav.)*
decipiens (Sharp)*
Nehemitropia sordida (Marsh.)*
Dochmonota clancula (Erichs.) (**N**)
Geostiba circellaris (Grav.)
Dinaraea aequata (Erichs.)
Plataraea brunnea (F.)*
Liogluta longiuscula (Grav.)*

Atheta amicula (Steph.)*
  aterrima (Grav.)*
  atramentaria (Gyll.)*
  benickiella Brundin* (N)
  cinnamoptera (Thoms.)*
  clientula (Erichs.)*
  crassicornis (F.)
  debilis (Erichs.)*
  deformis (Kraatz) (N)
  diversa (Sharp)* (N)
  elongatula (Grav.)
  fungi (Grav.)
  fungivora (Thoms.)*
  graminicola (Grav.)
  gyllenhali (Thoms.)*
  hepatica (Thoms.)*
  hygrobia (Thoms.) (N)
  intermedia (Thoms.)*
  ischnocera (Thoms.)*
  laticollis (Steph.)
  longicornis (Grav.)*
  luridipennis (Thoms.)*
  luteipes (Erichs.)*
  magniceps (Sahlb.)
  malleus Joy*
  melanaria (Mann.)*
  melanocera (Thoms.)*
  mortuorum Thoms.* (RDBK)
  muscorum (Brisout)*
  nigra (Kraatz)*
  nigricornis (Thoms.)*
  nigripes (Thoms.)
  oblita (Erichs.)*
  orbata (Erichs.)*
  orphana (Erichs.)* (N)
  palustris (Kiesenw.)*
  parvula (Mann.)*
  pygmaea (Grav.)
  setigera (Sharp)*
  triangulum (Kraatz)*
  trinotata (Kraatz)*
  volans (Erichs.)*
  xanthopus (Thoms.)
  zosterae (Thoms.) (N)
Alianta incana (Erichs.)
Pachnida nigella (Erichs.)
Drusilla canaliculata (F.)*
Zyras collaris (Payk.)
Ilyobates nigricollis (Payk.) (RDBK)
  subopacus Palm* (N)
Calodera riparia Erichs. (N)
Chiloporata longitarsis (Erichs.)
Meotica exilis (Grav.)
Deubelia picina (Aubé)
Ocyusa maura (Erichs.)
Oxypoda elongatula Aubé
  haemorrhoa (Mann.)*
  induta Muls. & Rey
  lividipennis Mann.*
  opaca (Grav.)
  umbrata (Gyll.)
Crataraea saturalis (Mann.)*
Aleochara bipustulata (L.)
  brevipennis Grav.* (N)
  curtula (Goeze)
  lanuginosa Grav.
  moerens Gyll.* (N)
  sparsa Heer*
  tristis Grav.*

PSELAPHIDAE

Bibloplectus ambiguus (Reich.)
Euplectus nanus (Reich.)* (RDB I)
  sanguineus Denny*
Bythinus macropalpus Aubé
Bryaxis bulbifer (Reich.)
  curtisi (Leach)
  puncticollis (Denny)*
Tychus niger (Payk.)*
Rybaxis laminata (Motsch.)
  longicornis (Leach)
Brachygluta fossulata (Reich.)*
Reichenbachia juncorum (Leach)
Pselaphaulax dresdensis Herbst (N)
Pselaphus heisei Herbst

Scirtiformia

SCIRTOIDEA

SCIRTIDAE

Elodes spp. [A closely related group of five recently-separated
  species. Those at Wicken have yet to be determined]
Microcara testacea (L.)
Cyphon coarctatus (Payk.)
  ochraceus Steph.
  padi (L.)
  phragmiticola Nyholm
  variabilis (Thunb.)
Prionocyphon serricornis (P. W. J. Müll.)* (Nb)
Hydrocyphon deflexicollis (P. W. J. Müll.)* (Nb)
Scirtes hemisphaericus (L.)

CLAMBIDAE

Calyptomerus dubius (Marsh.)
Clambus armadillo (DeGeer)
  gibbulus (LeConte)
  pubescens (Redtenb.)

Scarabaeiformia

SCARABAEOIDEA

LUCANIDAE

Dorcus parallelipipedus (L.)*

GEOTRUPIDAE

Geotrupes stercorarius (L.)

SCARABAEIDAE

Aphodiinae

Colobopterus erraticus (L.)*
  fossor (L.)
Aphodius ater (DeGeer)
  contaminatus (Herbst)
  fimetarius (L.)
  luridus (F.)*
  prodromus (Brahm)
  rufipes (L.)
Oxyomus sylvestris (Scop.)*

Melolonthinae

Melolontha melolontha (L.)
Hoplia philanthus (Fuessly)

Rutelinae
Phylloperta horticola (L.)

Elateriformia

DASCILLOIDEA

DASCILLIDAE
Dascillus cervinus (L.)

BUPRESTOIDEA

BUPRESTIDAE
Agrilus sinuatus (Olivier)

BYRRHOIDEA

BYRRHIDAE
Simplocaria semistriata (F.)
Cytilus sericeus (Forst.)
Byrrhus pilula (L.)*
  pustulatus (Forst.)*

DRYOPIDAE
Dryops anglicanus Edw. (RDB3)
  auriculatus (Geoff.) (Nb)
  ernesti des Gozis
  luridus (Erichs.)
  nitidulus (Heer) (RDB3)
  similaris Bollow (RDB3)

ELMIDAE
Elmis aenea (P. W. J. Müll.)
Oulimnius major (Rey) (Na)
  rivularis (Rosenh.) (Na)
  tuberculatus (P. W. J. Müll.)

LIMNICHIDAE
Limnichus pygmaeus (Sturm)* (Na)

HETEROCERIDAE
Heterocerus fenestratus (Thunb.)
  maritimus Guér.-Ménev.*

ELATEROIDEA

THROSCIDAE
Trixagus dermestoides (L.)
  obtusus (Curt.)

ELATERIDAE
Pyrophorinae
Agrypnus murinus (L.)

Hypnoidinae
Hypnoidus riparius (F.)

Denticollinae
Actenicerus sjaelandicus (O. F. Müll.)
Aplotarsus incanus (Gyll.)
Kibunea minuta (L.)
Denticollis linearis (L.)
Athous bicolor (Goeze)
  haemorrhoidalis (F.)
  vittatus (F.)
Hemicrepidius hirtus (Herbst)

Elaterinae
Adrastus pallens (F.)
Agriotes acuminatus (Steph.)
  lineatus (L.)
  obscurus (L.)
  pallidulus (Ill.)
  sputator (L.)
Dalopius marginatus (L.)

Melanotinae
Melanotus villosus (Fourc.)

Negastriinae
Oedostethus quadripustulatus (F.)*

LAMPYRIDAE
Lampyris noctiluca (L.)

CANTHARIDAE
Cantharis cryptica Ashe
  decipiens Baudi
  figurata Mann.
  fusca L.* (RDB3)
  lateralis L.
  livida L.
  nigra (DeGeer)
  nigricans (O. F. Müll.)
  pallida Goeze
  rufa L.*
  rustica Fall.
  thoracica (Olivier)
Rhagonycha femoralis (Brullé)
  fulva (Scop.)
  lutea (O. F. Müll.)* (Nb)
  testacea (L.)
Silis ruficollis (F.) (Nb)
Malthinus balteatus Suffr. (Nb)
  flaveolus (Herbst)
  seriepunctatus Kiesenw.
Malthodes dispar (Germar)
  flavoguttatus Kiesenw.*
  marginatus (Latr.)*
  minimus (L.)*
  mysticus Kiesenw.*
  pumilus (Brébisson)*

Bostrichiformia

BOSTRICHOIDEA

DERMESTIDAE
Attagenus pellio (L.)
Anthrenus fuscus Olivier
  musaeorum (L.)

ANOBIIDAE
Hedobiinae
Ptinomorphus imperialis (L.) (Nb)

Ernobiinae
Xestobium rufovillosum (DeGeer)

Anobiinae
Hemicoelus fulvicornis (Sturm)
Anobium inexspectatum Lohse* (Nb)
  punctatum (DeGeer)*

Ptilinae

Ptilinus pectinicornis (L.)

Dorcatominae

Caenocara bovistae (Hoffm.)* (**RDB3**)

Cucujiformia

CLEROIDEA

CLERIDAE

Korynetes caeruleus (DeGeer)* (**Nb**)

MELYRIDAE

Dasytinae

Dasytes aeratus Steph.
  plumbeus (O. F. Müll.) (**Nb**)
Axinotarsus ruficollis (Olivier)*

Malachiinae

Malachius bipustulatus (L.)
  marginellus Olivier (**Nb**)
  viridis F.
Cerapheles terminatus (Ménétr.) (**Na**)
Anthocomus fasciatus (L.)*
  rufus (Herbst)

CUCUJOIDEA

KATERETIDAE

Brachypterolus pulicarius (L.)
  vestitus (Kiesenw.)*
Brachypterus glaber (Steph.)
  urticae (F.)*
Kateretes pedicularius (L.)*
  pusillus (Thunb.)
  rufilabris (Latr.)

NITIDULIDAE

Epuraea aestiva (L.)
  limbata (F.)*
  melina Erichs.*
  silacea (Herbst)* (**RDB3**)
    (*deleta* Sturm)
  unicolor (Olivier)
Nitidula bipunctata (L.)*
  rufipes (L.)*
Soronia grisea (L.)*
Pria dulcamarae (Scop.)
Meligethes aeneus (F.)
  coracinus Sturm* (**Extinct**)
  difficilis (Heer)
  flavimanus Steph.*
  fulvipes Bris. (**N**)
  lugubris Sturm* (**N**)
  nigrescens Steph.
  pedicularius (Gyll.)*
    (*viduata* (Heer))
  viridescens (F.)
Glischrochilus hortensis (Geoff. in Fourc.)

RHIZOPHAGIDAE

Rhizophaginae

Rhizophagus bipustulatus (F.)
  perforatus Erichs.

Monotominae

Monotoma bicolor Villa*
  longicollis Gyll.*
  picipes Herbst*
  testacea Motsch.

SILVANIDAE

Silvaninae

Oryzaephilus surinamensis (L.)*
Silvanus unidentatus (Olivier)

Psammoecinae

Psammoecus bipunctatus (F.)

CUCUJIDAE

Cucujinae

Pediacus depressus (Herbst)* (**Na**)
  dermestoides (F.)

Laemophloeinae

Cryptolestes ferrugineus (Steph.)

PHALACRIDAE

Phalacrus caricis Sturm*
  corruscus (Panz.)
  fimetarius (F.)
Olibrus aeneus (F.)
  pygmaeus (Sturm) (**Nb**)
Stilbus atomarius (L.)* (**RDBK**)
  oblongus (Erichs.)
  testaceus (Panz.)

CRYPTOPHAGIDAE

Telmatophilinae

Telmatophilus brevicollis Aubé (**RDB3**)
  caricis (Olivier)*
  schoenherri (Gyll.) (**RDBK**)
  typhae (Fall.)

Cryptophaginae

Cryptophagus dentatus (Herbst)
  distinguendus Sturm*
  laticollis Lucas
  pallidus Sturm*
  pilosus Gyll.
  populi Payk.* (**N**)
  pseudodentatus Bruce
  pubescens Sturm
  saginatus Sturm
  scanicus (L.)
  schmidti Sturm* (**RDBK**)
  scutellatus Newm.
  setulosus Sturm*
Micrambe villosus (Heer)*
  vini (Panz.)
Antherophagus nigricornis (F.)
  pallens (L.)*

Atomariinae

Atomaria apicalis Erichs.*
  atra (Herbst)* (**N**)
  atricapilla Steph.
  basalis Erichs.*
  fuscata (Schoen.)
  gutta Newman
  lewisi Reitter

linearis Steph.*
mesomela (Herbst)*
munda Erichs.
nigrirostris Steph.
nitidula (Marsh.)*
pusilla (Payk.)
rhenana Kraatz* (N)
rubella Heer
testacea Steph.
Ootypus globosus (Waltl)
Ephistemus globulus (Payk.)

EROTYLIDAE

Triplax russica (L.)*
Dacne bipustulata (Thunb.)*
rufifrons (F.)

BYTURIDAE

Byturus ochraceus (Scriba)
tomentosus (DeGeer)

CERYLONIDAE

Euxestinae
Annomatus duodecimstriatus (P. W. J. Müll.)* (Na)

ENDOMYCHIDAE

Sphaerosominae
Mycetaea hirta (Marsh.)*

Endomychinae
Endomychus coccineus (L.)

COCCINELLIDAE

Epilachninae
Subcoccinella 24-punctata (L.)

Coccinellinae
Coccidula rufa (Herbst)
scutellata (Herbst)
Rhyzobius litura (F.)
Stethorus punctillum Weise*
Scymnus frontalis (F.)*
limbatus Steph. (Nb)
suturalis Thunb.*
Chilocorus renipustulatus (Scriba)
Adonia variegata (Goeze)* (Nb)
Anisosticta 19-punctata (L.)
Aphidecta obliterata (L.)*
Micraspis 16-punctata (L.)
Adalia bipunctata (L.)
10-punctata (L.)
Coccinella hieroglyphica L.*
7-punctata L.
11-punctata L.
Harmonia quadripunctata (Pont.)
Propylea 14-punctata (L.)
Anatis ocellata (L.)
Calvia 14-guttata (L.)
Psyllobora 22-punctata (L.)

CORYLOPHIDAE

Sericoderus lateralis (Gyll.)
Corylophus cassidoides (Marsh.)
Orthoperus brunnipes (Gyll.)* (RDB3)

LATHRIDIIDAE

Lathridiinae
Stephostethus angusticollis (Gyll.)*
lardarius (DeGeer)
Aridius bifasciatus (Reitt.)
nodifer (Westw.)
Cartodere constricta (Gyll.)*
Enicmus histrio Joy & Toml.
minutus (L.)
transversus (Olivier)
Dienerella ruficollis (Marsh.)

Corticariinae
Corticaria elongata (Gyll.)
ferruginea Marsh.*
impressa (Olivier)
inconspicua Wollaston* (N)
punctulata Marsh.
serrata (Payk.)*
Corticarina fuscula (Gyll.)
Cortinicara gibbosa (Herbst)
transversalis (Gyll.)*

TENEBRIONOIDEA

MYCETOPHAGIDAE

Pseudotriphyllus suturalis (F.)*
Mycetophagus multipunctatus F.
quadriguttatus P. W. J. Müll.* (Na)
quadripustulatus (L.)
Typhaea stercorea (L.)

CIIDAE (=CISIDAE)

Octotemnus glabriculus (Gyll.)
Cis boleti (Scop.)*

TETRATOMIDAE

Tetratoma fungorum F.

MELANDRYIDAE

Orchesia micans (Panz.)* (Nb)
Anisoxya fuscula (Ill.)* (Na)
Conopalpus testaceus (Olivier)* (Nb)

MORDELLIDAE

Mordellistena humeralis (L.) (RDBK)
neuwaldeggiana (Panz.)* (RDBK)

COLYDIIDAE

Bitoma crenata (F.)

TENEBRIONIDAE

Scaphidema metallicum (F.) (Nb)
Alphitophagus bifasciatus (Say)*
Tenebrio molitor L.
obscurus F.*
Lagria hirta (L.)
Isomira murina (L.)*
Cteniopus sulphureus (L.)*

OEDEMERIDAE

Oedemera lurida (Marsh.)

PYROCHROIDAE

Pyrochroa serraticornis (Scop.)

SALPINGIDAE

Rhinosimus planirostris (F.)

ANTHICIDAE

Notoxus monoceros (L.)*
Anthicus antherinus (L.)
  bifasciatus (Rossi)* (**Nb**)
  floralis (L.)
  formicarius (Goeze)

SCRAPTIIDAE

Anaspis frontalis (L.)
  humeralis (F.)
  maculata Fourc.
  pulicaria Costa*
  regimbarti Schils.

CHRYSOMELOIDEA

CERAMBYCIDAE

Lepturinae

Stenocorus meridianus (L.)
Grammoptera ruficornis (F.)
Anoplodera rubra (L.)
Strangalia maculata (Poda)
  quadrifasciata (L.)

Cerambycinae

Aromia moschata (L.) (**Nb**)
Callidium violaceum (L.)*
Clytus arietis (L.)
Anaglyptus mysticus (L.) (**Nb**)

Lamiinae

Lamia textor (L.) (**RDB1**)
Pogonocherus hispidus (L.)
Agapanthia villosoviridescens (DeGeer)
Saperda carcharias (L.)* (**Na**)
Oberea oculata (L.) (**RDB1**)
Phytoecia cylindrica (L.)* (**Nb**)
Tetrops praeusta (L.)

CHRYSOMELIDAE

Bruchinae

Bruchus atomarius (L.)* (**Nb**)
  rufimanus Boh.

Donaciinae

Donacia aquatica (L.)* (**RDB3**)
  bicolora Zschach* (**RDB2**)
  clavipes F. (**Nb**)
  crassipes F.* (**Nb**)
  dentata Hoppe* (**Na**)
  marginata Hoppe*
  semicuprea Panz.
  simplex F.
  sparganii Ahr. (**Na**)
  versicolorea (Brahm)*
  vulgaris Zschach*
Plateumaris affinis (Kunze)* (**Nb**)
  sericea (L.)*

Megalopidinae

Zeugophora subspinosa (F.)

Criocerinae

Lema cyanella (L.)
Oulema lichenis Voet
  ?*melanopus* (L.)
  rufocyanea (Suffr.)
Crioceris asparagi (L.)

Cryptocephalinae

Cryptocephalus bilineatus (L.)§ (**Nb**)
  fulvus Goeze
  pusillus F.

Chrysomelinae

Chrysolina brunsvicensis (Grav.)
  graminis (L.) (**Na**)
  haemoptera (L.)* (**Nb**)
  menthastri (Suffr.)*
  polita (L.)
  staphylaea (L.)*
  varians (Schall.)*
Gastrophysa polygoni (L.)*
  viridula (DeGeer)
Phaedon armoraciae (L.)
  cochleariae (F.)
  tumidulus (Germar)
Hydrothassa glabra (Herbst)
  marginella (L.)*
Prasocuris junci (Brahm)*
  phellandrii (L.)*
Chrysomela populi L.
Phyllodecta laticollis Suffr.
  vitellinae (L.)

Galerucinae

Galerucella calmariensis (L.)*
  lineola (F.)*
  pusilla (Duft.)
  tenella (L.)
Pyrrhalta viburni (Payk.)
Galeruca laticollis (Sahlb.)* (**RDB1**)
    (*interrupta* sensu auctt. Brit. nec. Ill.)
  tanaceti (L.)*
Lochmaea caprea (L.)
  crataegi (Forst.)
Phyllobrotica quadrimaculata (L.)
Luperus longicornis (F.)
Sermylassa halensis (L.)*

Halticinae

Phyllotreta atra (F.)
  exclamationis (Thunb.)
  flexuosa (Ill.)*
  nemorum (L.)
  nigripes (F.)
  nodicornis (Marsh.)*
  ochripes (Curt.)
  striolata (F.)
  tetrastigma (Comolli)*
  undulata Kutsch.
  vittula (Redten.)
Aphthona atrocaerulea (Steph.)*
  atrovirens Först.
  euphorbiae (Schr.)
  lutescens (Gyll.)
  melancholica Weise
  nonstriata (Goeze)
Longitarsus aeneicollis (Falderm.)* (**Nb**)
  (*suturalis* (Marsh.))
  agilis (Rye)* (**Na**)
  anchusae (Payk.)* (**Nb**)

atricillus (L.)*
ballotae (Marsh.)* (**Nb**)
brunneus (Duft.) (**Nb**)
ferrugineus (Foudr.)* (**RDB I**)
ganglbaueri Heiker.* (**Na**)
gracilis Kutsch.
holsaticus (L.)*
jacobaeae (Waterh.)
luridus (Scop.)
lycopi (Foudr.) (**Nb**)
melanocephalus DeGeer*
nigrofasciatus (Goeze)* (**Na**)
ochroleucus (Marsh.)* (**Nb**)
parvulus (Payk.) (**Na**)
pellucidus (Foudr.)*
pratensis (Panz.)
reichei (Allard)
rubiginosus (Foudr.)
succineus (Foudr.)*
suturellus (Duft.)
Altica lythri Aubé
palustris Weise
Batophila rubi (Payk.)
Lythraria salicariae (Payk.) (**Nb**)
Crepidodera ferruginea (Scop.)
transversa (Marsh.)
Chalcoides aurata (Marsh.)
aurea (Fourc.)
fulvicornis (F.)
plutus (Latr.)
Epitrix atropae (Foudr.)* (**Nb**)
pubescens (J. D. W. Koch)
Podagrica fuscicornis (L.) (**Nb**)
Mantura chrysanthemi (J. D. W. Koch)* (**Na**)
rustica (L.)* (**Nb**)
Chaetocnema concinna (Marsh.)
confusa (Boh.)*
hortensis (Fourc.)*
Sphaeroderma rubidum (Graëlls)
testaceum (F.)
Apteropeda orbiculata (Marsh.)
Psylliodes affinis (Payk.)*
chrysocephala (L.)
cuprea (J. D. W. Koch)
dulcamarae (J. D. W. Koch)
napi (F.)*
picina (Marsh.)
sophiae Heiker.* (**RDB3**)

Cassidinae

Cassida flaveola Thunb.*
hemisphaerica Herbst* (**Na**)
nobilis L. (**Nb**)
prasina Ill.* (**Nb**)
rubiginosa O. F. Müll.
vibex L.
viridis L.*

CURCULIONOIDEA

ATTELABIDAE

Rhynchitinae

Rhynchites aequatus (L.)
caeruleus (DeGeer)
germanicus Herbst*
nanus (Payk.)
Deporaus betulae (L.)

BRENTIDAE (=*APIONIDAE*)

Apioninae

Acanephodus onopordi (Kirby)
Catapion seniculus (Kirby)
Ceratapion gibbirostre (Gyll.)*
(*carduorum* auctt. nec (Kirby))
Diplapion confluens (Kirby)*
Aspidapion aeneum (F.)
radiolus (Marsh.)
Squamapion vicinum (Kirby)* (**Nb**)
Pseudapion rufirostre (F.)
Malvapion malvae (F.)
Protapion assimile (Kirby)
fulvipes (Geoff.)
(*dichroum* (Bedel))
nigritarse (Kirby)
ononicola (Bach)
trifolii (L.)
varipes Germar (**Nb**)
Perapion affine Kirby (**Na**)
curtirostre (Germar)
hydrolapathi (Marsh.)
lemoroi (Bris.)* (**RDBK**) (stubble field between W.Fen and Burw.Fen)
violaceum Kirby
Apion frumentarium (L.)
(*miniatum* Germar)
haematodes Kirby*
(*frumentarium* (Payk.))
Trichapion simile (Kirby)
Holotrichapion pisi (F.)
Oxystoma pomonae (F.)
Eutrichapion ervi (Kirby)
viciae (Payk.)
virens Herbst
vorax (Herbst)

Nanophyinae

Nanophyes marmoratus (Goeze)

CURCULIONIDAE

Entiminae

Otiorhynchus clavipes (Bonsd.)*
singularis (L.)*
Trachyphloeus asperatus Boh.* (**Nb**)
Phyllobius argentatus (L.)
maculicornis Germar*
oblongus (L.)
pomaceus Gyll.
pyri (L.)
roboretanus Gredl.
viridiaeris (Laich.)
Polydrusus cervinus (L.)
Sciaphilus asperatus (Bonsd.)
Liophloeus tessulatus (O. F. Müll.)
Barynotus obscurus (F.)*
Tanymecus palliatus (F.)
Sitona hispidulus (F.)
humeralis Steph.
lineatus (L.)
macularius (Marsh.)* (**Nb**)
puncticollis Steph.
striatellus Gyll.
sulcifrons (Thunb.)

Cleoninae

Lixus paraplecticus (L.)* (**RDB1**)

Hyperinae

Hypera arator (L.)
  fuscocinerea (Marsh.)* (**Nb**)
  meles (F.) (**Na**)
  nigrirostris (F.)*
  pollux (F.)*
    (*adspersa* (F.))
  postica (Gyll.)*
  punctata (F.)*
  rumicis (L.)*
  suspiciosa (Herbst)*

Cioninae

Cionus hortulanus (Fourc.)
  scrophulariae (L.)

Hylobiinae

Leiosoma deflexum (Panz.)

Magdalidinae

Magdalis armigera (Fourc.)*
  ruficornis (L.)

Anoplinae

Anoplus plantaris (Naezen)

Tanysphyrinae

Tanysphyrus lemnae (Payk.)

Cossoninae

Cossonus linearis (F.) (**Na**)
  parallelepipedus (Herbst) (**Nb**)

Rhyncophorinae

Rhyncolus lignarius (Marsh.)*
Sitophilus oryzae (L.)*

Cryptorhynchinae

Cryptorhynchus lapathi (L.)* (**Nb**)
Acalles roboris Curt.* (**Nb**)

Erirhinae

Bagous collignensis (Herbst)* (**RDB3**)
  subcarinatus Gyll.* (**Na**)
  tempestivus (Herbst)* (**Nb**)
Hydronomus alismatis (Marsh.)* (**Nb**)
Dorytomus dejeani Faust
  filirostris (Gyll.) (**Nb**)
  hirtipennis Bedel* (**Na**)
  longimanus (Forst.)*
  melanophthalmus (Payk.)*
  salicinus (Gyll.)
  taeniatus (F.)
  tortrix (L.)
Notaris acridulus (L.)
  scirpi (F.)* (**Nb**)
Thryogenes festucae (Herbst)
  nereis (Payk.) and/or *atrirostris* Lohse*
Pseudostyphlus pillumus (Gyll.)* (**Na**)
Orthochaetes setiger (Beck)* (**Nb**)

Ceutorhynchinae

Eubrychius velutus (Beck)* (**Nb**)
Phytobius leucogaster (Marsh.) (**Nb**)
  (=*Litodactylus leucogaster* (Marsh.))
Pelenomus canaliculatus (Fahraeus)* (**Nb**)
  (=*Phytobius canaliculatus* Fahraeus)
  comari (Herbst)* (**Nb**)
    (=*Phytobius comari* (Herbst))

  quadrituberculatus (F.)*
    (=*Phytobius quadrituberculatus* (F.))
Neophytobius muricatus (Bris.)* (**Na**)
  (=*Phytobius muricatus* Bris.)
Rhinoncus bruchoides (Herbst)*
  inconspectus (Herbst)
  pericarpius (L.)
  perpendicularis (Reich)
Amalus scortillum (Herbst)*
Poophagus sisymbrii (F.)
Coeliodes rubicundus (Herbst)
Thamiocolus viduatus (Gyll.)* (**Nb**)
  (=*Ceutorhynchus viduatus* (Gyll.))
Parethelcus pollinarius (Forst.)
  (=*C. pollinarius* (Forst.))
Datonychus angulosus (Boh.)* (**Na**)
  (=*C. angulosus* Boh.)
  melanostictus (Marsh.)*
    (=*C. melanostictus* (Marsh.))
Microplontus campestris (Gyll.) (**Nb**)
  (=*C. campestris* (Gyll.))
Hadroplontus litura (F.)
  (=*C. litura* (F.))
  trimaculatus (F.)* (**Nb**)
    (=*C. trimaculatus* F.)
Mogulones asperifoliarum (Gyll.)
  (=*C. asperifoliarum* (Gyll.))
Glocianus punctiger (Gyll.) (**Nb**)
  (=*C. punctiger* Gyll.)
Ceutorhynchus alliariae Bris.
  assimilis (Payk.)
    (*pleurostigma* (Marsh.))
  atomus Boh.
  chalybaeus Germar*
    (*timidus* Weise)
  cochleariae (Gyll.)*
  constrictus (Marsh.)
  contractus (Marsh.)*
  erysimi (F.)
  floralis (Payk.)
  obstrictus (Marsh.)
    (*assimilis* auctt. non (Payk.))
  pallidactylus (Marsh.)
    (*quadridens* (Panz.))
  pectoralis Weise* (**Na**)
  rapae Gyll.* (**Nb**)
  sulcicollis (Payk.)*
Sirocalodes depressicollis (Gyll.)*
  (=*Ceutorhynchus depressicollis* (Gyll.))
  mixtus (Muls. & Rey)* (**Nb**)
    (=*C. mixtus* Muls. & Rey)
Trichosirocalus troglodytes (F.)
  (=*Ceuthorhynchidius troglodytes* (F.))
Stenocarus ruficornis (Steph.)*
  (*umbrinus* (Gyll.))
Nedyus quadrimaculatus (L.)
  (=*Cidnorhinus quadrimaculatus* (L.))

Baridinae

Baris laticollis (Marsh.)* (**Na**)
Limnobaris dolorosa (Goeze)
  (*pilistriata* (Steph.))
  t-album (L.)

Anthonominae

Anthonomus bituberculatus Thoms.
  brunnipennis (Curt.)*
  pedicularius (L.)
  rubi (Herbst)
  ulmi (DeGeer)* (**Nb**)

Curculioninae

Curculio glandium Marsh.*
  salicivorus Payk.

Tychiinae

Tychius picirostris (F.)
Acalyptus carpini (F.) (**Nb**)

Mecininae

Miarus plantarum (Germar)* (**RDBK**)
Mecinus pyraster (Herbst)
Gymnetron antirrhini (Payk.)*
  labile (Herbst)*
  pascuorum (Gyll.)
  veronicae (Germar) (**Nb**)

Rhynchaeninae

Rhynchaenus alni (L.)*
  pratensis (Germar) (**Nb**)
  quercus (L.)*
  rusci (Herbst)
  salicis (L.)
Ramphus pulicarius (Herbst)

SCOLYTIDAE

Scolytus multistriatus (Marsh.)

STREPSIPTERA

Record: Gambles & Kerrich (1932)

[STYLOPIDAE

Stylops spp.

Unidentified spp. have been recorded from Wicken Fen as parasitic on *Andrena saundersella* R. C. L. Perkins and *A. chrysosceles* (Kirby) (Hymenoptera: Apidae)]

DIPTERA

List: compiled by I. Perry and P. H. Langton, with assistance from D. M. Ackland, P. J. Chandler, J. H. Cole, R. H. L. Disney, J. W. Ismay, I. F. G. McLean, J. Robbins, A. E. Stubbs, and others.
Checklist: P. J. Chandler (1998)

* Species probably extinct at Wicken Fen
† Species with no recent records
Species without a symbol attached have been recorded since 1960

Nematocera

TIPULIDAE

Ctenophorinae

Dictenidia bimaculata (L.)

Tipulinae

Nephrotoma analis (Schumm.)
  appendiculata (Pierre)
  flavescens (L.)
  guestfalica (Westh.)
  quadrifaria (Meig.)
Nigrotipula nigra L.
Prionocera turcica (F.)
Tipula confusa van der Wulp
  fascipennis Meig.
  lateralis Meig.
  livida van der Wulp (N)
  luna Westh.
  lunata L.
  luteipennis Meig.
  maxima Poda
  obsoleta Meig.
  oleracea L.
  pagana Meig.
  paludosa Meig.
  peliostigma Schumm. (N)
  pierrei Tonn.
  scripta Meig.
  signata Staeger
  staegeri Nielsen
  subcunctans Alex.
  submarmorata Schumm.
  unca Wied.
  variicornis Schumm.
  varipennis Meig.
  vernalis Meig.
  vittata Meig.

CYLINDROTOMIDAE

Diogma glabrata (Meig.) (N)
Phalacrocera replicata (L.) (N)

PEDICIIDAE

Pediciinae

Tricyphona immaculata (Meig.)

Ulinae

Ula mollissima Hal.

LIMONIIDAE

Chioneinae

Cheilotrichia cinerascens (Meig.)
  imbuta (Meig.)† (N)
Ellipteroides lateralis (Macq.)

Erioconopa trivialis (Meig.)
Erioptera bivittata (Loew) (**RDB2**)
  fusculenta Edw.
  griseipennis Meig.
  lutea Meig.
  meijerei Edw. (**RDB2**)
Gnophomyia viridipennis (Gimmer.) (**N**)
Gonomyia recta Tonn.
  tenella (Meig.)
Ilisia maculata (Meig.)
Molophilus appendiculatus (Staeger)
  bifidus Goetgh.
  griseus (Meig.)
  obscurus (Meig.)
  ochraceus (Meig.)
  pleuralis de Meij.
  serpentiger Edw.
Ormosia depilata Edw.
  hederae (Curt.)
  lineata (Meig.)
  nodulosa (Macq.)
Rhypholophus varius (Meig.)
Symplecta hybrida (Meig.)
  stictica (Meig.)
Tasiocera murina (Meig.)
  robusta (Bangert.)

Limnophilinae

Austrolimnophila ochracea (Meig.)
Epiphragma ocellare (L.)
Neolimnomyia adjuncta (Walk.)
  nemoralis (Meig.)
Phylidorea ferruginea (Meig.)
  fulvonervosa (Schumm.)
Pilaria discicollis (Meig.)

Limoniinae

Atypophthalmus inustus (Meig.)
Dicranomyia chorea (Meig.)
  danica Kuntze (**RDB3**)
  lucida de Meijere (**N**)
  mitis sensu Edw.
  modesta (Meig.)
  morio (F.)
  ventralis (Schumm.)
Helius flavus (Walk.)
  longirostris (Meig.)
  pallirostris Edw. (**N**)
Limonia flavipes (F.)
  macrostigma (Schumm.)
  maculipennis (Meig.)
  nubeculosa Meig.
  phragmitidis (Schr.)
Metalimnobia quadrinotata (Meig.)
Neolimonia dumetorum (Meig.)
Rhipidia maculata (Meig.)
  uniseriata Schiner (**RDB3**)

BIBIONIDAE

Bibio ferruginatus (L.)
  hortulanus (L.)
  johannis (L.)
  lepidus Loew
  leucopterus (Meig.)
  marci (L.)
  nigriventris Hal.
  varipes Meig.
  venosus (Meig.)
Dilophus febrilis (L.)
  femoratus Meig.
  humeralis Zett.

BOLITOPHILIDAE

Bolitophila cinerea Meig.
  hybrida (Meig.)
  occlusa Edw.
  pseudohybrida Landr.
  saundersii (Curt.)

DIADOCIDIIDAE

Diadocidia ferruginosa (Meig.)

DITOMYIIDAE

Ditomyia fasciata (Meig.) **(N)**
Symmerus annulatus (Meig.)

KEROPLATIDAE

Keraplatinae

Isoneuromyia semirufa (Meig.)
Keroplatus testaceus Dalman **(N)**
Macrorrhyncha flava Winn.
Neoplatyura modesta (Winn.)
Orfelia fasciata (Meig.)
  nemoralis (Meig.)
  unicolor (Staeger)
Pyratula perpusilla (Edw.) **(RDB3)**
Rutylapa ruficornis Zett. **(RDB1)**

Macrocerinae

Macrocera centralis Meig.
  fasciata Meig.
  lutea Meig.
  maculata Meig. **(N)**
  phalerata Meig.
  stigmoides Edw.
  vittata Meig.

MYCETOPHILIDAE

Gnoristinae

Boletina gripha Dziedz.
  griphoides Edw.
  plana Walk.
  trivittata (Meig.)
Palaeodocosia janickii (Dziedz.)
Synapha fasciata Meig.

Leiinae

Docosia gilvipes (Walk.)
  pallipes Edw. **(N)**
Leia bimaculata (Meig.)
  winthemii Lehmann
Megophthalmidia crassicornis (Curt.) **(N)**

Mycetophilinae

Allodia grata (Meig.)
  neglecta (Edw.) **(N)**
  ornaticollis (Meig.)
  pistillata Lund. **(N)**
  silvatica Landr. **(N)**
Allodiopsis maculosa (Meig.) **(N)**
  rustica (Edw.)
Anatella flavomaculata Edw.
  setigera Edw.
  unguigera Edw.
Brevicornu auriculatum (Edw.)
  fissicauda (Lund.)
  griseicolle (Staeger)
  sericoma (Meig.)

Cordyla crassicornis Meig.
  fissa Edw.
Dynatosoma fuscicorne (Meig.)
Exechia dorsalis (Staeger)
  exigua (Lund.) **(N)**
  fusca (Meig.)
  pseudofestiva Lacksch. **(N)**
  repandoides Caspers
  spinuligera Lund.
Exechiopsis hammi (Edw.)
Mycetophila autumnalis Lund. **(RDB3)**
  blanda Winn.
  britannica Last. & Kidd
  cingulum Meig.
  confusa Dziedz. **(RDB3)**
  curviseta Lund.
  edwardsi Lund.
  forcipata Lund.
  formosa Lund.
  fraterna Winn.
  fungorum (DeGeer)
  luctuosa Meig.
  lunata Meig.
  marginata Winn.
  mitis (Johanns.) **(N)**
  occultans Lund.
  ocellus Walk.
  pumila Winn.
  ruficollis Meig.
  signatoides Dziedz.
  sordida van der Wulp
  tridentata Lund.
  trinotata Staeger
  uliginosa Chandl.
  unicolor Stann.
  unipunctata Meig.
  vittipes Zett.
Phronia biarcuata (Becker)
  braueri Dziedz.
  conformis (Walk.)
  disgrega (Dziedz.) **(N)**
  flavipes Winn.
  forcipata Winn.
  humeralis Winn.
  nigricornis (Zett.)
  siebeckii Dziedz.
  strenua Winn.
  tenuis Winn.
  triangularis Winn.
Platurocypta punctum (Stann.)
  testata (Edw.)
Pseudexechia trisignata (Edw.)
  trivittata (Staeger)
Pseudobrachypeza helvetica (Walk.)
Rymosia fasciata (Meig.)
Sceptonia cryptocauda Chandl.
  membranacea Edw.
  nigra (Meig.)
Synplasta excogitata (Dziedz.)
Tarnania fenestralis (Meig.)
Trichonta apicalis Strobl
  fragilis Gagné **(RDB3)**
  melanura (Staeger)
  terminalis (Walk.)
  vitta (Meig.)
Zygomyia humeralis (Wied.)
  notata (Stann.)
  pictipennis (Staeger)
  pseudohumeralis Caspers
  valida Winn.

Mycomyinae

Mycomya annulata (Meig.)
  cinerascens (Macq.)
  marginata (Meig.)
  tenuis (Walk.)
  winnertzi (Dziedz.)

Sciophilinae

Acnemia nitidicollis (Meig.)
Leptomorphus walkeri Curt.
Megalopelma nigroclavatum (Strobl) (N)
Monoclona rufilatera (Walk.)
Neuratelia nemoralis (Meig.)
Phthinia mira (Ostroverk.)
  winnertzi Mik
Sciophila antiqua Chandl. (RDB1)
  fenestella Curt. (N)
  lutea Macq.

SCIARIDAE

Bradysia aprica (Winn.)
  brunnipes (Meig.)
  confinis (Winn.)
  fungicola (Winn.)
  giraudii (Egger)
  rufescens (Zett.)
Bradysiopsis vittata (Meig.)
Corynoptera curvispinosa Freeman
  flavicauda (Zett.)
  forcipata (Winn.)
Leptosciarella rejecta (Winn.)
  subpilosa (Edw.)
  viatica (Winn.)
Lycoriella castanescens (Lengersd.)
Phytosciara flavipes (Meig.)
  ungulata (Winn.)
Pseudolycoriella bruckii (Winn.)
Scatopsciara atomaria (Zett.)
  vitripennis (Meig.)
Schwenckfeldina carbonaria (Meig.)
Sciara hemerobioides (Scop.)
Trichosia glabra (Meig.)
  morio (F.)
  splendens Winn.
Zygoneura sciarina Meig.

CECIDOMYIIDAE

Cecidomyiinae

Dasineura crataegi (Winn.)
  galiicola (F. Löw)
  glechomae (Kieff.)
  pustulans (Rübsaamen)
  ulmaria (Bremi)
  urticae (Perris)
Geocrypta galii (Loew)
Wachtliella rosarum (Hardy)

PSYCHODIDAE

Psychodinae

Boreoclytocerus ocellaris (Meig.)
Panimerus albifacies Tonn.
  goetghebueri Tonn.
Pericoma compta Eaton
  nubila (Meig.)
  pilularia Tonn.
  pseudoexquisita Tonn.
  trivialis Eaton

Philosepedon humeralis (Meig.)
Psychoda albipennis Zett.
Telmatoscopus vaillanti Withers

TRICHOCERIDAE

Trichocera annulata Meig.
  hiemalis (DeGeer)
  regelationis (L.)
  saltator (Harris)

ANISOPODIDAE

Sylvicola cinctus (F.)
  punctatus (F.)

SCATOPSIDAE

Psectrosciarinae

Anapausis dalmatina Duda
  nigripes (Zett.)
  soluta (Loew)

Scatopsinae

Apiloscatopse flavicollis (Meig.)
  picea (Meig.)
Coboldia fuscipes (Meig.)
Efcookella albitarsis (Zett.)
Reichertella geniculata (Zett.)
Rhexoza subnitens (Verrall)
Scatopse notata (L.)
Thripomorpha bifida (Zilahi-Sebess)
  coxendix (Verrall)

PTYCHOPTERIDAE

Ptychoptera albimana (F.)
  contaminata (L.)
  minuta Tonn.
  scutellaris Meig.

DIXIDAE

Dixa nebulosa Meig.
Dixella aestivalis (Meig.)
  amphibia (DeGeer)
  autumnalis Meig.
  serotina Meig. (N)

CHAOBORIDAE

Chaoborus crystallinus (DeGeer)†
  flavicans (Meig.)†

CULICIDAE

Anophelinae

Anopheles claviger (Meig.)
  messeae Falleroni

Culicinae

Aedes annulipes (Meig.)
  cinereus Meig.
  geniculatus (Olivier)†
  rusticus (Rossi)
Coquillettidia richiardii (Ficalbi)
Culex pipiens L.
  torrentium Martini
Culiseta annulata (Schr.)
  morsitans (Theobald)†

SIMULIIDAE

Simuliinae

Simulium angustipes Edw.
 erythrocephalum (DeGeer)
 lundstromi (Enderl.)

CERATOPOGONIDAE

Ceratopogoninae

Bezzia annulipes (Meig.)
 circumdata (Staeger)
 coracina (Zett.)
 leucogaster (Zett.)
 ornata (Meig.)
Clinohelea unimaculata (Macq.)
Mallochohelea nitida (Macq.)
Palpomyia flavipes (Meig.)
 lineata (Meig.)
 spinipes (Meig.)
Probezzia seminigra (Panz.)
Schizohelea leucopeza (Meig.)
Serromyia femorata (Meig.)
 morio (F.)
Sphaeromias pictus (Meig.)
Stilobezzia flavirostris (Winn.)

Dasyheleinae

Dasyhelea flavoscutellata (Zett.)
 versicolor (Winn.)

Forcipomyiinae

Forcipomyia pulchrithorax Edw.

CHIRONOMIDAE

Chironominae

Chironomus annularius (auctt. nec DeGeer, misident.)
 cingulatus Meig.
 commutatus Keyl
 longipes (Staeger)
 longistylus Goetgh.
 lugubris Zett.
 luridus Strenzke
 nuditarsis Keyl
 plumosus (L.)
 tentans (F.)
Cladopelma edwardsi (Krus.)
 viridula (L.)
Cladotanytarsus nigrovittatus (Goetgh.)
Cryptochironomus obreptans (Walk.)
 supplicans (Meig.)
Cryptotendipes holsatus Lenz
 nigronitens (Edw.)
Dicrotendipes lobiger (Kieff.)
 nervosus (Staeger)
 notatus (Meig.)
 objectans (Walk.)
 tritomus (Kieff.)
Einfeldia pagana (Meig.)
Endochironomus albipennis (Meig.)
 tendens (F.)
Glyptotendipes foliicola Kieff.
 gripekoveni (Kieff.)
 pallens (Meig.)
 paripes (Edw.)
Harnischia curtilamellata (Malloch)
Kiefferulus tendipediformis (Goetgh.)
Micropsectra contracta Reiss

Microtendipes chloris (Meig.)
 pedellus (DeGeer)
Parachironomus arcuatus (Goetgh.)
 biannulatus (Staeger)
 parilis (Walk.)
 vitiosus (Goetgh.)
Paratanytarsus bituberculatus (Edw.)
 dissimilis (Johanns.)
 grimmii (Schneider)
 inopertus (Walk.)
 laccophilus (Edw.)
 lauterborni (Kieff.)
 tenellulus (Goetgh.)
Phaenopsectra flavipes (Meig.)
Polypedilum arundineti (Goetgh.)
 bicrenatum Kieff.
 cultellatum Goetgh.
 laetum (Meig.)
 nubeculosum (Meig.)
 sordens (Wulp)
 tritum (Walk.)
Stempellina bausei (Kieff.)
Stempellinella minor (Edw.)
Stenochironomus gibbus (F.)
Tanytarsus brundini Lind.
 ejuncidus (Walk.)
 eminulus (Walk.)
 glabrescens Edw.
 lestagei Goetgh.
 medius Reiss & Fittk.
 mendax Kieff.
 pallidicornis (Walk.)
 usmaensis Pagast
Xenochironomus xenolabis (Kieff.)
Zavrelia pentatoma Kieff.

Orthocladiinae

Acricotopus lucens (Zett.)
Corynoneura carriana Edw.
 coronata Edw.
 edwardsi Brundin
 gratias Schlee
 scutellata Winn.
Cricotopus albiforceps (Kieff.)
 bicinctus (Meig.)
 festivellus (Kieff.)
 fuscus (Kieff.)
 intersectus (Staeger)
 ornatus (Meig.)
 sylvestris (F.)
 trifasciatus (Meig.)
Limnophyes asquamatus Anders.
 minimus (Meig.)
 ninae Saether
Metriocnemus fuscipes (Meig.)
Orthocladius holsatus Goetgh.
 oblidens (Walk.)
Paracladius conversus (Walk.)
Paralimnophyes hydrophilus (Goetgh.)
Paraphaenocladius exagitans (Johanns.)
 impensus (Walk.)
Psectrocladius barbimanus (Edw.)
 limbatellus (Holm.)
 obvius (Walk.)
 oxyura Langton
 psilopterus (Kieff.)
 sordidellus (Zett.)
Pseudosmittia obtusa Strenzke
 trilobata (Edw.)

Smittia aterrima (Meig.)
  edwardsi Goetgh.
  foliacea (Kieff.)
Trissocladius brevipalpis Kieff.

Prodiamesinae

Prodiamesa olivacea (Meig.)

Tanypodinae

Ablabesmyia longistyla Fittk.
Arctopelopia barbitarsis (Zett.)
Clinotanypus nervosus (Meig.)
Guttipelopia guttipennis (Wulp)
  monilis (L.)
  phatta (Egger)
Monopelopia tenuicalcar (Kieff.)
Paramerina cingulata (Walk.)
Procladius choreus (Meig.)
  sagittalis (Kieff.)
Psectrotanypus varius (F.)
Telmatopelopia nemorum (Goetgh.)
Xenopelopia nigricans (Goetgh.)

Brachycera

RHAGIONIDAE

Chrysopilus asiliformis (Preyssler)
  cristatus (F.)
Rhagio lineola F.
  scolopaceus (L.)
  tringarius (L.)

TABANIDAE

Chrysopsinae

Chrysops caecutiens (L.)
  relictus Meig.

Tabaninae

Haematopota crassicornis Wahlb.
  pluvialis (L.)
Hybomitra bimaculata (Macq.)
Tabanus autumnalis L.

XYLOMYIDAE

Solva marginata (Meig.) (N)

STRATIOMYIDAE

Beridinae

Beris chalybata (Forst.)
  geniculata Curt.
  vallata (Forst.)
Chorisops nagatomii Rozk. (N)
  tibialis (Meig.)

Clitellariinae

Nemotelus nigrinus Fall.
  pantherinus (L.)
  uliginosus (L.)
Oxycera morrisii Curt. (N)
  nigricornis Olivier†
  rara (Scopoli)
  trilineata (F.)
Vanoyia tenuicornis (Macq.) (N)

Pachygasterinae

Neopachygaster meromelas (Dufour) (N)
Pachygaster atra (Panz.)
  leachii Curt.

Sarginae

Chloromyia formosa (Scop.)
Microchrysa flavicornis Meig.
  polita (L.)
Sargus bipunctatus (Scop.)

Stratiomyinae

Odontomyia angulata (Panz.)* (RDB1)
  argentata (F.) (RDB2)
  tigrina (F.)
Oplodontha viridula (F.)
Stratiomys chamaeleon (L.)* (RDB1)
  longicornis (Scop.)* (RDB2)
  potamidus (Meig.) (N)
  singularior (Harris) (N)

BOMBYLIIDAE

Bombyliinae

Bombylius major L.

THEREVIDAE

Therevinae

Thereva nobilitata (F.)

SCENOPINIDAE

Scenopinus fenestralis (L.)
  niger (DeGeer) (N)

ASILIDAE

Asilinae

Machimus atricapillus (Fall.)

Leptogasterinae

Leptogaster cylindrica (DeGeer)

Stenopogoninae

Dioctria atricapilla Meig.
  linearis (F.)
  rufipes (DeGeer)

HYBOTIDAE

Hybotinae

Hybos culiciformis (F.)
  femoratus (Mull.)

Ocydromiinae

Bicellaria mera Coll. (N)
  simplicipes (Zett.)
  spuria (Fall.)
  vana Coll.
Euthyneura halidayi Coll. (N)
Leptopeza flavipes (Meig.)
Ocydromia glabricula (Fall.)
Oedalea flavipes Zett.
  holmgreni Zett.
  stigmatella Zett.
  tibialis Macq. (N)
Oropezella sphenoptera (Loew)

Trichina clavipes Meig.
  elongata Hal.
  pallipes (Zett.) (N)

Tachydromiinae

Crossopalpus humilis (Frey)
  minimus Meig.
  nigritellus (Zett.)
Drapetis assimilis (Fall.)
  ephippiata Fall.
  exilis Meig.
  parilis Coll.
  simulans Coll. (N)
Platypalpus agilis (Meig.)
  albicornis (Zett.) (N)
  albiseta (Panz.) (N)
  albocapillatus (Fall.) (N)
  annulatus (Fall.)
  annulipes (Meig.)
  aristatus (Coll.) (N)
  articulatoides (Frey) (N)
  articulatus Macq. (N)
  aurantiacus (Coll.) (RDB3)
  calceatus (Meig.)
  candicans (Fall.)
  cothurnatus Macq. (N)
  excisus (Becker) (RDB3)
  exilis (Meig.)
  flavicornis (Meig.)
  infectus (Coll.) (RDB2)
  ingenuus (Coll.) (RDB2)
  interstinctus (Coll.)
  kirtlingensis Grootaert
  leucocephalus (von Roser)
  longicornis (Meig.)
  longiseta Zett.
  maculipes (Meig.)
  minutus (Meig.)
  niger (Meig.) (N)
  pallidicornis (Coll.)
  pallidiventris (Meig.)
  pallipes (Fall.)
  pictitarsis (Becker)
  politus (Coll.) (N)
  pseudofulvipes Frey
  ruficornis (von Roser) (N)
  stabilis (Coll.)† (N)
Stilpon graminum (Fall.)
Symballophthalmus dissimilis (Fall.) (N)
  fuscitarsis (Zett.)
Tachydromia aemula (Loew)
  connexa Meig.† (RDB3)
  umbrarum Hal.
Tachypeza fuscipennis (Fall.)† (N)
  nubila (Meig.)

EMPIDIDAE

Clinocerinae

Clinocera stagnalis (Hal.)
Dolichocephala irrorata (Fall.)
  oblongoguttata (Dale)

Empidinae

Empis aestiva Loew
  caudatula Loew
  chioptera Meig.
  femorata F.
  grisea Fall.
  livida L.

  nigripes F.
  nigritarsis Meig.
  nuntia Meig.
  opaca Meig.
  picipes Meig. (N)
  scutellata Curt.
  stercorea L.
  tessellata F.
  trigramma Meig.
Hilara anglodanica Lundb.
  brevistyla Coll.
  curtisi Coll.
  litorea (Fall.)
  lugubris (Zett.) (N)
  lurida (Fall.)
  maura (F.)
  monedula Coll.
  nigrina (Fall.)
  nitidula Zett.
  quadriseta Coll. (RDB3)
  recedens Walk.† (RDB3)
  subpollinosa Coll.
  thoracica Macq.
Rhamphomyia albitarsis Coll. (N)
  anomalipennis Meig.
  atra Meig.
  barbata (Macq.)
  caesia Meig.
  caliginosa Coll. (N)
  crassirostris (Fall.)
  geniculata Meig.
  laevipes (Fall.)
  maculipennis Zett.
  nigripennis (F.)
  pilifer Meig.
  stigmosa Macq.
  subcinerascens Coll.
  sulcata (Meig.)
  sulcatella Coll.
  tarsata Meig.
  tibiella Zett.

Hemerodromiinae

Chelifera precatoria (Fall.)
Hemerodromia baetica Coll.
  raptoria Meig.
Phyllodromia melanocephala (F.)

Oreogetoninae

Ragas unica Walk. (N)

MICROPHORIDAE

Microphorinae

Microphor anomalus (Meig.)
  crassipes Macq.
  holosericeus (Meig.)

DOLICHOPODIDAE

Achalcinae

Achalcus bimaculatus Pollet
  cinereus (Hal.)
  flavicollis (Meig.)
  melanotrichus Mik (N)
  thalhammeri Lichtw.

Diaphorinae

Argyra argentina (Meig.)
  argyria (Meig.)

diaphana (F.)
elongata (Zett.) (**RDB3**)
leucocephala (Meig.)
perplexa Becker
vestita (Wied.)
Chrysotus cilipes Meig.
gramineus (Fall.)
neglectus (Wied.)
palustris Verrall (**N**)
pulchellus Kowarz
suavis Loew (**N**)
Diaphorus oculatus (Fall.)

Dolichopodinae

Dolichopus campestris Meig.
cilifemoratus Macq.(**RDBK**)
festivus Hal.
latilimbatus Macq.
linearis Meig.† (**N**)
longicornis Stann.
longitarsis Stann.
notatus Staeger† (**N**)
nubilus Meig.
pennatus Meig.
planitarsis Fall.
plumipes (Scop.)
popularis Wied.
signifer Hal. (**RDB2**)
simplex Meig.
ungulatus (L.)
urbanus Meig.
Hercostomus assimilis (Staeger)
blankaartensis Pollet
celer (Meig.)
chalybeus (Wied.)
chrysozygos (Weid.)
fulvicaudis (Hal.) (**RDB3**)
gracilis (Stann.)†
metallicus (Stann.)
nanus (Macq.)
plagiatus (Loew) (**N**)
sylvestris Pollet
Ortochile nigrocoerulea Latr.* (**N**)
Poecilobothrus nobilitatus (L.)
Sybistroma obscurellum (Fall.)

Hydrophorinae

Hydrophorus balticus (Meig.)
bipunctatus (Lehmann)
litoreus Fall.
Scellus notatus (F.)
Schoenophilus versutus (Hal.) (**N**)

Medeterinae

Medetera ambigua (Zett.) (**N**)
diadema (L.)†
flavipes Meig.
impigra Coll.
jacula (Fall.)
pallipes (Zett.)
saxatilis Coll.
truncorum Meig.
Systenus leucurus Loew (**N**)
scholtzii (Loew) (**N**)
Thrypticus bellus Loew
divisus (Strobl) (**RDB3**)
laetus Verrall (**N**)
pollinosus Verrall (**N**)
tarsalis Parent (**RDB3**)

Neurigoninae

Neurigona pallida (Fall.)
quadrifasciata (F.)

Rhaphiinae

Rhaphium antennatum Carlier (**N**)
appendiculatum (Zett.)
caliginosum Meig.
fasciatum Meig.
monotrichum Loew

Sciapodinae

Sciapus longulus (Fall.)
platypterus (F.)

Sympycninae

Campsicnemus curvipes (Fall.)
loripes (Hal.)
picticornis (Zett.)
scambus (Fall.)
Chrysotimus molliculus (Fall.)
Lamprochromus bifasciatus (Macq.) (**N**)
Micromorphus albipes (Zett.) (**N**)
Sympycnus aeneicoxa (Meig.)
desoutteri (Parent)
Syntormon bicolorellum (Zett.)
denticulatum (Zett.)
pallipes (F.)
pumilum (Meig.)
Teuchophorus monacanthus Loew
simplex Mik
spinigerellus (Zett.)
Xanthochlorus ornatus (Hal.)

Muscomorpha (Cyclorrhapha) Aschiza

OPETIIDAE

Opetia nigra Meig.

PLATYPEZIDAE

Callomyiinae

Agathomyia elegantula (Fall.) (**N**)
unicolor Oldenb.
viduella (Zett.)
Callomyia amoena Meig.

Platypezinae

Bolopus furcatus (Fall.)
Platypeza consobrina Zett.
fasciata Meig.
Protoclythia modesta (Zett.)

PHORIDAE

Anevrina curvinervis (Becker)
thoracica (Meig.)
unispinosa (Zett.)
urbana (Meig.)
Borophaga incrassata (Meig.)
Chaetopleurophora erythronata (Strobl)
Conicera dauci Meig.
floricola Schmitz
similis (Hal.)
Diplonevra funebris (Meig.)
nitidula (Meig.)
Gymnophora arcuata (Meig.)
Gymnoptera longicostalis Schmitz

Megaselia aequalis (Wood)
  affinis (Wood)
  basispinata (Lundb.)
  bovista (Gimmer.)
  brevicostalis (Wood)
  ciliata (Zett.)
  clemonsi Disney
  collini (Wood)
  crassipes (Wood)
  diversa (Wood)
  elongata (Wood)
  emarginata (Wood)
  errata (Wood)
  flavicans Schmitz
  frameata Schmitz
  fusca (Wood)
  fusciclava Schmitz
  fuscinervis (Wood)
  fuscovariana Schmitz
  giraudii (Egger)
  glabrifrons (Wood)
  gregaria (Wood)
  halterata (Wood)
  hendersoni Disney
  hirtiventris (Wood)
  hortensis (Wood)
  involuta (Wood)
  latifrons (Wood)
  latior Schmitz
  longicostalis (Wood)
  longiseta (Wood)
  lucifrons (Schmitz)
  lutea (Meig.)
  manicata (Wood)
  meconicera (Speiser)
  melanocephala (von Roser)
  minuta (Aldrich)
  nasoni (Malloch)
  nigra (Meig.)
  nigriceps (Loew)
  obscuripennis (Wood)
  pallidizona (Lundb.)
  paludosa (Wood)
  parva (Wood)
  pectoralis (Wood)
  pleuralis (Wood)
  propinqua (Wood)
  protarsalis Schmitz
  pulicaria (Fall.)
  pumila (Meig.)
  pusilla (Meig.)
  rufipes (Meig.)
  scutellaris (Wood)
  stichata (Lundb.)
  subconvexa (Lundb.)
  subfuscipes Schmitz
  subpleuralis (Wood)
  subtumida (Wood)
  sulphuripes (Meig.)
  tarsalis (Wood)
  tarsella (Lundb.)
  tumida (Wood)
  unguicularis (Wood)
  unwini Disney
  verna Schmitz
  wickenensis Disney [**new to science** (Disney & Perry, 2000)]
  woodi (Lundb.)
Metopina oligoneura (Mik)
  pileata Schmitz
Phalacrotophora fasciata (Fall.)

Phora atra (Meig.)
  edentata Schmitz
  hamata Schmitz
  holosericea Schmitz
  tincta Schmitz
Plectanocnema nudipes (Becker) (**RDBK**)
Spiniphora bergenstammi (Mik)
  maculata (Meig.)
Triphleba citreiformis (Becker)
  distinguenda (Strobl)
  papillata (Wingate)

LONCHOPTERIDAE

Lonchoptera bifurcata (Fall.)
  lutea Panz.

SYRPHIDAE

Anasimyia contracta Claus. & Torp
  interpuncta Harris (**RDB3**)
  lineata (F.)
  transfuga (L.)
Baccha elongata (F.)
Chalcosyrphus nemorum (F.)
Cheilosia albipila Meig.
  albitarsis Meig.
  bergenstammi Becker
  cynocephala Loew* (**N**)
  fraterna (Meig.)
  griseiventris Loew
  grossa (Fall.)
  illustrata (Harris)
  impressa Loew
  lasiopa Kowarz
  pagana (Meig.)
  proxima (Zett.)
  variabilis (Panz.)
  vernalis (Fall.)
  vulpina (Meig.)
Chrysogaster solstitialis (Fall.)
Chrysotoxum bicinctum (L.)
  cautum (Harris)
  festivum (L.)
  verralli Coll.
Criorhina berberina (F.)
  floccosa (Meig.)
Dasysyrphus albostriatus (Fall.)
  tricinctus (Fall.)
  venustus (Meig.)
Epistrophe eligans (Harris)
  grossulariae (Meig.)
Episyrphus balteatus (DeGeer)
Eristalinus sepulchralis (L.)
Eristalis abusivus Coll.
  arbustorum (L.)
  horticola (DeGeer)
  interruptus (Poda)
  intricarius (L.)
  pertinax (Scop.)
  tenax (L.)
Eumerus strigatus (Fall.)
  tuberculatus Rond.
Eupeodes corollae (Fall.)
  latifasciatus (Macq.)
  luniger (Meig.)
Helophilus hybridus Loew
  pendulus (L.)
  trivittatus (F.)
Heringia brevidens (Egger) (**N**)
  latitarsis (Egger) (**N**)
  vitripennis (Meig.)

Lejogaster metallina (F.)
  tarsata (Meig.) **(N)**
Leucozona lucorum (L.)
Melangyna labiatarum (Verrall)
  lasiophthalma (Zett.)
  umbellatarum (F.)
Melanogaster hirtella Loew
  aerosa (Loew)* **(N)**
Melanostoma mellinum (L.)
  scalare (F.)
Meliscaeva auricollis (Meig.)
Merodon equestris (F.)
Myathropa florea (L.)
Myolepta dubia (F.)* **(N)**
Neoascia geniculata (Meig.)† **(N)**
  interrupta (Meig.) **(N)**
  meticulosa (Scop.)
  podagrica (F.)
  tenur (Harris)
Orthonevra brevicornis Loew **(N)**
  geniculata Meig. **(N)**
Parasyrphus punctulatus (Verrall)
Parhelophilus frutetorum (F.)
  versicolor (F.)
Pipiza austriaca Meig.
  bimaculata Meig.
  fenestrata Meig.†
  luteitarsis Zett.
  noctiluca (L.)
Pipizella virens (F.) **(N)**
Platycheirus albimanus (F.)
  ambiguus (Fall.)
  angustatus (Zett.)
  clypeatus (Meig.)
  fulviventris (Macq.)
  granditarsa (Forst.)
  manicatus (Meig.)
  occultus Goel., Maib. & Speight
  peltatus (Meig.)
  rosarum (F.)
  scutatus (Meig.)
Rhingia campestris Meig.
Riponnensia splendens (Meig.)
Scaeva pyrastri (L.)
Sericomyia silentis (Harris)
Sphaerophoria interrupta (F.)*
  rueppellii (Wied.)
  scripta (L.)
Syritta pipiens (L.)
Syrphus ribesii (L.)
  torvus Osten-Sacken
  vitripennis Meig.
Trichopsomyia flavitarsis (Meig.)
Triglyphus primus Loew **(N)**
Tropidia scita (Harris)
Volucella bombylans (L.)
  pellucens (L.)
Xanthandrus comtus (Harris) **(N)**
Xanthogramma pedissequum (Harris)
Xylota abiens Meig. **(N)**
  segnis (L.)

PIPUNCULIDAE

Chalarinae

Chalarus decorus Jervis
  fimbriatus Coe
  latifrons Hardy
  pughi Coe
  spurius (Fall.)

Jassidophaga pilosa (Zett.)
Verrallia aucta (Fall.)

Pipunculinae

Cephalops chlorionae Frey
  pannonicus (Aczél) **(RDB1)**
  semifumosus (Kowarz)
Dorylomorpha extricata (Coll.)
  hungarica Aczél **(N)**
  infirmata (Coll.) **(N)**
  maculata (Walk.)
  xanthopus (Thomson)
Eudorylas fascipes (Zett.)
  fuscipes (Zett.)
  kowarzi (Becker) **(N)**
  longifrons Coe
  obliquus Coe **(N)**
  obscurus Coe
  subfascipes Coll.
  subterminalis Coll.
  zonellus Coll.
Pipunculus campestris Latr.
  tenuirostris (Kozanek)
  thomsoni Becker
  varipes Meig.
  zugmayeriae Kowarz **(N)**
Tomosvaryella kuthyi (Aczél)
  palliditarsis (Coll.) **(N)**
  sylvatica (Meig.)

Muscomorpha (Cyclorrhapha) Schizophora Acalyptratae

MICROPEZIDAE

Calobatinae

Neria cibaria (L.)
  commutata (Czerny)

Micropezinae

Micropeza corrigiolata (L.)

TANYPEZIDAE

Tanypeza longimana Fall. **(RDB2)**

MEGAMERINIDAE

Megamerina dolium (F.) **(N)**

PSILIDAE

Loxocerinae

Loxocera albiseta (Schr.)
  aristata (Panz.)

Psilinae

Chamaepsila nigricornis Meig.
  rosae (F.)
Chyliza leptogaster (Panz.)
Psila fimetaria (L.)
  merdaria Coll.

CONOPIDAE

Conopinae

Conops flavipes L.
  quadrifasciatus DeGeer
Physocephala rufipes (F.)

Myopinae

Myopa tessellatipennis Motsch.
Sicus ferrugineus (L.)
Zodion cinereum (F.)* (N)

LONCHAEIDAE

Dasiopinae

Dasiops hennigi Morge
  mucronatus Morge

Lonchaeinae

Earomyia viridana (Meig.)
Lonchaea chorea (F.)
  fugax Becker
  laticornis Meig.
  laxa Coll. (N)
  patens Coll.
  peregrina Becker (N)
  postica Coll.
  scutellaris Rond.
Protearomyia nigra (Meig.)
Setisquamalonchaea fumosa Egger

PALLOPTERIDAE

Pallopterinae

Palloptera muliebris (Harris)
  quinquemaculata (Macq.)
  saltuum (L.)
  scutellata (Macq.)
  trimacula (Meig.)
  umbellatarum (F.)
  ustulata Fall.

PIOPHILIDAE

Piophilinae

Parapiophila vulgaris Fall.
Protopiophila latipes Meig.
Stearibia nigriceps (Meig.)

ULIDIIDAE

Otitinae

Ceroxys urticae (L.)
Herina frondescentiae (L.)
  longistylata (Rivosecchi)
  oscillans (Meig.) (RDB3)
Melieria crassipennis (F.)
  omissa (Meig.)†
Otites guttatus (Meig.)
Physiphora alceae (Preyssler)
Seioptera vibrans (L.)
Ulidia erythrophthalma Meig.† (RDB3)

PLATYSTOMATIDAE

Platystoma seminationis (L.)

TEPHRITIDAE

Tephritinae

Acinia corniculata (Zett.) (RDB1)
Campiglossa misella (Loew)
Chaetorellia jaceae (Rob.-Des.)
Chaetostomella cylindrica (Rob.-Des.)
Dioxyna bidentis (Rob.-Des.) (N)
Merzomyia westermanni (Meig.) (N)
Myopites inulaedyssentericae Blot (RDB3)

Oxyna parietina (L.)
Sphenella marginata (Fall.)
Tephritis bardanae (Schr.)
  cometa (Loew)
  formosa (Loew)
  hyoscyami (L.)
  neesii (Meig.)
Terellia ruficauda (F.)
  serratulae (L.)
  tussilaginis (F.)
Trupanea stellata (Fuessly)
Urophora cardui (L.)
  jaceana (Hering)
  quadrifasciata (Meig.)
  solstitialis (L.)† (RDB3)
  stylata (F.)
Xyphosia miliaria (Schr.)

Trypetinae

Acidia cognata (Wied.)
Anomoia purmunda (Harris)
Euleia heraclei (L.)
Philophylla caesio (Harris)
Rhagoletis alternata (Fall.)

LAUXANIIDAE

Homoneurinae

Homoneura subnotata Papp

Lauxaniinae

Calliopum aeneum (Fall.)
  elisae (Meig.)
  simillimum (Coll.)
Lauxania cylindricornis (F.)
Lyciella affinis (Zett.)
  decempunctata (Fall.)
  decipiens (Loew)
  rorida (Fall.)
Minettia inusta (Meig.)
  longipennis (F.)
  lupulina (F.)
  plumicornis (Fall.)
  rivosa (Meig.)
Peplomyza litura (Meig.)
Sapromyza hyalinata (Meig.)
  opaca Becker (N)
  quadripunctata (L.)
  sexpunctata Meig.
  sordida Hal.
Tricholauxania praeusta (Fall.)
Trigonometopus frontalis (Meig.)

CHAMAEMYIIDAE

Chamaemyiinae

Chamaemyia elegans Panz. (N)
  fasciata Loew (N)
  herbarum Rob.-Des.
  nigripalpis Coll.
  paludosa Coll. (RDB2)
  polystigma (Meig.)

Leucopinae

Leucopis argentata Heeger
  geniculata Zett.
  psyllidiphaga McLean
Lipoleucopis praecox de Meij.
Neuleucopis obscura (Hal.)
  tapiae (Blanchard)

DRYOMYZIDAE

Dryomyzinae

Neuroctena anilis Fall.

PHAEOMYIIDAE

Pelidnoptera fuscipennis (Meig.)

SCIOMYZIDAE

Sciomyzinae

Antichaeta analis (Meig.) (**RDB3**)
  obliviosa Enderl. (**RDB2**)
Colobaea bifasciella (Fall.) (**N**)
  distincta (Meig.)
  punctata (Lundb.) (**N**)
Coremacera marginata (F.)
Dichetophora finlandica Verbeke (**RDB3**)
Elgiva cucularia (L.)
  solicita (Harris)
Euthycera fumigata (Scop.)
Hydromya dorsalis (F.)
Ilione albiseta (Scop.)
Limnia paludicola Elberg
  unguicornis (Scop.)
Pherbellia albocostata (Fall.)
  cinerella (Fall.)
  dorsata (Zett.) (**N**)
  dubia (Fall.)
  griseola (Fall.) (**N**)
  grisescens (Meig.) (**N**)
  nana (Fall.) (**N**)
  schoenherri (Fall.)
  ventralis (Fall.)
Pherbina coryleti (Scop.)
Psacadina verbekei Rozkosny (**N**)
  vittigera (Schiner)† (**RDB2**)
Pteromicra angustipennis (Staeger)
  pectorosa (Hendel) (**RDB2**)
Renocera pallida (Fall.)
Sciomyza simplex Fall. (**N**)
Sepedon sphegea (F.)
  spinipes (Scop.)
Tetanocera arrogans (Meig.)
  elata (F.)
  ferruginea Fall.
  hyalipennis von Roser
  robusta Loew
  silvatica Meig.
Trypetoptera punctulata (Scop.)

SEPSIDAE

Nemopoda nitidula (Fall.)
Saltella sphondylii (Schr.)
Sepsis cynipsea (L.)
  duplicata Hal.
  flavimana Meig.
  fulgens Meig.
  orthocnemis Frey
  punctum (F.)
  thoracica (Rob.-Des.)
Themira annulipes (Meig.)
  lucida (Staeger)
  minor (Hal.)
  nigricornis (Meig.) (**RDB3**)
  pusilla (Zett.)
  superba (Hal.)

CLUSIIDAE

Clusia flava (Meig.)
Clusiodes albimanus (Meig.)
  verticalis (Coll.)

ODINIIDAE

Odinia boletina (Zett.)

AGROMYZIDAE

Agromyzinae

Agromyza albipennis Meig.
  alnibetulae Hendel
  anthracina Meig.
  bromi Spencer
  cinerascens Macq.
  ferruginosa van der Wulp
  filipendula Spencer
  frontella (Rond.)
  intermittens (Becker)
  lathyri Hendel
  luteitarsis (Rond.)
  mobilis Meig.
  myosotidis Kalt.
  nana Meig.
  nigrella (Rond.)
  nigrescens Hendel
  nigripes Meig.
  nigrociliata Hendel
  phragmitidis Hendel
  potentillae (Kalt.)
  pseudoreptans Nowak.
  reptans Fall.
  rondensis Strobl
  vicifoliae Hering
Melanagromyza aenea (Meig.)
  aeneoventris (Fall.)
  angeliciphaga Spencer
  lappae (Loew)
  symphyti Griff.

Phytomyzinae

Amauromyza flavifrons (Meig.)
  labiatarum (Hendel)
  monfalconensis (Strobl)
Aulagromyza anteposita (Strobl)
  discrepans (van der Wulp)
  hendeliana (Hering)
  orphana (Hendel)
  trivittata (Loew)
Calycomyza artemisiae (Kalt.)
Cerodontha atra (Meig.)
  atronitens (Hendel)
  biseta (Hendel)
  calamagrostidis Nowak.
  caricicola (Hering)
  crassiseta (Strobl)
  denticornis (Panz.)
  flavocingulata (Strobl)
  fulvipes (Meig.)
  geniculata (Fall.)
  hennigi Nowak.
  incisa (Meig.)
  iraeos (Gour.)
  lateralis (Macq.)
  luctuosa (Meig.)
  muscina (Meig.)
  phragmitidis Nowak.
  pygmaea (Meig.)
  venturii Nowak.

Chromatomyia horticola Gour.
  milii (Kalt.)
  nigra (Meig.)
  ramosa (Hendel)
Liriomyza amoena (Meig.)
  artemisicola de Meij.
  centaureae Hering
  congesta (Becker)
  demaeijerei Hering
  erucifolii de Meij.
  eupatorii (Kalt.)
  flaveola (Fall.)
  lutea (Meig.)
  occipitalis Hendel
  orbona (Meig.)
  ptarmicae de Meij.
  pusilla (Meig.)
  richteri Hering
  sonchi Hendel
  soror Hendel
  strigata (Meig.)
Metopomyza flavonotata (Hal.)
Napomyza hirticornis Hendel
  lateralis (Fall.)
  nigriceps van der Wulp
Ophiomyia aquilegiana Lund.
  beckeri (Hendel)
  collini Spencer
  cunctata (Hendel)
  curvipalpis (Zett.)
  heringi Stary
  labiatarum Hering
  ranunculicaulis Hering
  senecionina Hering
Phytoliriomyza ornata (Meig.) (**N**)
Phytomyza albipennis (Fall.)
  angelicae Kalt.
  angelicastri Hering
  artemisivora Spencer
  cecidonomia Hering
  chaerophylli Kalt.
  cirsii Hendel
  conii Hering
  continua Hendel
  conyzae Hendel
  crassiseta Zett.
  eupatorii Hendel
  evanescens Hendel
  fallaciosa Brischke
  flavicornis Fall.
  glechomae Kalt.
  heracleana Hering
  lappae Gour.
  leucanthemi Hering
  minuscula Gour.
  notata Meig.
  plantaginis Rob.-Des.
  ranunculi (Schr.)
  rufipes Meig.
  spinaciae Hendel
  spoliata Strobl
  spondylii Gour.
  symphyti Hendel
  thysselini Hendel
  varipes Macq.
  wahlgreni Ryden
Pseudonapomyza atra (Meig.)

OPOMYZIDAE

Geomyza balachowskyi Mesnil
  hendeli Czerny (**RDB3**)
  majuscula (Loew) (**N**)
  subnigra Drake
  tripunctata Fall.
Opomyza florum (F.)
  germinationis (L.)
  petrei Mesnil

ANTHOMYZIDAE

Anagnota bicolor (Meig.) (**N**)
Anthomyza collini Anders.
  gracilis Fall.
  macra Czerny
  neglecta Coll.
  pallida (Zett.)
Paranthomyza nitida (Meig.)
Stiphrosoma sabulosum (Hal.)

STENOMICRIDAE

Stenomicra cogani Irwin (**RDB3**)

ASTEIIDAE

Asteiinae

Asteia amoena Meig.
  concinna Meig.

Siggaloessinae

Leiomyza dudai Sabrosky
  laevigata (Meig.)

MILICHIIDAE

Madizinae

Leptometopa latipes (Meig.)
Madiza britannica Hennig (**RDB2**)
  pachymera Becker (**RDB3**)
Phyllomyza securicornis Fall.

CARNIDAE

Meoneura flavifacies Coll.
  minutissima (Zett.) (**N**)
  vagans (Fall.)

CHLOROPIDAE

Chloropinae

Camarota curvipennis (Latr.)
Cetema elongatum (Meig.)
  neglectum Tonn.
Chlorops calceatus Meig.
  frontosus (Meig.)
  gracilis Meig. (**N**)
  hypostigma Meig.
  limbatus Meig.
  pumilionis (Bjerk.)
  rossicus Smirnov
  scalaris Meig.
  serenus Loew
  speciosus Meig.
Chloropsina pulicaria Ismay
  varleyi Ismay
Cryptonevra consimilis (Coll.) (**RDB2**)
  diadema (Meig.)
  flavitarsis (Meig.)
  nigritarsis (Duda) (**N**)
Diplotoxa messoria (Fall.)

Lasiosina intermedia Dely-Drask.
Meromyza femorata Macq.
  nigriventris Macq.
  ornata (Wied.)
  pluriseta Péterfi (**N**)
Neohaplegis tarsata (Fall.)
Platycephala planifrons (F.)
Thaumatomyia glabra (Meig.)
  notata (Meig.)

Oscinellinae

Aphanotrigonum trilineatum (Meig.)
Calamoncosis aprica (Meig.)
  duinensis (Strobl)
  glyceriae Nartshuk
  minima (Strobl)
Conioscinella mimula Coll.
Dicraeus fennicus Duda
  ingratus (Loew)
  tibialis (Macq.) (**N**)
  vagans (Meig.)
Elachiptera brevipennis (Meig.)
  cornuta (Fall.)
  diastema Coll.
  megaspis (Loew)
  scrobiculata (Strobl)
  tuberculifera (Corti)
  uniseta Coll. (**N**)
Eribolus hungaricus (Becker)
Gaurax fascipes (Becker)
Incertella albipalpis (Meig.)
  kerteszi (Becker)
  zuercheri (Duda)
Lipara lucens Meig.
  rufitarsis Loew (**N**)
  similis Schiner (**RDB2**)
Microcercis trigonella (Duda)
Oscinella angularis (Coll.) (**N**)
  frit (L.)
  maura (Fall.)
  nigerrima (Macq.)
  nitidissima (Meig.)
  pusilla (Meig.)
  trochanterata Coll.
  vastator (Curt.)
Oscinimorpha minutissima (Strobl)
  sordissima (Strobl) (**N**)
Oscinisoma cognata (Meig.)
  gilvipes (Loew) (**N**)
Rhopalopterum anthracinum (Meig.)
  femorale (Coll.) (**N**)
Speccafrons halophila (Duda) (**N**)
Tricimba cincta (Meig.)
  lineella (Fall.)

HELEOMYZIDAE

Heleomyzinae

Eccoptomera longiseta (Meig.)
  obscura (Meig.)
Neoleria inscripta (Meig.)
  maritima (Ville.)

Heteromyzinae

Heteromyza rotundicornis (Zett.)
Tephrochlamys flavipes (Zett.)
  rufiventris (Meig.)

Suilliinae

Suillia affinis (Meig.)
  atricornis (Meig.)
  bicolor (Zett.)
  dumicola (Coll.) (**N**)
  notata (Meig.)
  pallida (Fall.)
  variegata (Loew)

CHYROMYIDAE

Chyromya flava (L.)

SPHAEROCERIDAE

Copromyzinae

Alloborborus pallifrons (Fall.)
Borborillus vitripennis (Meig.)
Copromyza equina Fall.
  nigrina (Gimmerthal)
  stercoraria (Meig.)
Crumomyia fimetaria (Meig.)
  nitida (Meig.)
  notabilis (Coll.)
  pedestris (Meig.)
  roserii (Rond.)
Lotophila atra (Meig.)

Limosininae

Apteromyia claviventris (Strobl)
Chaetopodella scutellaris (Hal.)
Coproica acutangula (Zett.)
  ferruginata (Stenh.)
  hirticula Coll.
  lugubris (Hal.)
  pusio (Zett.)
  vagans (Hal.)
Gonioneura spinipennis (Hal.)
Leptocera breviceps (Stenh.)
  fontinalis (Fall.)
  limosa (Fall.)
  lutosa (Stenh.)
  lutosoides (Duda)
  nigra Olivier
  oldenbergi (Duda)
Limosina silvatica (Meig.)
Minilimosina fungicola (Hal.)
  vitripenis (Zett.)
Opacifrons coxata (Stenh.)
Opalimosina liliputana (Rond.)
  mirabilis (Coll.)
Pseudocollinella humida (Hal.)
Pteremis fenestralis (Fall.)
Pullimosina heteroneura (Hal.)
  moesta (Ville.)
  pullula (Zett.)
Spelobia clunipes (Meig.)
  ochripes (Meig.)
  palmata (Richards)
  rufilabris (Stenh.)
Trachyopella coprina (Duda)

Sphaerocerinae

Ischiolepta denticulata (Meig.)
  pusilla (Fall.)
Sphaerocera curvipes Latr.
  monilis Hal.

DROSOPHILIDAE

Drosophilinae

Drosophila andalusiaca Strobl
  busckii Coq.
  fenestrarum Fall.
  funebris (F.)
  hydei Sturt.
  immigrans Sturt.
  obscura Fall.†
  phalerata Meig.
  picta Zett.
  subobscura Coll.
  transversa Fall.†
Scaptomyza flava (Fall.)
  griseola (Zett.)
  pallida (Zett.)

CAMPICHOETIDAE

Campichoeta obscuripennis (Meig.)
  punctum (Meig.)

DIASTATIDAE

Diastata adusta Meig.
  costata Meig.
  fuscula (Fall.)

CAMILLIDAE

Camilla flavicauda Duda

EPHYDRIDAE

Discomyzinae

Psilopa nigritella Stenh.
  nitidula (Fall.)
  pulicaria (Hal.)
Trimerina madizans (Fall)

Ephydrinae

Coenia curvicauda (Meig.)
  palustris (Fall.)
Limnellia quadrata (Fall.)
  surturi Anders.
Paracoenia fumosa (Stenh.)
Parydra aquila (Fall.)
  coarctata (Fall.)
  fossarum (Hal.)
  littoralis (Meig.)
Scatella paludum (Meig.)
  stagnalis (Fall.)
  tenuicosta Coll.
Scatophila unicornis Czerny
Setacera aurata (Stenh.)
  trina Coll.

Gymnomyzinae

Discocerina obscurella (Fall.)
Ditrichophora calceata (Meig.)
  fuscella (Stenh.)
Ochthera manicata (F.) (RDB3)

Hydrellinae

Hydrellia albilabris (Meig.)
  cochleariae Hal.
  flaviceps (Meig.)
  flavicornis (Fall.)
  fusca (Stenh.)
  griseola (Fall.)
  maura Meig.

  nigricans (Stenh.)
  obscura (Meig.)
  ranunculi Hal.
  subalbiceps Coll.
  tarsata Hal.
  thoracica Hal.
Notiphila brunipes (Rob.-Des.)
  cinerea Fall.
  dorsata Stenh.
  maculata Stenh.
  riparia Meig.

Ilytheinae

Axysta cesta (Hal.)
Hyadina guttata (Fall.)
  humeralis Becker
  rufipes (Meig.)
Ilythea spilota (Curt.)
Pelina aenea (Fall.)
  nitens Loew
  similis Papp
Philygria flavipes (Fall.)
  maculipennis (Rob.-Des.)
  stictica (Meig.)
  vittipennis (Zett.)

Muscomorpha (Cyclorrapha) Schizophora Calyptratae

HIPPOBOSCIDAE

Ornithomyinae

Ornithomya avicularia (L.)
  fringillina Curt.

SCATHOPHAGIDAE

Delininae

Delina nigrita (Fall.)
Leptopa filiformis Zett.

Scathophaginae

Chaetosa punctipes (Meig.)
Cleigastra apicalis (Meig.)
Conisternum tinctinerve (Becker) (RDB2)
Cordilura aemula Coll. (RDB3)
  albipes Fall.
  ciliata Meig.
  impudica Rond.
  pubera (L.)
Gimnomera tarsea (Fall.)* (N)
Hydromyza livens (F.)
Megaphthalma pallida (Fall.)
Nanna fasciata (Meig.)
  flavipes (Fall.)
  multisetosa (Hackman)
  tibiella (Zett.)
Norellisoma lituratum (Meig.)
  opacum (Loew)
  spinimanum (Fall.)
Scathophaga furcata (Say)
  inquinata (Meig.)
  stercoraria (L.)
  suilla (F.)
Spaziphora hydromyzina (Fall.)
Trichopalpus fraternus (Meig.)

ANTHOMYIIDAE

Anthomyiinae

Adia cinerella (Fall.)
Anthomyia confusanea Michel.
  liturata (Rob.-Des.)
  mimetica (Malloch)
  monilis (Meig.)
  pluvialis (L.)
  procellaris Rond.
Botanophila brunneilinea (Zett.)
  dissecta (Meig.)
  fugax (Meig.)
  gnava (Meig.)
  laterella (Coll.)
  lobata (Coll.)
  phrenione (Seguy)
  sonchi (Hardy)
  striolata (Fall.)
Delia carduiformis (Schn.)
  coarctata (Fall.)
  florilega (Zett.)
  lamelliseta (Stein)
  platura (Meig.)
  radicum (L.)
Egle bicaudata (Malloch)
  ciliata (Walk.)
  minuta (Meig.)
  parva Rob.-Des.
  parvaeformis Schn.
  rhinotmeta (Pand.)
  steini Schn.
  subarctica (Huckett) (**RDBK**)
Eustalomyia festiva (Zett.)
Hydrophoria lancifer (Harris)
  ruralis (Meig.)
  silvicola Rob.-Des.
Hylemya urbica (van der Wulp)
  vagans (Panz.)
  variata (Fall.)
Hylemyza partita (Meig.)
Lasiomma picipes (Meig.)
  seminitidum (Zett.)
  strigilatum (Zett.)
Leucophora obtusa (Zett.)
  personata (Coll.)
Paregle audacula (Harris)
Phorbia bartaki Ackl. & Michel.
  fumigata (Meig.)
  moliniaris (Karl)
  nuceicornis (Pandellé)
  sepia (Meig.)
Zaphne divisa (Meig.)

Pegomyinae

Alliopsis bilbergi (Zett.)
Calythea nigricans (Rob.-Des.)
Emmesomyia grisea (Rob.-Des.)
Eutrichota schineri (Schn.)
Paradelia intersecta (Meig.)
Pegomya bicolor (Wied.)
  caesia Stein
  dulcamarae Wood
  flavifrons (Walk.)
  fulgens (Meig.)
  geniculata (Bouché)
  interruptella Zett.†
  laticornis (Fall.)
  nigrisquama (Stein)
  rubivora (Coq.)

rufina (Fall.)
solennis (Meig.)
steini Hendel
ulmaria Rond.
Pegoplata aestiva (Meig.)
  infirma (Meig.)
  juvenilis nitidicauda (Schn.)
  palposa (Stein)

FANNIIDAE

Fannia armata (Meig.)
  canicularis (L.)
  coracina (Loew)
  corvina (Verrall)
  fuscula (Fall.)
  genualis (Stein)
  glaucescens (Zett.)
  lepida (Wied)
  lustrator (Harris)
  manicata (Meig.)
  mollissima (Hal.)
  monilis (Hal.)
  polychaeta (Stein)
  postica (Stein)
  serena (Fall.)
  similis (Stein)
  sociella (Zett.)
  speciosa (Ville.) (**N**)
  umbrosa (Stein)
Piezura graminicola (Zett.)

MUSCIDAE

Acantheripterinae

Achanthiptera rohrelliformis (Rob.-Des.)

Coenosiinae

Coenosia atra Meig. (**N**)
  humilis Meig.
  infantula Rond.
  mollicula (Fall.)
  pumila (Fall.)
  testacea (Rob.-Des.)
  tigrina (F.)
Dexiopsis lacteipennis (Zett.)
Limnophora riparia (Fall.)
  tigrina (Am Stein)
  triangula (Fall.)
Lispe pygmaea Fall.
  tentaculata (DeGeer)
  uliginosa Fall. (**N**)
Lispocephala erythrocera (Rob.-Des.)
  falculata Coll.
Schoenomyza litorella (Fall.)
Spanochaeta dorsalis (von Roser)
Spilogona scutulata (Schn.) (**RDB3**)

Muscinae

Azelia aterrima (Meig.)
  cilipes (Hal.)
  nebulosa Rob.-Des.
  trigonica Hennig
  triquetra (Wied.)
  zetterstedtii Rond.
Haematobia irritans (L.)
Hydrotaea albipuncta (Zett.)
  armipes (Fall.)
  capensis (Wied.)
  dentipes (F.)
  diabolus (Harris)

floccosa Macq.
ignava (Harris)
irritans (Fall.)
meteorica (L.)
parva Meade (**N**)
similis (Meade)
Mesembrina meridiana (L.)
Morellia aenescens Rob.-Des.
simplex (Loew)
Musca autumnalis DeGeer
domestica L.
Muscina levida (Harris)
prolapsa (Harris)
Neomyia cornicina (F.)
Polietes domitor (Harris)
lardarius (F.)
Potamia littoralis Rob.-Des.
Pyrellia rapax (Harris)† (**RDB2**)
Stomoxys calcitrans (L.)
Thricops nigrifrons (Rob.-Des.)
semicinereus (Wied.)

Mydaeinae

Brontaea humilis (Zett.)
Graphomya maculata (Scop.)
minor Rob.-Des.
Hebecnema nigra (Rob.-Des.)
umbratica (Meig.)
vespertina (Fall.)
Mydaea urbana (Meig.)
Myospila meditabunda (F.)

Phaoniinae

Helina evecta (Harris)
impuncta (Fall.)
lasiophthalma (Macq.)
maculipennis (Zett.)
obscurata (Meig.)
pertusa (Meig.)
pubiseta (Zett.)
reversio (Harris)
setiventris Ringd.
Phaonia angelicae (Scop.)
atriceps (Loew) (**N**)
canescens Stein (**RDB3**)
errans (Meig.)
falleni (Michelsen) (**N**)
fuscata (Fall.)
gobertii (Mik)
halterata (Stein)
incana (Wied.)
mystica (Meig.)
nymphaearum (Rob.-Des.) (**RDB2**)
pallida (F.)
palpata (Stein)
perdita (Meig.)
rufiventris (Scop.)
subventa (Harris)
trimaculata (Bouché)
tuguriorum (Scop.)
valida (Harris)

CALLIPHORIDAE

Calliphorinae

Bellardia vulgaris (Rob.-Des.)
Calliphora vicina Rob.-Des.
vomitoria (L.)
Cynomya mortuorum (L.)

Chrysomyiinae

Protocalliphora azurea (Fall.)

Luciliinae

Lucilia caesar (L.)
illustris (Meig.)
richardsi Coll.
silvarum (Meig.)

Melanomyinae

Eggisops pecchiolii Rond. (**N**)
Melanomya nana (Meig.)
Melinda viridicyanea (Rob.-Des.)

Polleniinae

Pollenia angustigena Wainwr.
griseotomentosa (Jacentk.)
labialis Rob.-Des.
rudis (F.)
viatica Rob.-Des.

RHINOPHORIDAE

Paykullia maculata (Fall.)
Phyto melanocephala (Meig.)
Rhinophora lepida (Meig.)
Tricogena rubricosa (Meig.)

SARCOPHAGIDAE

Miltogramminae

Macronychia striginervis (Zett.) (**N**)
Oebalia cylindrica (Fall.)
minuta (Fall.)

Paramacronychiinae

Brachicoma devia (Fall.)
Nyctia halterata (Panz.)

Sarcophaginae

Ravinia pernix (Harris)
Sarcophaga anaces (Walk.)
arcipes Pand. (**N**)
carnaria (L.)
crassimargo (Pand.)
dissimilis Meig.
haemorrhoa Meig.
incisolobata (Pand.)
pumila Meig.
sinuata Meig.
subvicina Rohdend.
vagans Meig.
variegata (Scopoli)

TACHINIDAE

Dexiinae

Athrycia trepida (Meig.)
Dufouria chalybeata (Meig.)
Eriothrix rufomaculata (DeGeer)
Ramonda spathulata (Fall.)
Rondania fasciata (Macq.) (**N**)
Trixa conspersa (Harris)
Voria ruralis (Fall.)

Exoristinae

Admontia blanda (Fall.)
Bessa selecta (Meig.)
Carcelia lucorum (Meig.)
tibialis Rob.-Des.

Cyzenis albicans (Fall.)
Eumea linearicornis (Zett.)
Exorista rustica (Fall.)
Ligeria angusticornis (Loew)
Lydella stabulans (Meig.)
Medina collaris (Fall.)
  luctuosa (Meig.)
Meigenia dorsalis (Meig.)
  mutabilis (Fall.)
Nemorilla floralis (Fall.)
Ocytata pallipes (Fall.)
Pales pavida (Meig.)
Phryxe nemea (Meig.)
  vulgaris (Fall.)

Phasiinae

Cinochira atra Zett.
Phania funesta (Meig.)
Phasia obesa (F.)
  pusilla Meig.

Tachininae

Actia crassicornis (Meig.)
  infantula (Zett.)
  pilipennis (Fall.)
Eloceria delecta (Meig.) (**N**)
Ernestia rudis (Fall.)
Eurithia vivida (Zett.)
Gymnocheta viridis (Fall.)
Loewia foeda (Meig.)
Lydina aenea (Meig.)
Lypha dubia (Fall.)
Macquartia grisea (Fall.)
  praefica (Meig.)
Pelatachina tibialis (Fall.)
Phytomyptera nigrina (Meig.)
Siphona cristata (F.)
  geniculata (DeGeer)
  pauciseta Rond.
Tachina ursina (Meig.)
Triarthria spinipennis (Meig.)
Zophomyia temula (Scop.) (**N**)

SIPHONAPTERA
(fleas)

List: R. S. George
Checklist: Smit (1957a, 1957b), updated by R. S. George
(pers.comm.)

HYSTRICHOPSYLLIDAE

Hystrichopsylla talpae talpae (Curt.)

Rhadinopsylla pentacantha (Rothsch.)
Palaeopsylla soricis soricis (Dale)
Ctenophthalmus nobilis nobilis (Rothsch.)

LEPTOPSYLLIDAE

Peromyscopsylla spectabilis (Rothsch.)

CERATOPHYLLIDAE

Amalaraeus penicilliger mustelae (Dale)

Megabothris turbidus (Rothsch.) *walkeri* (Rothsch.)

Orchopeas howardi howardi (Baker)
Ceratophyllus gallinae (Schr.)
  garei Rothsch.

Hosts at Wicken:

Talpa europaea (Mole: in nest)
Arvicola terrestris (Water Vole)
Clethrionomys glareolus (Bank Vole)
Microtus agrestis (Field Vole)
Clethrioniomys glareolus (in lab.)
Sorex araneus (Common Shrew)
Talpa europaea (in nest)
Clethrionomys glareolus
Sorex araneus
Apodemus sylvaticus (Wood Mouse: in nest)
Microtus agrestis

Microtus agrestis

Clethrioniomys glareolus
Sorex araneus
Clethrioniomys glareolus
Sorex sp. (Shrew)
Arvicola terrestris
Apodemus sylvaticus (in nest)
Pyrrhula pyrrhula (Bullfinch)
Carduelis cannabina (Linnet)
Clethrionomys glareolus (a casual)

HYMENOPTERA
(sawflies, wasps, ants, bees)

Symphyta
(sawflies and wood wasps)

Lists: Benson (1928, 1932, 1938), updated by D. A. Sheppard
Checklists: Kloet & Hincks, edn 2 (1978), Quinlan & Gauld
(1981), Liston (1995, 1996); classification of higher taxa after
Gauld & Bolton (1988)

* Records from Benson (1928)
† Records from Benson (1932)
‡ Records from VCH (Benson, 1938)

MEGALODONTOIDEA

PAMPHILIIDAE

Pamphiliinae

Neurotoma saltuum (L.)‡ (also as *N. flaviventris* Retz.*)
 (*flaviventris* Retz.)
Pamphilius sylvaticus (L)*‡

TENTHREDINOIDEA

ARGIDAE

Arginae

Arge ciliaris (L.)†‡ (Sedge Fen)
 cyanocrocea (Först.)*‡ (Adv.Fen)
 ochropa (Gmel. in L.) (as *A. rosincola* Schrank,† and *A.*
  ochropus Gmel.‡ (= *rosae* auctt. nec. L.)
 (*rosincola* Schr.)

CIMBICIDAE

Abiinae

Abia sericea (L.)*‡

TENTHREDINIDAE

Selandriinae

Nesoselandria morio (F.) (as *Selandria morio* (F.)*‡)
Brachythops flavens (Klug) (as *S. flavens* Klug†‡)
Selandria serva (F.)*‡
Dolerus aeneus Hartig*‡
 aericeps Thoms.*‡ (Adv.Fen)
 cothurnatus Lep. (as *D. palustris* Klug†)
  (*palustris* Klug)
 ferrugatus Lep.†‡
 gonager (F.)*‡
 haematodes Schr.*‡
 madidus (Klug)†‡
 nigratus (O. F. Müll.)*‡
 picipes (Klug)*‡
 planatus Hartig (as *D. oblongus* Cam.,† and *D. asper*
  Zadd. (=*carbonarius* Zadd. and *oblongus* Cam.)‡)
  (*asper* Zadd.)
  (*carbonarius* Zadd.)
  (*oblongus* Cam.)
 possilensis Cam.
  (?*nitens* misident.)
 sanguinicollis (Klug) (as *D. sanguinicollis* L. var. *fumosus*
  Steph.*‡)
  (*fumosus* Steph.)
 triplicatus Klug†‡

Blennocampinae

Athalia circularis (Klug)‡ (also as *A. lineolata* Lep.*)
 (*lineolata* Lep.)
 cordata Lep.†‡
 glabricollis Thoms.*‡
Monostegia abdominalis (F.) (as *Empria abdominalis* F.*‡)
Empria excisa (Thoms.)*‡
 liturata (Gmel. in L.)*‡
 pumila (Konow)*‡
 tridens (Konow)*‡
Ametastegia equiseti (Fall.)†‡
 glabrata (Fall.)*‡
Protoemphytus pallipes (Spin.) (as *Allantus pallipes* Spin.,*
 and *Emphytina pallipes* (Spin.)‡)
 tener (Fall.) (as *A. tener* Fall.,* and *Emphytina tener*
  (Fall.)‡)
Allantus calceatus (Klug) (as *Emphytus calceatus* Klug‡)
 cinctus (L.)* (as *E. cinctus* (L.)‡)
 cingulatus (Scop.) (as *E. cingulatus* Scopoli*‡)
 truncatus (Klug) (as *A. melanarius* Klug misident.,* and
  Emphytus truncatus (Klug)†‡)
  (*melanarius* misident.)
Endelomyia aethiops (F.)‡ (also as *Caliroa aethiops* F.*)
Tomostethus nigritus (F.)*‡
Eutomostethus ephippium (Panz.) (as *Tomostethus ephippium*
 Panz.,† and *Atomostethus ephippium* (Panzer)‡)
 gagathinus (Klug)‡ (also as *T. funereus* Kl.†*)
  (*funereus* misident.)
 luteiventris (Klug)‡ (also as *T. luteiventris* Klug)‡
Rhadinoceraea micans (Klug)‡
Monophadnus pallescens (Gmel. in L.)*‡
Pareophora pruni (L.)*‡
Claremontia alternipes (Klug) (as *Blennocampa alternipes*
 (Klug)*‡)
 tenuicornis (Klug) (as *B. tenuicornis* (Klug)*)
 waldheimii (Gimmer.) (as *B. subcana* (Zadd.)*)
  (*subcana* (Zadd.))
Monophadnoides confusa (Konow) (as *Monophadnus genicu-*
 latus Hartig,* and [*Pseudomonophadnus*]
  Pseudomonophadnum geniculatus (Hartig)‡)
  (*geniculata* (Hartig))
 ruficruris (Brullé) (as *Monophadnus ruficruris* Brullé,* and
  Pseudomonophadnus ruficruris (Brullé)‡)
Halidamia affinis (Fall.) (as *Blennocampa affinis* Fall.*‡)
Fenusella hortulana (Klug) (as *Messa hortularia* Klug †‡)
Kaliofenusa ulmi (Sund.) (as *Febusa* (=*Fenusa*) *ulmi* Kl.*†)

Heterarthrinae

Heterarthrus microcephalus (Klug) (as *Phyllotoma micro-*
 cephala (Klug)*‡

Tenthredininae

Perineura rubi (Panz.) (?as *Monophadnoides rubi* (Harris))
Aglaostigma aucupariae (Klug) (as *Laurentia aucuparia*
 (Klug) (=*Rhogaster aucuparia* Klug*)‡)
 fulvipes (Scop.) (as *Rhogaster fulvipes* Scop.,* and
  Laurentia fulvipes (Scop.)‡)
Tenthredopsis nassata L.*‡ (also as *T. coqueberti* (Kl.),* *T.*
 inornata Cam.,* and *T. thornleyi* Konow*)
 (*coqueberti* (Klug) misident.)
 (*inornata* Cam.)
 (*thornleyi* Konow)
Rhogogaster viridis (L.)* (also as *Tenthredo viridis* L.
 (=*Rhogaster viridis* L.)‡)
Tenthredo arcuata Först. (also as *Tenthredella arcuata* Först.
 (=*Allantus arcuatus* (Först.)‡)
 atra L.‡ (as *Tenthredella atra* L.*)
 celtica Benson (as *Tenthredella temula* Scop.,* and
  Tenthredo temula Scop.‡)
  (*temula* misident.)

colon Klug ‡ (also as *Tenthredella colon* Klug var.
    nigriventris Enslin*)
livida L. (also as *Tenthredella livida* L.*)
mesomelas L.‡ (as *Tenthredella mesomela* L.*)
notha Klug (as *Tenthredo perkinsi* Morice†)
    (*perkinsi* (Morice))
omissa (Först.)†‡
pseudorossi Taeger (as *Tenthredo rosii* Panz.††*)
    (*rossii* Panz., misident.)
scrophulariae L.†*
Pachyprotasis rapae (L.)*
Macrophya duodecimpunctata (L.) *‡
    ribis (Schr.) *‡
    rufipes (L.) *‡

Nematinae

Cladius pectinicornis (Geoff. in Fourc.) *‡
Priophorus morio (Lep.) (as *Priophorus tener* Zadd.‡ var.
    tristis*)
    (*tener* Zadd.)
  pallipes (Lep.)‡ (as *P. padi* L.*)
    (*padi* misident.)
  pilicornis (Curt.) (as *Trichiocampus eradiatus* Htg. and *T.*
    drewsoni [missp.] Thoms.,* and *Priophorus eradiatus*
    (Hartig)‡)
    (*eradiatus* (Hartig))
    (*drewensi* Thoms.)
  rufipes (Lep.)
  ulmi (L.)‡ (as *Trichiocampus ulmi* L.*)
Hoplocampa crataegi (Klug)†‡
  pectoralis Thoms.*‡
Dineura stilata (Klug)† (as *Nematus stilatus* (Klug)‡)
Pseudodineura fuscula (Klug)‡ (as *Pelmatopus fusculus*
    Klug*)
Pristiphora aphantoneura (Först.) (as *P. fulvipes* (Fallen)*‡)
    (*fulvipes* (Fall.) preocc.)
    (*vicina* (Lep.))
  melanocarpa (Hartig)*
  monogyniae (Hartig)‡
  pallidiventris (Fall.)‡ (and as *P. pallidiventris* var. *denudata*
    Kon.*)
    (*denudata* Konow)
  ruficornis (Olivier)*‡
Decanematus viduatus (Zett.) (as *Amauronematus viduatus*
    (Zett.)†‡)
Euura atra (Jurine)*‡
  mucronata (Hartig) (as *Euura saliceti* Fallén‡)
    (*saliceti* misident.)
Phyllocolpa leucosticta (Hartig) (as *Pontania leucosticta*
    Htg.,* and as *Nematus leucostictus* Hartig‡)
Pontania nigricantis Kolp.
  pedunculi (Hartig) (as *P. bella* Zadd.*)
    (*bella* (Zadd.))
  proxima (Lep.) (as *P. capreae* L.,* *P. femoralis* Cam.,* and
    Nematus proximus Le Peletier (=*Pontania proxima* Le
    Peletier)‡)
    (*capreae* L.)
    (*femoralis* misident.)
  viminalis (L.)* (and as *Nematus viminalis* (L.)‡)
Nematus bergmanni Dahlb. (as *Pteronidea curtispina*
    Thoms.,* and *Nematus curtispina* C. F. Thomson‡)
    (*curtispina* Thoms.)
  hypoxanthus Först.* (as *P. hypoxantha* Först.)
  lucidus (Panz.)*‡
  melanaspis Hartig‡ (as *P. melanaspis* Htg.†) (St.Edm.Fen)
  myosotidis (F.) (as *P. myosotidis* F.*)
  oligospilus Först. (as *P. oligospila* Först.*)
  ribesii (Scop.)‡ (as *P. ribesii* (Scop.))
  sulcipes Lep. (as *Nematus crassus* (Fall.)*‡)
    (*crassus* (Fall.), preocc.)

viridis Steph. (as *Pteronidea* ?*dispar* Brischke and *Nematus*
    dispar Brischke‡)
    (*dispar* misident.)
Pachynematus albipennis (Hartig)
  kirbyi (Dahlb.) (as *Pachynematus diaphanus* Eversmann††‡)
    (*diaphanus* (Eversm.))
    (*umbripennis* (Eversm.))
  lichtwardti Konow (as *Pachynematus apricalis* Htg.
    missp.,* and *P. apicalis* Htg.†‡)
    (*apicalis* (Hartig) preocc.)
  obductus (Hartig)†‡
  trisignatus (Först.) (as *Pachynematus clitellatus* Le Pel.*‡)
    (*clitellatus* Lep., preocc.)
  vagus (F.)*‡
  xanthocarpus (Hartig)†‡

SIRICOIDEA

XIPHYRIIDAE

Xiphydria prolongata (Geoff. in Fourc.)†‡

CEPHOIDEA

CEPHIDAE

Cephinae

Hartigia linearis Schr.*

Cephus pygmeus (L.)*

Trachelus tabidus (F.)*

Apocritica

(wasp-waisted Hymenoptera)

Parasitica (group of superfamilies)

(the parasitoids)

* Records from Hancock, 1925
† Records from Kerrich, 1932
‡ Records from Kerrich, 1936, 1938

Lists of Cynipoidea, Proctotrupoidea and Ceraphronoidea
(both as Serphoidea), and Chalcidoidea which appeared in the
Victoria County History of Cambridge (Kerrich, 1938), and of
Evanoidea and Ichneumonoidea (Ichneumonidae and
Braconidae) which appeared in the Natural History of Wicken
Fen and the Victoria County History (Hancock, 1925;
Kerrich, 1932, 1936, 1938) are reprinted here with nomen-
clature, where possible, amended to conform with Kloet &
Hincks, edn 2 (1978); Quinlan (1978); Nixon (1980);
Fergusson (1986); and Fitton et al. (1988). However, it is
difficult to relate to current nomenclature some of the names
used in these early lists, all of which have been checked against
Yu & Horstmann (1977) for Ichneumonidae, or Shenefelt
(1969-78) and Shenefelt & Marsh (1976) for Braconidae, and
difficult indeed to be certain that all the species recorded had
been correctly identified even at the time. The subsequent rein-
terpretation of the application of some of the names raises a
further complication, as current catalogues equate names
according to their formal status rather than their past
currency. The majority of records cited here were published by
Kerrich (1938), a leading authority in his day and Curator of
Insects at the Cambridge University Museum of Zoology from
1931-36. He collected widely at Wicken, and deposited all his
specimens of Wicken Parasitica in that museum, where they
can still be consulted in the Insect Room alongside those of
other earlier collectors who have contributed to the Wicken
record. The inclusion in this list of the names by which they
were recorded in the literature, alongside the current names, is
intended to make examination of museum material easier.

Parasitic wasps

Modern records from the Fen for these groups on which little recent work has been done, with voucher specimens placed in a cited depository, would be welcome.

Classification of higher taxa follow Gauld & Bolton (1988); subfamily Pimplinae in the Ichneumonidae follows Fitton *et al.* (1988); and subfamilies and generic nomenclature of the Braconidae follow Shaw & Huddleston (1991).

EVANOIDEA

GASTERUPTIONIDAE

Gasteruption rugulosum Ab.‡ (ex *Hylaeus pectoralis* Först. (Hymen.: Apidae))
  jaculator (L.) (as *G. thomsoni* Schlett.‡)
  (*thomsoni* Schlett.)

CYNIPOIDEA

FIGITIDAE

Figitinae

Figites consobrinus Gir.‡ (Adv.Fen.)

Anacharitinae

Anacharis eucharioides (Dalman) (as *Anacharis typica* Walk.‡)
  (*typica* Walk.)

EUCOILIDAE

Eucoilinae

Microstilba heterogena (Gir.)‡
Kleidotoma pygmaea (Dahlb.)‡
Eucoila crassinerva Westw.‡

CYNIPIDAE

Cynipinae

Diplolepis eglanteriae (Hart.) (as *Rhodites eglanteriae* Hart.‡)
  nervosa (Curt.) (as *R. nervosus* Curt.‡)
  rosae (L.) (as *R. rosae* L.‡)

Periclistus caninae (Hart.)‡ (ex gall of *Diplolepis nervosa* (Curt.) (Hymen.: Cynipidae))

CHALCIDOIDEA

EURYTOMIDAE

Eurytoma appendigaster (Swed.)‡ (hyperparasite on *Cephus pygmeus* (L.) (Hymen.: Cephidae) through *Bracon terebella* (Wesm.) (Hymen.: Braconidae) in wheat stubble)

TORYMIDAE

Toryminae

Torymus arundinis Walk. (as *T. lasiopterae* Gir.‡) (parasite of *Cecidomyia* sp. (Dipt.: Cecidomyiidae) on *Phragmites)*
  (*lasiopterae* (Gir.))
  ventralis (Fonsc.)‡

PTEROMALIDAE

Spalangiinae

Spalangia nigra Latr.‡

Asaphinae

Asaphes vulgaris Walk.‡ (hyperparasite through *Aphidius* spp. (Hymen.: Braconidae))

Miscogastrinae

Cyrtogaster vulgaris Walk.‡
Miscogaster maculata Walk. (as *Lamprotatus maculatus* Walk.‡)
Stenomalina liparae (Gir.) (as *Pteromalus liparae* Gir.‡) (ex puparia of *Lipara lucens* Meig. (Dipt.: Chloropidae))
  gracilis (Walk.) (as *Stenomalus muscarum* L.‡)
  (*muscarum* misident.)

EULOPHIDAE

Tetrastichinae

Melittobia acasta (Walk.)‡ (hyperparasite through *Alysia manducator* (Panz.) (Hymen.: Braconidae))
Tetrastichus arundinis Gir.‡ (also as *T. flavimanus* Thoms.‡) (parasite of *Cecidomyia* sp. (Dipt.: Cecidomyiidae) on *Phragmites*)
  (*flavimanus* Thoms.)
Aprostocetus ciliatus (Nees)‡ (ex *Lipara* galls (Dipt.: Chloropidae))
  gaus Walk. (as *Tetrastichus rosellae* Deg.‡) (ex *Lipara* galls (Dipt.: Chloropidae))
  (*rosellae* misident.)

MYRMARIDAE

Alaptinae

Ooctonus vulgatus Hal.‡

PROCTOTRUPOIDEA (as SERPHOIDEA)

HELORIDAE

Helorus ruficornis Först. (as *H. coruscus* Hal.‡)
  (*coruscus* Hal.)

PROCTOTRUPIDAE

Codrus ligatus Nees (as *Exallonyx ligatus* Nees‡)
  niger Panz. (as *E. niger* Hal.‡)
Cryptoserphus laricis (Hal.)‡
Paracodrus apterogynus (Hal.)‡
Phaenoserphus calcar (Hal.)‡
Proctotrupes gravidator (L.) (as *Serphus gravidator* Hal.‡)

DIAPRIIDAE

Belytinae

Belyta depressa Thoms.‡
Acanosema nervosa (Thoms.) (as *Cardiopsilus rufiventris* Kieff.‡)
  (*rufiventris* (Kieff.))

Diapriinae

Basalys abrupta Thoms. (as *Loxotropa convexa* Kieff.‡)
  (*convexa* (Kieff.))
  fumipennis Westw. (as *L. atricrus* Kieff.‡)
  (*atricrus* (Kieff.))

SCELIONIDAE

Baeus seminulum Hal.‡
Trimorus aratus (Walk.) (as *Hoplogryon anatus* Walk.‡)
  flavipes (Walk.) (as *H. fimbriatus* Kieff.‡)
  (*fimbriatus* (Kieff.))

PLATYGASTERIDAE

Platygaster pleuron Walk. (as *Polygnotus* pleuron Walk.‡) (ex *Cecidomyia* sp. (Dipt.: Cecidomyiidae) on *Phragmites*)

CERAPHRONOIDEA

MEGASPILIDAE (as *CALLICERATIDAE*)

Dendrocerus aphidivorus (Kieff.) (as *Lygocerus aphidivorus* Kieff.‡) (from aphidiine braconid on *Salix purpurea* L.)

ICHNEUMONOIDEA

ICHNEUMONIDAE

Pimplinae

Dolichomitus terebrans (Ratz.) (as *Epiurus terebrans* Ratz.‡)
Fredegunda diluta (Ratz.) (as *E. dilutus* Ratz.‡)
Endromopoda arundinator (F.) (as *Epiurus melanopygus* Grav.,‡ and *Pimpla culpator* Morl.*)
(*melanopyga* (Grav.))
(*culpator* (Morl.))
  detrita (Holmgr.) (as *Epiurus detritus* Holmgr.,‡ and *Pimpla brunnea* Brischke*)
  (*brunneus* (Brischke))
  phragmitidis (Perkins) (as *Ephialtes* (*Scambus*) *phragmitidis* Perkins) [new to science (Perkins, 1957)]
Iseropus stercorator (F.) (as *Epiurus graminellae* Holmgr.‡) (ex cocoon of *Euthrix potatoria* (L.) (Lepid.: Lasiocampidae))
  (*graminellae* (Schrank))
Scambus brevicornis (Grav.) (as *Epiurus brevicornis* Grav.,‡ and *Pimpla brevicornis* var. *depositor* Först.*)
  (*depositor* (Först.))
  nigricans (Thoms.) (as *Epiurus similis* Bridg.,‡ *Pimpla robusta* Morl.,* and *P. arundinator* F. var. *habermehli* Schmied.*) (ex gall of *Lipara lucens* Meig. (Dipt.: Chloropidae))
  (*similis* (Bridg.))
  (*robusta* (Morl.) preocc.)
  (*habermehli* (Schmied.))
Tromatobia oculatoria (F.)‡
Zaglyptus varipes (Grav.) (as *Polysphincta* (*Zaglyptus*) *varipes* Grav.‡)
Clistopyga rufator Holmgr.‡ (bred from spider's eggs)
Schizopyga circulator (Panz.)‡
  podagrica Grav.‡
Itoplectis alternans (Grav.)‡
  aterrima Jussila (as *Pimpla alternans* Grav. var. *kohlthoffi* Aur.*)
  (*kolthoffi* ?misident.)
  maculator (F.)‡
Pimpla flavicoxis Thoms.‡
  hypochondriaca (Retz.) (as *P. instigator* F.*)
  (*instigator* (F.) preocc.)
  spuria Grav.‡
  turionellae (L.)* (also as *P. turionellae* auctt.,‡ and *P. examinator* F.*‡)
  (*examinator* (F.))
Apechthis compunctor (L.) (as *A. brassicariae* Poda‡)
  (*brassicariae* (Poda))
  rufatus (Gmel. in L.) (as *Pimpla rufata* Gmel.*) [but not in Kerrich, 1936, 1938]
Hybomischos septemcinctorius (Thunb.) (as *Perithous varius* Grav.‡)
  (*varius* (Grav.))

Tryphoninae

Netelia melanura (Thoms.) (as *Paniscus melanurus* Thoms.‡)
  vinulae (Scop.) (as *P. cephalotes* Holmgr.‡) (ex *Cerura vinula* (L.) (Lepid.: Notodontidae))
  (*cephalotes* (Holmgr.))
Polyblastus varitarsus (Grav.) (as *Polyblastus strobilator* Thunb. (=*varsitarsus* Grav.)‡)
  (*strobilator* misident.)

Erromenus brunnicans (Grav.)‡
  junior (Thunb.)‡ (also as *E. junior* Thunb. (*frenator* Grav.)*)
  (*frenator* (Grav.))
Dyspetes arrogator Heinr. (as *Dyspetes praerogator* L.‡)
  (*praerogator* misident.)
Tryphon atriceps Steph. (as *Psiloage ephippium* Holmgr.‡)
  (*ephippium* Holmgr.)
  bidentatus (Steph.) (as *T. incestus* Holmgr.‡)
  (*incestus* Holmgr.)
  nigripes Holmgr.‡ (also as *T. nigripes* Grav.*)
  relator (Thunb.) (as *T. vulgaris* Holmgr.‡)
  (*vulgaris* Holmgr.)
  rutilator (L.)‡
  signator (Grav.)‡
  trochanteratus Holmgr.‡
Kristotomus laticeps (Grav.) (as *Acrotomus laticeps* Grav.‡)
Eridolius aurifluus (Hal.) (as *Ctenicus aurifluus* Hal.‡)
  bimaculatus (Holmgr.)‡
  flavomaculatus (Grav.) (as *Exenterus flavilabris* Holmgr.†)
  (*flavilabris* (Holmgr.))

Xoridinae

Xorides fuligator (Thunb.) (as *Xylonomus pilicornis* Grav.‡)
  (*pilicornis* (Grav.))

Cryptinae

'**Hemiteles niger** Taschb.'‡ [This name is now applied to a species of *Thymaris* (Tryphoninae), but it is certain that Kerrich (if it was he) would have misapplied it to a small Cryptinae, the identity of which could be established only by examining his material in Cambridge.]
Acrolyta mediovittata (Schmied.) (as *Hemiteles mediovittatus* Schmied.‡)
Lysibia nanus (Grav.) (as *H. fulvipes* Grav.‡)
  (*fulvipes* (Grav.))
Xiphulcus floricolator (Grav.) (as *H. floricolator* Grav.‡)
Stibeutes breviareolatus (Thoms.) (as *H. breviareolatus* Thoms.‡)
Sulcarius nigricornis (Thoms.) (as *H. homocerus* Thoms.‡)
  (*homocerus* (Thoms.))
Encrateola laevigata (Ratz.) (as *H. laevigatus* Ratz.‡)
Mastrus rufulus (Thoms.) (as *H. rufulus* Thoms.‡)
Dichrogaster aestivalis (Grav.) (as *H. aestivalis* Grav.‡)
Gelis agilis (F.) (as *G. instabilis* Först.‡)
  (*instabilis* (Först.))
  areator (Panz.) (as *Hemiteles areator* Panz.†‡)
  balteatus (Thoms.) (as *H. balteatus* Thoms.‡)
  hortensis (Christ)) (as *Gelis gentilis* Först.‡)
  (*gentilis* (Först.))
  mangeri (Grav.) (as *Catalytus fulveolatus* Grav.‡)
  (*fulveolatus* (Grav.))
  melanocephalus (Schr.) (as *Gelis fasciatus* F.‡)
  (*fasciatus* (F.) preocc.)
  proximus (Först.) (as *G. corruptor* Först.‡)
  (*corruptor* (Först.))
  rufipes (Först.)‡ (Burw.Fen)
  rugifer (Thoms.) (as *Hemiteles rugifer* Thoms.‡)
  trux (Först.) (as *Gelis comes* Först.‡)
  (*comes* (Först.))
Thaumatogelis audax (Olivier) (as *G. zonatus* Först.‡)
  (*zonatus* (Först.))
Isadelphus inimicus (Grav.) (as *Cecidonomus inimicus* Grav.‡)
Rhembobius quadrispinus (Grav.) (as *Acanthocryptus quadrispinus* Grav. (=*quadrispinosus* Thoms.)‡)
  (♀♀ hibernating in grass tufts)
Endasys erythrogaster (Grav.) (as *Glyphicnemis erythrogaster* Grav.‡)
Glyphicnemis profligator (F.)‡
  vagabunda (Grav.)‡

Parasitic wasps

Bathythrix argentata (Grav.) (as *Leptocryptus lacustris*
 Schmied.‡) (common hyperparasite of *Euthrix
 potatoria* (L.) (Lepid.: Lasiocampidae))
 (*lacustris* (Schmied.))
Theroscopus essenbeckii (Grav.) (as *Hemiteles subzonatus*
 (Grav.)‡) (reared from *Phorbia fumigata* (Meig.) (Dipt.:
 Anthomyiidae) from wheat stubble, Wicken)
 (*subzonatus* (Grav.))
 rufulus (Gmel.) (as *H. politus* Bridg.‡)
 (*politus* (Bridg.))
Aclastus ungularis (Thoms.) (as *H. ungularis* Thoms.‡)
Platyrhabdus monodon (Thoms.) (as *H. monodon* Thoms.‡)
Zoophthorus palpator (Müll.) (as *H. incisus* Bridg.‡)
 (*incisus* (Bridg.))
Phygadeuon cubiceps Thoms.‡
 dimidiatus Thoms.‡ (Adv.Fen)
 exiguus Grav.‡
 hercynicus Grav.‡
 infelix Dalla Torre (as *P. inflatus* Thoms.‡)
 (*inflatus* Thoms. preocc.)
 laeviventris Thoms.‡
 leucostigmus Grav.‡ (Adv.Fen)
 rugipectus Thoms.‡
 trichops Thoms. (as *Phygadeuon ocularis* Thoms.‡) (hibernating in grass tufts)
 (*ocularis* Thoms.)
Stilpnus gagates (Grav.)‡
Mesoleptus filicornis (Thoms.) (as *Exolytus filicornis*
 Thoms.‡) (Burw.Fen)
 laevigatus (Grav.) (as *E. laevigatus* Grav.‡)
 petiolaris (Thoms.) (as *E. petiolaris* Thoms.‡)
Atractodes foveolatus Grav. (as *Asyncrita foveolata* Grav.‡)
 oreophilus Först.‡ (Adv.Fen)
Cubocephalus erythrinus (Grav.) (as *Microcryptus erythrinus*
 Grav.‡)
Oresbius arridens (Grav.) (as *M. arridens* Grav.‡)
 galactinus (Grav.) (as *M. galactinus* Grav.‡) (Burw.Fen)
Polytribax rufipes (Grav.) (as *Plectopcryptus rufipes* Grav.‡)
Schenkia spinolae (Grav.) (as *Microcryptus spinolae* Grav.‡)
Pleolophus brachypterus (Grav.) (as *M. brachypterus* Grav.
 var. *micropterus* Grav.‡)
 sperator (O. F. Müll.) (as *M. sperator* Müll.‡)
Aptesis jejunator (Grav.) (as *M. abdominator* Grav.‡) (ex
 cocoon of *Euthrix potatoria* (L.) (Lepid.:
 Lasiocampidae))
 (*abdominator* (Grav.))
 nigrocincta (Grav.) (as *M. nigrocinctus* Grav.‡) (hibernating
 in grass tufts)
Agrothereutes abbreviatus (F.) f. *hopei* (Grav.) (as *Spilocryptus
 abbreviator* F. var. *hopei* Först.‡)
 saturniae (Boie) (as Spilocryptus saturniae Boie‡)
Gambrus carnifex (Grav.) (as *Aritranis carnifex* Grav.‡)
 incubitor (L.) (as *Gambrus incubitor* L. = *ornatus* Grav.‡)
 (parasite of *Euthrix potatoria* (L.) (larva in cocoon)
 (Lepid.: Lasiocampidae))
 (*ornatus* (Grav.))
Aritranis director (Thunb.) (as *Pycnocryptus director* Thunb.
 (= *peregrinator* Grav.)‡)
 (*peregrinator* misident.)
Trychosis legator (Thunb.) (as *Goniocryptus plebejus*
 Tschek.‡)
 (*plebejus* (Tschek.))
 insularis van Rossem [**new British record** (Schwarz & Shaw,
 1998)]
Buathra laborator (Thunb.) (as *Cryptus laborator* Thunb.‡)
Cryptus armator F. (as *C. albatorius* Vill.‡)
 (*albatorius* misident.)
 titubator (Thunb.) (as *C. albatorius* Vill. var. *difficilis*
 Tschek.‡)
 (*difficilis* Tschek.)

Banchinae

Apophua bipunctoria (Thunb.) (as *Glypta bipunctoria* Thunb.
 (=*flavolineata* Grav.)‡)
 (*flavolineata* (Grav.))
Glypta ceratites Grav. (as *Conoblasta ceratites* Grav.‡)
 cylindrator (F.) (as *Diblastomorpha bicornis* Boie‡)
 (*bicornis* Boie)
 incisa Grav.‡
 monoceros Grav. (as *Conoblasta monocerus* Grav.‡)
 pictipes Taschenb.‡
 rufata Bridg.‡ (ex *Phalonidia manniana* (F.v.R.) (Lepid.))
 sculpturata Grav. (as *Glypta macrura* Haberm.‡)
 (*macrura* Haberm.)
 similis Bridg.‡
Lissonata ?clypeator (Grav.) (as *Lissonata cylindrator* Vill.)
 coracina (Gmel.) (as *L. bellator* Grav.‡)
 (*bellator* (Grav.) preocc.)
 folii Thoms. (as *L. transversa* Bridg.*)
 (*transversa* Bridg.)
 fundator (Thunb.) (as *L. sulphurifera* Grav.‡)
 (*sulphurifera* Grav.)
 punctiventris Thoms. (as *L. errabunda* Holmgr.‡)
 (*errabunda* Holmgr.)
 variabilis Holmgr.‡ (Adv.Fen)
Alloplasta piceator (Thunb.) (as *Alloplasta murina* Grav.,*
 and *A. piceator* Thunb. (=*murina* Grav.)‡)
 (*murina* (Grav.))
Exetastes adpressorius (Thunb.) (as *Exetastes adpressorius*
 Thunb. (=*guttatorius* Grav.),‡ and *E. guttatorius*
 Grav.†)
 (*guttatorius* Grav.)
 fornicator (F.)‡
Banchus falcatorius (F.)‡
 volutatorius (L.)‡

Ctenopelmatinae

Glyptorhaestus punctulatus (Woldst.) (as *Glyptorhaestus
 wüstneii* Thoms.‡)
 (*wuestneii* Thoms.)
Rhorus chrysopus (Gmel. in L.) (as *Monoblastus chrysopus*
 Gmel.‡)
 exstirpatorius (Grav.) (as *M. exstirpatorius* Grav.‡)
 neustriae (Schr.) (as *M. neustriae* Schr.‡)
 palustris (Holmgr.) (as *M. palustris* Holmgr.‡)
Sympherta antilope (Grav.) (as *Stiphrosomus antilope* Grav.‡)
 (Adv.Fen)
Perilissus pallidus (Grav.)‡
 spilonotus (Steph.) (as *P. thuringiacus* Schmied.‡)
 (*thuringiacus* Schmied.)
 variator (Müll.) (as *P. filicornis* Grav.‡)
 (*filicornis* (Grav.))
Lagarotis semicaligata (Grav.) (as *Lagarotus semicaligatus*
 Grav.‡)
Alexeter multicolor (Grav.) (as *Mesoleius multicolor* Grav.‡)
 niger (Grav.)‡
Himerta sepulchralis (Holmgr.) (as *Himertus sepulchralis*
 Holmgr.‡)
Campodorus ignavus (Holmgr.) (as *Mesoleius ignavus*
 Holmgr.‡)
 scapularis (Steph.) (as *M. scapularis* Steph.‡)
 variegatus (Jur.) (as *M. variegatus* Jur.‡)
Mesoleius armillatorius (Grav.)‡ (ex *Ametastegia glabrata*
 (Fall.) (Hymen.: Tenthredinidae))
 aulicus (Grav.)‡
 filicornis Holmgr.‡ (Adv.Fen)
Synomelix albipes (Grav.)‡
Mesoleptidea cingulata (Grav.) (as *Mesoleptus cingulatus*
 Grav.‡)
Gunomeria sordida (Grav.) (as *G. macrodactyla* Holmgr.‡)
 (*macrodactyla* (Holmgr.))

Hadrodactylus tiphae (Geoff. in Fourc.) (as *Hadrodactylus typhae* Geoff.‡) (Burw.Fen)
Phobetes chrysostomus (Grav.) (as *Ipoctonus chrysostomus* Grav.‡)
Euryproctus mundus (Grav.)* [but not in Kerrich 1936, 1938]
  nemoralis (Geoff. in Fourc.)*

Campopleginae

Sinophorus juniperinus (Holmgr.) (as *Eulimneria juniperana* Holmgr.‡) (Adv.Fen)
xanthostomus (Grav.) (as *E. xanthostoma* Grav.‡)
Campoplex cursitans (Holmgr.) (as *Omorgus cursitans* Holmgr.‡) (Burw.Fen)
  difformis (Gmel. in L.) (as *O. difformis* Gmel.,‡ and *O. mutabilis* Holmgr.‡)
    (*mutabilis* (Holmgr.))
  melanostictus (Grav.) (as *O. melanostictus* Grav.‡)
  molestus (Grav.) (as *O. molestus* Grav.‡)
  multicinctus (Grav.) (as *O. multicinctus* Grav.‡)
  variabilis (Bridg.) (as *Angitia variabilis* Bridg.‡) (ex *Teleiodes notatella* (Hb.) (Lepid.: Gelechiidae))
Bathyplectes infernalis (Grav.) (as *Canidiella tristis* Grav.‡)
    (*tristis* (Grav.))
Dusona angustifrons (Först.) (as *Campoplex obreptans* Först.‡) (Adv.Fen)
    (*obreptans* (Först.))
  erythrogaster (Först.) (as *C. erythrogaster* Först.‡)
  infesta (Först.) (as *C. infestus* Först.‡)
  insignita (Först.) (as *C. insignitus* Först.‡) (Adv.Fen)
  pugillator (L.) (as *C. canaliculatus* Först.‡)
    (*canaliculatus* (Först.))
  rugifer (Först.) (as *C. rugifer* Först.‡)
  terebrator (Först.) (as *C. terebrator* Först.‡)
Diadegma armillatum (Grav.) (as *Angitia armillata* Grav.‡ (Burw.Fen), and *A. tibialis* Grav.‡)
    (*tibiale* (Grav.))
  crassicorne (Grav.) (as *Diadegma crassicornis* Grav.‡)
  ?*cylindricum* (Brischke) (as *Angitia cylindrica* Brischke (=*tenuipes* Thoms.)‡)
  fenestrale (Holmgr.) (as *A. fenestralis* Holmgr.‡)
  ?*gracile* (Grav.) (as *A. gracilis* Bridg.‡)
  litorale (Holmgr.) (as *Meloboris litoralis* Holmgr.‡)
  neocerophaga Horstm. (as *A. cerophaga* Grav.‡)
    (*cerophaga* misident.)
Hyposoter didymator (Thunb.) (as *Anilasta ruficincta* Grav.,* and *A. didymator* Thunb. (=*ruficincta* Grav.)‡)
    (*ruficinctus* (Grav.))
  virginalis (Grav.) (as *Angitia virginalis* Grav.‡)
Olesicampe fulviventris (Gmel. in L.‡)
  paludicola (Holmgr.) (as *Meloboris inculcator* Grav.‡)
    (*inculcator* misident.)

Tersilochinae

Thersilocus moderator Holmgr.'‡ [This name cannot be interpreted.]
Tersilochus curvator Horst. (as *Thersilocus saltator* F.‡)
    (*saltator* (F.))
  jocator Holmgr. (as *Thersilocus jocator* F.‡)
Aneuclis melanaria (Holmgr.) (as *Thersilocus melanarius* Holmgr.‡)
Phradis morionellus (Holmgr.) (as *Thersilocus morionellus* Holmgr.‡)
Diaparsis nutritor (F.) (as *Diaparsis genalis* Thoms.‡)
    (*genalis* (Thoms.))

Ophioninae

Ophion luteus (L.) (as *O. distans* Thoms.‡)
    (*distans* Thoms.)
  obscuratus F. (as *O. obscurus* F.‡)
    (*obscurus* F.)

scutellaris Thoms.†‡
Enicospilus merdarius (Grav.)‡

Mesochorinae

Mesochorus nuncupator (Panz.) (as *M. vittator* Zett.‡)
    (*vittator* (Zett.))
  orbitalis Holmgr.‡
  stigmator (Thunb.)‡ (Adv.Fen)
  tenuiscapus Thoms.‡
  unicinctor (Thunb.) (as *Stictopisthus laticeps* Thoms.‡) (ex *Teleiodes notatella* (Hb.) (Lepid.: Gelechiidae))
    (*laticeps* Thoms.)

Metopiinae

Chorinaeus cristator (Grav.)‡
  funebris (Grav.)‡
  talpa (Hal.)‡
Trieces tricarinatus (Holmgr.) (as *Chorinaeus tricarinatus* Holmgr.‡)
Triclistus podagricus (Grav.)‡
Hypsicera curvator (F.) (as *Triclistus curvator* F.‡)
Exochus albicinctus Holmgr.‡
  consimilis Holmgr. (as *E. parvispina* Thoms.‡) (Adv.Fen)
    (*parvispina* Thoms.)
  flavomarginatus Holmgr.‡
  fletcheri Bridg.‡ (ex *Teleiodes notatella* (Hb.) (Lepid.: Gelechiidae))
  frontellus Holmgr.‡
  gravipes Grav.‡
  nigripalpis Thoms.‡

Anomaloninae

Agrypon flaveolatum (Grav.)‡

Acaenitinae

Phaenolobus terebrator (Scop.) (as *Acaenitus arator* Rossi.‡)
    (*arator* (Rossi.))

Oxytorinae

Oxytorus luridator (Grav.) (as *Callidiotes luridator* Grav.‡)

Orthocentrinae

Helictes borealis (Holmgr.)‡ (Burw.Fen)
Orthocentrus ?*monilicornis* Holmgr.‡

Orthopelmatinae

Orthopelma brevicorne Morl. (as *Orthopelma brevicornis* Morl.‡)
  mediator Thunb. (as *O. mediator* Thunb. (=*luteolator* Grav.)‡) (parasite of *Diplolepis rosae* (L.) (Hymen.: Cynipidae))
    (*luteolator* (Grav.))

Collyriinae

Collyria coxator (Vill.) (as *Collyria calcitrator* Grav.,*‡ and *C. puncticeps* (Thoms.)*) (bred from *Cephus pygmeus* (L.) (Hymen.: Cephidae))
    (*calcitrator* (Grav.))
    (*puncticeps* (Thoms.))

Diplazontinae

Syrphoctonus dimidiatus (Schr.) (as *Homotropus dimidiatus* Schr.‡) (Adv.Fen)
  elegans (Grav.) (as *H. elegans* Grav.‡) (Adv.Fen)
  fissorius (Grav.) (as *H. fissorius* Grav.‡)
  pictus (Grav.) (as *H. pictus* Grav.‡)
  signatus (Grav.) (as *H. signatus* Grav.‡)
  tarsatorius (Panz.) (as *H. tarsatorius* Panz.‡)

Enizemum ornatum (Grav.) (as *H. deplanatus* Grav. (=*ornatus* Grav.)‡)
  (*deplanatum* (Grav.))
Campocraspedon caudatus (Thoms.) (as *H. caudatus* Thoms.‡)
Phthorima compressa (Desv.)‡ (Adv.Fen)
Syrphophilus bizonarius (Grav.) (as *H. bizonarius* Grav.‡)
Tymmophorus rufiventris (Grav.) (as *Zootrephes rufiventris* Grav.‡)
Diplazon annulatus (Grav.) (as *Bassus annulatus* Grav.‡)
  laetatorius (F.) (as *B. laetatorius* F.‡)
  pectoratorius (Grav.) (as *Homotropus pectoratorius* Grav.‡)
  tetragonus (Thunb.) (as *Bassus trincinctus* Grav.‡)
    (*trincinctus* (Grav.))
  tibiatorius (Thunb.) (as *B. albosignatus* Grav.‡)
    (*albosignatus* (Grav.))
Promethes sulcator (Grav.)‡
Sussaba pulchella (Holmgr.) (as *Promethes pulchellus* Holmgr.*‡, and *P. laticarpus* Thoms.‡)
  (*laticarpus* (Thoms.))

Ichneumoninae

Trogus lapidator (F.)‡
Amblyjoppa proteus (Christ) (as *Amblyjoppa laminatoria* F.‡)
  (ex *Deilephila elpenor* (L.) (Lepid.: Sphingidae))
  (*laminatoria* (F.))
Coelichneumon comitator (L.) (as *Coelichneumon comitator* L. (=*lineator* auctt.)‡, and *C. lineator* F.*)
  (*lineator* misident.)
Callajoppa cirrogaster (Schr.) (as *Callajoppa lutoria* F.‡)
  (*lutoria* (F.))
Stenichneumon culpator Schr.‡ (♀♀ hibernating under bark)
Syspasis eburnifrons (Wesm.) (as *Stenichneumon puerulus* Kreichb.‡)
  (*puerulus* (Kreichb.))
  lineator (F.) (as *Stenichneumon lineator* F. (=*trilineatus* Gmel.‡) (ex *Abraxas grossulariata* (L.) (Lepid.: Geometridae))
    (*trilineatus*) (Gmel. in L.)
Aoplus ochropis (Gmel. in L.) (as *Stenichneumon ochropis* Gmel.‡) (ex *Abraxas grossulariata* (L.) (Lepid.: Geometridae))
Cratichneumon culex (O. F. Müll.) (as *C. annulator* F.‡)
  (*annulator* (F.))
  dissimilis (Grav.)‡
  fabricator (F.)‡
  fugitivus (Grav.)‡
Vulgichneumon deceptor (Scop.) (as *Barichneumon vestigator* Wesm.‡)
  (*vestigator* (Wesm.) preocc.)
  saturatorius (L.) (as *Melanichneumon saturatorius* L.‡)
  suavis (Grav.) (as *Barichneumon lepidus* Grav.‡)
    (*lepidus* (Grav.))
Barichneumon bilunulatus (Grav.)‡
  heracleanae (Bridg.)‡
  sedulus (Grav.)‡
Homotherus locutor (Thunb.) (as *B. locutor* Thunb. (=*albicinctus* Grav.)‡)
  (*albicinctus* (Grav.) preocc.)
Virgichneumon maculicauda (Perkins) (as *Melanichneumon perscrutator* Wesm.‡)
  (*perscrutator* (Wesm.) preocc.)
Chasmias motatorius (F.)‡ (♀♀ hibernating in grass tufts and under bark)
Ichneumon albiger Wesm. (as *I. tempestivus* Holmgr.‡) (♀♀ hibernating in grass tufts)
  (*tempestivus* Holmgr.)
  confusor Grav. (as *I. confusorius* Grav.‡) (hibernating in grass tufts)
    (*confusorius* Grav.)
  insidiosus Wesm.‡

  latrator F.‡ (♀♀ hibernating in grass tufts)
  lautatorius Desv.‡ (♀♀ hibernating in grass tufts)
  melanotis (Holmgr.) (as *Ichneumon molitorius* Grav. var. *melanotis* Holmgr.‡) (hibernating under bark)
  molitorius L. (as *I. molitorius* Grav.‡) (hibernating under bark)
  sarcitorius L.‡ (♀♀ hibernating in grass tufts)
  simulans Tischb. (as *I. subquatratus* Thoms.‡) (hibernating in grass tufts)
    (*subquatratus* Thoms.)
  suspiciosus Wesm.‡ (♀♀ hibernating in grass tufts)
  xanthorius Först.‡
Probolus ?*alticola* (Grav.) (as *P. culpatorius* L. (=*alticola* Grav.)‡)
  ?*culpatorius* (L.) (as *P. culpatorius* L. (=*alticola* Grav.)‡)
Ctenichneumon castigator (F.)‡
  divisorius (Grav.)‡
Diphyus fossorius (L.) (as *Amblytes fossorius* L. (=*subsericans* auctt.)‡)
  ochromelas (Gmel.) (as *A. negatorius* F. var. *nubilis* Berth.‡)
    (*negatorius* (F.))
  palliatorius (Grav.) (as *A. palliatorius* (Grav.)‡)
  raptorius (L.) (as *Spilichneumon quadriguttorius* Thunb. (=*gravenhorstii* Wesm.)‡)
    (*quadriguttorius* (Thunb.))
    (*gravenhorstii* (Wesm.) preocc.)
Achaius oratorius (F.) (as *Amblytes oratorius* F. var. *cingulipes* Steph.‡)
  (*cingulipes* (Steph.))
Limerodops subsericans Grav. (as *Amblytes subsericans* Grav.*)
Limerodes arctiventris (Boie)‡ (hibernating in grass tuft)
Exephanes ischioxanthus (Grav.) (as *Exephanes hilaris* Grav.‡) (Burw.Fen)
  (*hilaris* (Grav.) preocc.)
  occupator (Grav.) (as *E. occupator* Grav. var. *nigromaculatus* Ulbricht‡) (Adv.Fen)
Linycus exhortator (F.) (as *Platylabus exhortator* F. (=*dimidiatus* Grav.)‡)
  (*dimidiatus* (Grav.))
Apaeliticus bellicosus Wesm.‡
Heterischnus nigricollis (Wesm.) (as *Ischnus nigricollis* Wesm.‡)
Dicaelotus pumilus (Grav.)‡
Colpognathus celerator (Grav.) (as *Phygadeuon procerus* Grav.‡)
  (*procerus* (Grav.))
  divisus Thoms.‡ (♀♀ hibernating in grass tufts)
Centeterus rubiginosus (Gmel.) (as *C. opprimator* Grav.‡) (in straw-stack refuse) (Burw.Fen)
  (*opprimator* Grav.)
Aethecerus discolor Wesm.‡
  pallicoxa Thoms.‡
Dirophanes rusticatus (Wesm.) (as *Phaeogenes rusticatus* Wesm.‡) (♀♀ hibernating in grass tufts)
Phaeogenes melanogonos (Gmel.) (as *P. melanogonus* Gmel.‡)
  mysticus Wesm.‡
Alomya debellator (F.) (as *Alomyia debellator* F.‡)

BRACONIDAE

Braconinae

Bracon discoideus (Wesm.)‡
  epitriptus Marsh.‡
  exarator Marsh.‡
  fulvipes Nees‡
  fuscicoxis (Wesm.)‡
  minutator (F.)‡
  osculator Nees‡
  terebella (Wesm.)‡ (parasite of *Cephus pygmeus* (L.) (Hymen.: Cephidae))
  variator Nees‡

Rogadinae

Clinocentrus exsertor (Nees)‡
Aleiodes alternator (Nees) (as *Rhogas geniculator* Nees‡) (ex young larvae of *Euthrix potataria* (L.) (Lepid.: Lasiocampidae))
  (*geniculator* (Nees))
  ?*circumscriptus* (Nees) (as *R. circumscriptus* Nees‡)
  dispar (Hal. in Curt.) (as *Heterogamus dispar* Hal.‡)
  rugulosus (as *Rhogas rugulosus* Nees‡) (ex larvae of *Simyra albovenosa* (Goeze) (Lepid.: Noctuidae))
Rhyssalus clavator Hal.‡
Hormius moniliatus (Nees)‡

Alysiinae

Alysia manducator (Panz.)‡ (parasite of blowfly spp. (Dipt.: Calliphoridae))
Coelinidea niger (Nees) (as *Coelinius niger* Nees‡)
  ruficollis (H.-S.) (as *Coelinius procerus* Hal.‡)
  (*procerus* (Hal.))
Coelinius anceps (Curt.) (as *Chaenon anceps* Curt.‡)
  elegans (Curt.) (as *Coelinius elegans* Hal.‡)
Polemochartus liparae (Gir.) (as *Polemon liparae* Gir.‡) (parasite of *Lipara lucens* Meig. (Dipt.: Chloropidae))
Dacnusa areolaris (Nees)‡
  stramineipes Hal.‡
Symphya hians (Nees) (as *Oenone hians* Nees‡)

Helconinae

Diospilus morosus Reinh.‡
  oleraceus Hal.‡

Meteorinae

Meteorus colon (Hal.) (as *Perilitus fragilis* Wesm.‡) (ex *Nola cucullatella* (L.) (Lepid.: Nolidae))
  (*fragilis* (Wesm.))
  ictericus (Nees) (as *M. minutor* Thunb. (=*ictericus* Nees)‡, and *M. confinis* Ruthé‡)
  (*minutus* (Thunb.))
  (*confinis* Ruthe)
  pulchricornis (Wesm.)‡

Blacinae

Blacus armatulus Ruthe‡
  ruficornis (Nees)‡

Euphorinae

Pygostolus falcatus (Nees) (as *Pygostylus falcatus* Nees‡)
Centistes cuspidatus (Hal.) (as *C. lucidator* Nees‡) (Adv.Fen)
  (*lucidator* Nees)
  ?*subsulcatus* (Thoms.)‡ (Adv.Fen)
Peristenus pallipes (Curt.) (as *Euphorus pallidipes* Curt.‡)

Agathidinae

Agathis griseifrons (Thoms.)‡
Earinus gloriatorius (Panz.) (as *E. ochropes* Curt.‡)
  (*ochropes* Lyle)
Bassus clausthalianus (Ratz.) (as *Microdus clausthalianus* Marsh. non Ratz.‡)
  rufipes (Nees) (as *Microdus rufipes* Nees‡)
  tumidulus (Nees) (as *M. tumidulus* Nees‡)

Macrocentrinae

Macrocentrus infirmus (Nees)‡
  linearis (Nees) (as *M. abdominalis* (F.)†‡)
  (*abdominalis* (F.))
  marginator (Nees)†‡

Orgilinae

Orgilus obscurator (Nees)‡ (Adv.Fen)

Cheloninae

Microchelonus exilis (Marsh.) (as *Chelonella exilis* Marsh.‡)
  latrunculus (Marsh.) (as *Chelonella latruncula* Marsh.‡) (Adv.Fen)
Chelonus inanita (L.) (as *Chelonus inanitus* L.‡)
Ascogaster quadridentata Wesm. (as *Ascogaster quadridentatus* Wesm.‡)
  rufipes (Latr.)‡

Microgastrinae

Hygroplitis russatus (Hal.)‡
Microgaster ?*laeviscuta* Thoms. (as *M. globatus* L.‡)
  (?*globata* misident.)
  tibialis Nees†‡
Apanteles obscurus (Nees)‡
Dolichogenidea gagates (Nees) (as *Apanteles gagates* Nees‡)
Cotesia congesta (Nees) (as *A. congestus* Nees‡)
  ferruginea (Marsh.) (as *A. ferrugineus* Reinh.‡)
Glyptapanteles pallipes (Reinh.) (as *A. pallidipes* Reinh.‡)
Protapanteles incertus (Ruthe) (as *A. jugosus* Lyle‡) (ex larvae of *Cabera exanthemata* (Scop.) (Lepid.: Geometridae))
  (*jugosus* (Lyle))
Microplitis ocellatae (Bouché)‡ (ex *Laothoe populi* (L.) (Lepid.: Sphingidae))
  mediator (Hal.) (as *Microplitis mediana* Ruthé‡)
  (*mediana* (Ruthe))
  tuberculifera (Wesm.)‡

Aculeata (group of superfamilies)
(stinging Hymenoptera)

List from Kerrich (1938), updated by G. R. Else; nomenclature: Kloet & Hincks, edn 2 (1978), Richards (1980), Morgan (1984), and Day (1988); classification after Gauld & Bolton (1988)

‡ Records from VCH (Kerrich, 1938)

Dates in square brackets are for newly-recorded species

NOTE. As with the Parasitica (p.83), there have been many taxonomic revisions and changes to nomenclature of Aculeata. Some species listed in 1938 may now have a different identity. There are many Wicken specimens in major collections which need to be re-examined in order to establish their correct determination and to augment this list.

CHRYSIDOIDEA

DRYINIDAE

Anteoninae

Prenanteon subapterus (Kieff.) (as *Mystrophorus subapterus* Kieff.‡)
Chelogynus ephippiger (Dalman) (as *C. brevifilis* (Kieff.)‡)
  (*brevifilis* (Kieff.))

BETHYLIDAE

Epyrinae

Cephalonomia formiciformis Westw.‡

Bethylinae

Bethylus cephalotes Först.‡

CHRYSIDIDAE

Elampinae

Omalus aeneus (F.)‡
  auratus (L.)‡

Chrysidinae

Chrysis fulgida L.‡ (**RDB1**)
  ignita (L.)‡
  ruddii Shuck.
Chrysura radians (Harris) (as *Chrysis pustulosa* Ab. de Perr.‡)
  (**Na**)
  (*pustulosa* Ab. de Perr.)
Trichrysis cyanea (L.) (as *Chrysis cyanea* L.‡)

VESPOIDEA

SAPYGIDAE

Sapyginae

Monosapyga clavicornis (L.)‡ (**Nb**)
Sapyga quinquepunctata (F.)‡

FORMICIDAE

Myrmicinae

Myrmica rubra (L.)‡
  (*laevinodis* Nyl.)
  ruginodis Nyl.
  scabrinodis Nyl.‡

Formicinae

Lasius flavus (F.) (as *Acanthomyops flavus* (F.)‡)

POMPILIDAE

Pepsinae

Priocnemis agilis (Shuck.) (as *P. obtusiventris* Schiød.‡) (**Nb**)
  (*obtusiventris* Schiød.)
  exaltata (F.)‡
  hyalinata (F.) (as *P. femoralis* (Dahlb.)‡) (**Nb**)
  (*femoralis* (Dahlb.))
Dipogon bifasciatus (Geoff. in Fourc.) (as *Deuteragenia hircana* (F.)‡) (**RDB3**)
  (*hircanus* (F.))

Pompilinae

Anoplius caviventris (Auriv.) (as *Psammochares piliventris* (Mor.) (*cardui* Perk.)‡) (**Nb**)
  (*cardui* R.C.L. Perkins)

Ceropalinae

Ceropales maculata (F.)‡

VESPIDAE

Eumeninae

Odynerus spinipes (L.) (as *Hoplomerus spinipes* (L.)‡)
Ancistrocerus nigricornis (Curt.) (as *A. callosus* (Thoms.)‡)
  (*callosus* (Thoms.))
  oviventris (Wesm.) (as *A. pictus* (Curt.)‡)
  (*pictus* (Curt.))
  parietinus (L.)*
  parietum (L.)*
  trifasciatus (O. F. Müll.) (as *A. trimarginatus* Zett. (=*trifasciatus* Oliv.)‡)
  (*trimarginatus* misident.)

Symmorphus gracilis (Brullé)‡
  mutinensis (Baldini) (as *S. sinuatissimus* Richards (=*sinuatus* (F.)‡)
  (*sinuatissimus* Richards)

Vespinae

Dolichovespula media (Retz.) [1998] (**Na**)
  sylvestris (Scop.)
Vespula germanica (F.)‡
  rufa (L.)‡
  vulgaris (L.)‡

APOIDEA

SPHECIDAE

Larrinae

Trypoxylon attenuatum F. Smith‡
  clavicerum Lep.‡
  figulus (L.)‡

Crabroninae

Crossocerus annulipes (Lep. & Brullé) (as *Coelocrabo ambiguus* (Dahlb.) (*gonager*)‡)
  (*ambiguus* (Dahlb.))
  (*gonager* (Lep. & Brullé))
  binotatus Lep. & Brullé (as *Cuphopterus confusus* (Schulz) (*signatus*)‡) (**Na**)
  (*confusus* Schulz)
  (*signatus* misident.)
  capitosus (Shuck.) (as *Coelocrabo capitosus* (Shuck.)‡)
  cetratus (Shuck.) (as *Coelocrabo cetratus* (Shuck.)‡)
  megacephalus (Ross.) (as *Coelocrabo leucostomoides* Richards (*leucostomus*)‡)
  (*leucostomoides* (Richards))
  nigritus (Lep. & Brullé) (as *Coelocrabo pubescens* Shuck. (*nigritus*)‡)
  (*pubescens* (Shuck.))
  podagricus (Vander Lind.) (as *Ablepharipus podagricus* (Vander Lind.)‡)
  pusillus Lep. & Brullé (as *Crossocerus varus* Lep.‡)
  (*varus* Lep. & Brullé)
  quadrimaculatus (F.) (as *Hoplocrabro 4-maculatus* (F.)‡)
  tarsatus (Shuck.) (as *Crossocerus tarsatus* (Schuck.) (*palmipes* L.)‡)
  (*palmipes* misident.)
  vagabundus (Panz.) (as *Acanthocrabro vagabundus* (Panz.)‡) (? extinct nationally) (**RDB1**)
Ectemnius cavifrons (Thoms.) (as *Clytochrysus cavifrons* Thoms.‡) (parasitized at Wicken by *Macronychia striginerva* (Dipt.: Sarcophagidae))
  cephalotes (Olivier) (as *Metacrabro quadricinctus* (F.) (*interruptus*)‡) (predator at Wicken on *Episyrphus balteatus* (DeGeer) (Dipt.: Syrphidae))
  (*quadricinctus* misident.)
  (*interruptus* misident.)
  continuus (F.) (as *Solenius contiguus* (F.) (*vagus* L.)‡)
  (*vagus* misident.)
  lapidarius (Panz.) (as *Clytochrysus chrysostomus* (Lep.)‡)
  (*chrysostomus* (Lep. & Brullé))
  lituratus (Panz.) (as *Metacrabo lituratus* (Panz.)‡)
Entomognathus brevis (Vander Lind.)‡
Rhopalum clavipes (L.)‡
  coarctatum (Scop.)
  gracile Wesm. (as *Corynopus nigrionum* Kiesenw. (*kiesenwetteri* Mor.)‡) (**RDB2**)
  (*nigrinum* Kiesenw. preocc.)
  (*kiesenwetteri* Mor.)

Pemphredoninae

Psenulus pallipes (Panz.) (as *P. atratus* F. (*pallipes*)‡)
  (*atratus* F.)
Spilomena spp. [a group of 4 closely related spp.] (as *S.
  troglodytes* (Vander Lind.)‡)
Stigmus solskyi A. Moraw.‡ and/or *pendulus* Panz. (**RDBK**)
Pemphredon inornatus Say (as *Cemonus shuckardi* Mor.)‡)
  (*shuckardi* (Mor.))
  lugubris (F.)‡
  morio Vander Lind. (as *Ceratophorus morio* (Vander
    Lind.)‡) (**Nb**)
Diodontus luperus Shuck.‡
Passaloecus clypealis Faest. (**RDB3**)
  corniger Shuck.‡
  gracilis (Curt.)‡
  ?monilicornis Dahlb.‡ [a northern species]
  singularis Dahlb.‡

Nyssoninae

Gorytes quadrifasciatus (F.) (as *Hoplisus quadrifasciatus*
  (F.)‡)

APIDAE

Colletinae

Hylaeus annularis (Kirby)‡

  (*dilatatus* (Kirby))
  brevicornis Nyl.‡
  communis Nyl.‡
  confusus Nyl.‡
  cornutus Curt. (**Na**)
  hyalinatus F. Smith‡
  pectoralis Först. (as *H. pectoralis* Först. (*palustris* Perk.,
    kriechbaumeri Först.)‡) (in galls of *Lipara lucens* Meig.
    (Dipt.: Chloropidae))
    (*kriechbaumeri* Först.)
    (*palustris* (R. C. L. Perkins))
  pictipes Nyl. (**Na**)
  signatus (Panz.) (as *H. pratensis* (Geoff.) (*signata*)‡) (**Nb**)
    (*pratensis* (Geoff.))

Andreninae

Andrena barbilabris (Kirby) (as *A. barbilabris* (K.) (*sericeus,
  albicrus*)‡)
    (*sericea* (Christ) preocc.)
    (*albicrus* (Kirby))
  bicolor F. [1998]
    (*gwynana* (Kirby))
  chrysosceles (Kirby)‡
  coitana (Kirby)‡
  dorsata (Kirby)‡
  haemorrhoa (F.) (as *A. albicans* (Müll.)‡)
    (*albicans* misident.)
  helvola (L.)‡
  labialis (Kirby)‡
  nitida (O. F. Müll.) (as *A. pubescens* Oliv. (*nitida*)‡)
    (*pubescens* Olivier)
  nigroaenea (Kirby)‡
  niveata Friese‡ (**RDB2**)
  praecox (Scop.)‡
  scotica R. C. L. Perkins (as *A. jacobi* Perk. (*trimmerana*
    auctt.)‡)
    (*jacobi* R. C. L. Perkins)
  semilaevis Pérez (as *A. saundersella* R. C. L. Perkins‡)
    (*saundersella* R. C. L. Perkins)
  subopaca Nyl. [1998]
  synadelpha R. C. L. Perkins‡
  tibialis (Kirby)‡ (**Na**)
  wilkella (Kirby)‡

Halictinae

Halictus rubicundus (Christ)‡
  tumulorum (L.)‡

Lasioglossum albipes (F.) (as *Halictus albipes* (K.)‡)
  calceatum (Scop.) (as *H. calceatus* (Scop.) (*cylindricus*)‡)
    (*cylindricum* (F.))
  fulvicorne (Kirby) (as *H. fulvicornis* (K.)‡)
  nitidiusculum (Kirby) (as *H. nitidiusculus* (K.)‡)
  villosulum (Kirby) (as *H. villosulus* (Kirby)‡)
Sphecodes ephippius (L.) (as *S. divisus* K.) (*similis*)‡) (clep-
    toparasite of *Halictus rubicundus* (Christ))
    (*divisus* (Kirby))
    (*similis* Wesm.)
  rubicundus Hagens‡ (**Na**) (parasite of *Andrena labialis*
    (Kirby))

Melittinae

Macropis europaea Warncke (as *M. labiata* F.)‡) (**Na**)
  (*labiata* misident.)

Megachilinae

Anthidium manicatum (L.)
Stelis phaeoptera (Kirby)‡ (cleptoparasite of *Osmia leaiana*
    (Kirby) and ?*O. caerulescens* (L.)) (**RDB2**)
Chelostoma florisomne (L.) (as *Heriades florisomne* (L.)‡)
Osmia caerulescens (L.) (as *Osmia coerulescens* (L.)‡)
  leaiana (Kirby)‡ (associates with *O. caerulescens*)
    (*fulviventris* misident.)
  rufa (L.)‡
Hoplitis spinulosa (Kirby) (as *Osmia spinulosa* (Kirby)‡)
Megachile centuncularis (L.)‡
  ligniseca (Kirby)‡
  maritima (Kirby)‡
  versicolor F. Smith‡
  willughbiella (Kirby)‡ (parasitized at Wicken by
    Cryptophagus populi Payk. (Coleopt.:
    Cryptophagidae))
Coelioxys inermis (Kirby)‡ (cleptoparasite at Wicken of
    Megachile versicolor F. Smith and *M. centuncularis*
    (L.))
    (*acuminata* Nyl.)
  rufescens Lep. & Serv.‡ (cleptoparasite of *Megachile* spp.)

Apinae

Nomada fulvicornis F. (as *N. lineola* Panz.‡) (**RDB3**) (clep-
    toparasite of *Andrena tibialis* (Kirby))
    (*lineola* Panz.)
  obtusifrons Nyl.‡ (cleptoparasite of *A. coitana* (Kirby))
  ruficornis (L.) (as *N. bifida* Thoms.‡) (cleptoparasite of *A.
    haemorrhoa* (F.))
    (*bifida* Thoms.)
  sheppardana (Kirby) (as *N. rufocincta* (K.) (*furva*)‡) (clep-
    toparasite of *Lasioglossum nitidiusculus* (Kirby))
    (*furva* misident.)
  striata F. (as *N. hillana* (K.) (*ochrostoma*)‡) (cleptoparasite
    of *Andrena wilkella* (Kirby))
    (*ochrostoma* (Kirby))
    (?*hillana* (Kirby))
Anthophora furcata (Panz.)‡
  plumipes (Pall.) (as *A. pilipes* (F.) (=*retusa* of Jenyns)‡)
    (*pilipes* (F.))
    (*retusa* auctt.)
Melecta albifrons (Forst.) (as *M. punctata* F.) (*armata*)‡) (clep-
    toparasite of *Anthophora plumipes* (Pall.))
    (*punctata* F.)
    (*armata* (Panz.) preocc.)
Bombus barbutellus (Kirby)‡
  bohemicus (Seidl)‡ (inquiline on *Bombus lucorum* (L.))
    (*distinctus* (Peréz))

   distinguendus F. Moraw. (**Nb**)
   hortorum (L.)‡
   humilis Ill.‡
   jonellus (Kirby)‡
   lapidarius (L.)‡
   lucorum (L.)‡
   muscorum (L.)‡
   pascuorum (Scop.) (as *Bombus agrorum* F.‡)
      (*agrorum* (F.))
   pratorum (L.)‡
   ruderarius (O. F. Müll.) (as *B. donovanella* (K.) (*ruderarius*,
         derhamellus)‡)
      (*derhamellus* (Kirby))
   ruderatus (F.)‡ (**Nb**)
   rupestris (F.)‡ (**Nb**) (inquiline on *Bombus lapidarius* (L.))
   soroeensis (F.)‡
   subterraneus (L.)‡ (?now extinct in Britain) (**Na**)
      (*latreillellus* Kirby)
   sylvarum (L.)‡ (**Nb**)
   terrestris (L.)‡
   vestalis (Geoff. in Fourc.)‡
Apis mellifera L. (Honeybee)

DEUTEROSTOMA

CHORDATA

FRESHWATER FISHES

Lists: Gardiner (1932); D. C. Aldridge (pers.comm.); hybrids:
Johnson (1985)
Checklist: Maitland & Campbell (1992)

Agnatha (vertebrates without jaws)

CYCLOSTOMATA
(lampreys)

HYPEROARTIA

PETROMYZONIDAE
Lampetra fluviatilis (L.) (River Lamprey)

Gnathostomata (jawed vertebrates)

PISCES
(fishes)

HAPLOMI

ESOCIDAE
Esox lucius L. (Pike)

OSTARIOPHYSI

CYPRINIDAE
Gobio gobio (L.) (Gudgeon)
Tinca tinca (L.) (Tench)
Blicca bjoerkna (L.) (Silver Bream)
Abramis brama (L.) (Common Bream)
  brama × *Blicca bjoerkna*
Phoxinus phoxinus (L.) (Minnow)
Rhodeus sericeus (Bloch) (Bitterling)
Scardinius erythrophthalmus (L.) (Rudd)
Rutilus rutilus (L.) (Roach)
  rutilus × *A. brama*
  rutilus × *B. bjoerkna*
  rutilus × *Scardinius erythrophthalmus*
Leuciscus cephalus (L.) (Chub)
  leuciscus (L.) (Dace)

COBITIDAE
Cobitis taenia L. (Spined Loach)

APODES

ANGUILLIDAE
Anguilla anguilla (L.) (European Eel)

ANACANTHINI

GADIDAE
Lota lota (L.) (Burbot)

PERCOMORPHI

PERCIDAE
Perca fluviatilis L. (Perch)
Gymnocephalus cernua (L.) (Ruffe)

COTTIDAE
Cottus gobio L. (Bullhead or Miller's Thumb)

GASTEROSTEIDAE
Gasterosteus aculeatus L. (Three-spined Stickleback)
Pungitius pungitius (L.) (Ten-spined Stickleback)

TETRAPODA

AMPHIBIA
(amphibians)
List: Gardiner (1932)
Checklist: Frazer (1983)

CAUDATA

SALAMANDRIDAE
Triturus vulgaris (L.) (Smooth Newt)
  cristatus (Laurenti) (Great Crested Newt)

SALIENTIA

BUFONIDAE
Bufo bufo (L.) (Common Toad)

RANIDAE
Rana temporaria L. (Common Frog)

REPTILIA
(reptiles)
List: Gardiner (1932)

SQUAMATA

ANGUIDAE
Anguis fragilis L. (Slow Worm)

LACERTIDAE
Lacerta vivipara Jacq. (Common Lizard)

COLUBRIDAE
Natrix natrix (L.) (Grass Snake)

AVES
(birds)

Lists: Evans (1923a); Thorne & Bennett (1982, 1989, 1995)
Nomenclature: Scientific and vernacular names follow Brooks
& Mitchell (1998). These differ only slightly from those used
by Cramp *et al.* (1977–94).

Feral species and 'escapes' are in square brackets

Key:
B Breeds regularly
O Very occasional breeder
R Resident all year round
S Summer visitor
W Winter visitor
P Regular passage migrant
V Vagrant, fairly uncommon
X Exceptional, five or fewer records
\# Subspecies recognizable in the field

PODICIPEDIFORMES
(grebes)

PODICIPEDIDAE

Tachybaptus ruficollis (Pall.) (Little Grebe) **BR**
Podiceps cristatus (L.) (Great Crested Grebe) **BR**
  grisegena (Bodd.) (Red-necked Grebe) **X**
  auritus (L.) (Slavonian Grebe) **X**
  nigricollis C. L. Brehm (Black-necked Grebe) **X**

PELICANIFORMES
(gannets, cormorants)

SULIDAE

Morus bassanus (L.) (Gannet) **X**

PHALACROCORACIDAE

Phalacrocorax carbo (L.) (Cormorant) **R**
  aristotelis (L.) (Shag) **X**

CICONIIFORMES
(herons, storks, spoonbills)

ARDEIDAE

Botaurus stellaris (L.) (Bittern) **W**
Egretta garzetta (L.) (Little Egret) **X**
Ardea cinerea L. (Grey Heron) **OR**
  purpurea L. (Purple Heron) **X**

THRESKIORNITHIDAE

Platalea leucorodia L. (Spoonbill) **X**

ANSERIFORMES
(swans, geese, ducks)

ANATIDAE

Cygnus olor (Gmel.) (Mute Swan) **BR**
  columbianus bewickii (Yarr.) (Bewick's Swan) **WV**
  cygnus (L.) (Whooper Swan) **WV**
Anser fabalis (Latham) (Taiga Bean Goose) **X**
  brachyrhynchus Baill. (Pink-footed Goose) **WV**
  albifrons (Scop.) (White-fronted Goose) **X**
  anser (L.) (Greylag Goose) **BR**
  [*indicus* (Latham) (Bar-headed Goose)] **X**
  [*caerulescens* (L.) (Snow Goose)] **X**

Branta canadensis (L.) (Canada Goose) **BR**
  leucopsis Bechst. (Barnacle Goose) **X**
  bernicla (L.) (Brent Goose) **X**
Alopochen aegyptiacus (L.) (Egyptian Goose) **X**
Tadorna [*ferruginea* (Pall.) (Ruddy Shelduck)] **X**
  tadorna (L.) (Shelduck) **P**
[*Aix galericulata* (L.) (Mandarin)] **X**
Anas penelope L. (Wigeon) **W**
  americana Gmel. (American Wigeon) **X**
  [*sibilatrix* Poeppig (Chiloe Wigeon)] **X**
  strepera L. (Gadwall) **OR**
  crecca L. (Common Teal) **OW/R**
  platyrhynchos L. (Mallard) **BR**
  acuta L. (Pintail) **W**
  querquedula L. (Garganey) **OS**
  clypeata L. (Shoveler) **BR**
Netta rufina (Pall.) (Red-crested Pochard) **X**
Aythya ferina (L.) (Pochard) **OW**
  nyroca (Güldenst.) (Ferruginous Duck) **X**
  fuligula (L.) (Tufted Duck) **BR**
  marila (L.) (Scaup) **X**
Melanitta nigra (L.) (Common Scoter) **X**
Bucephala clangula (L.) (Common Goldeneye) **WV**
Mergus albellus L. (Smew) **X**
  serrator L. (Red-breasted Merganser) **X**
  merganser L. (Goosander) **W**
Oxyura jamaicensis (Gmel.) Ruddy Duck **X**

FALCONIFORMES
(hawks, falcons)

ACCIPITRIDAE

Pernis apivorus (L.) (Honey Buzzard) **X**
Milvus milvus (L.) (Red Kite) **X**
Circus aeruginosus (L.) (Marsh Harrier) **BS**
  cyaneus (L.) (Hen Harrier) **W**
  pygargus (L.) (Montagu's Harrier) **O**
Accipiter gentilis (L.) (Goshawk) **X**
  nisus (L.) (Sparrowhawk) **BR**
Buteo buteo (L.) (Buzzard) **PV**
  lagopus (Pontopp.) (Rough-legged Buzzard) **WV**

PANDIONIDAE

Pandion haliaetus (L.) (Osprey) **PV**

FALCONIDAE

Falco tinnunculus L. (Kestrel) **OR**
  vespertinus L. (Red-footed Falcon) **X**
  columbarius L. (Merlin) **WV**
  subbuteo L. (Hobby) **S**
  peregrinus Tunst. (Peregrine Falcon) **WV**

GALLIFORMES
(game birds)

PHASIANIDAE

Alectoris rufa (L.) (Red-legged Partridge) **BR**
Perdix perdix (L.) (Grey Partridge) **O**
Coturnix coturnix (L.) (Quail) **X**
Phasianus colchicus L. (Pheasant) **BR**
[*Chrysolophus amherstiae* (Leadb.) (Lady Amherst's Pheasant)] **X**
[*Pavo cristatus* L. (Peacock)] **X**

GRUIFORMES
(crakes, rails)

RALLIDAE
Rallus aquaticus L. (Water Rail) **BR**
Porzana porzana (L.) (Spotted Crake) **OSV**
Gallinula chloropus (L.) (Moorhen) **BR**
Fulica atra L. (Coot) **BR**

GRUIDAE
Grus grus (L.) (Common Crane) **X**
   [*antigone* (L.) (Sarus Crane)] **X**
[*Balearica pavonina* (L.) (Crowned Crane)] **X**

CHARADRIIFORMES
(waders, gulls, terns, auks)

HAEMATOPODIDAE
Haematopus ostralegus L. (Oystercatcher) **PS**

RECURVIROSTRIDAE
Recurvirostra avosetta L. (Avocet) **X**

BURHINIDAE
Burhinus oedicnemus (L.) Stone-curlew **X**

CHARADRIIDAE
Charadrius dubius Scop. (Little Ringed Plover) **OP**
   hiaticula L. (Ringed Plover) **P**
Pluvialis apricaria (L.) (Golden Plover) **W**
   squatarola (L.) (Grey Plover) **X**
Vanellus vanellus (L.) (Lapwing) **BR**

SCOLOPACIDAE
Calidris minuta (Leisl.) (Little Stint) **X**
   melanotos (Vieill.) (Pectoral Sandpiper) **X**
   ferruginea (Pontopp.) (Curlew Sandpiper) **X**
   alpina (L.) (Dunlin) **P**
Philomachus pugnax (L.) (Ruff) **P**
Lymnocryptes minimus (Brünn.) (Jack Snipe) **W**
Gallinago gallinago (L.) (Common Snipe) **BRW**
Scolopax rusticola L. (Woodcock) **BR**
Limosa limosa (L.) (Black-tailed Godwit) **P**
   lapponica (L.) (Bar-tailed Godwit) **X**
Numenius phaeopus (L.) (Whimbrel) **P**
   arquata (L.) (Curlew) **P**
Tringa erythropus (Pall.) (Spotted Redshank) **PV**
   totanus (L.) (Redshank) **BS**
   nebularia (Gunner.) (Greenshank) **P**
   ochropus L. (Green Sandpiper) **P**
   glareola L. (Wood Sandpiper) **PV**
Actitis hypoleucos (L.) (Common Sandpiper) **P**
Arenaria interpres (L.) (Turnstone) **X**

STERCORARIIDAE
Stercorarius parasiticus (L.) (Arctic Skua) **X**

LARIDAE
Larus ridibundus L. (Black-headed Gull) **R**
   canus L. (Common Gull) **WP**
   fuscus L. (Lesser Black-backed Gull) **P**
   argentatus Pontopp. (Herring Gull) **WP**
   marinus L. (Great Black-backed Gull) **W**

STERNIDAE
Sterna sandvicensis Latham (Sandwich Tern) **X**
   hirundo L. (Common Tern) **SP**
   paradisaea Pontopp. (Arctic Tern) **X**
Chlidonias niger (L.) (Black Tern) **P**

ALCIDAE
Alle alle (L.) (Little Auk) **X**

COLUMBIFORMES
(pigeons & doves)

COLUMBIDAE
Columba [*livia* Gmel. (Rock Dove, Feral Pigeon)] **R**
   oenas L. (Stock Dove) **BR**
   palumbus L. (Wood Pigeon) **BR**
Streptopelia decaocto (Frivalds.) (Collared Dove) **BR**
   turtur (L.) (Turtle Dove) **BS**

[PSITTACIFORMES]
(parrots)

[CACATUIDAE]
[*Cacatua galerita* (Latham) (Sulphur-crested Cockatoo)] **X**
[*Nymphicus hollandicus* (Kerr) (Cockatiel)] **X**

[PSITTACIDAE]
[*Melopsittacus undulatus* (Shaw & Nodder) (Budgerigar)] **X**
[*Poicephalus senegalus* (L.) (Senegal Parrot)] **X**
[*Psittacula krameri* (Scop.) (Ring-necked Parakeet)] **X**

CUCULIFORMES
(cuckoos)

CUCULIDAE
Cuculus canorus L. (Cuckoo) **BS**

STRIGIFORMES
(owls)

TYTONIDAE
Tyto alba (Scop.) (Barn Owl) **OR**

STRIGIDAE
Athene noctua (Scop.) (Little Owl) **OR**
Strix aluco L. (Tawny Owl) **BR**
Asio otus (L.) (Long-eared Owl) **BR**
   flammeus (Pontopp.) (Short-eared Owl) **OW**

CAPRIMULGIFORMES
(nightjars)

CAPRIMULGIDAE
Caprimulgus europaeus L. (Nightjar) **X**

APODIFORMES
(swifts)

APODIDAE
Apus apus (L.) (Common Swift) **BS**
Tachymarptis melba (L.) (Alpine Swift) **X**

CORACIIFORMES
(kingfishers, hoopoes)

ALCEDINIDAE

Alcedo atthis (L.) (Kingfisher) **OR**

UPUPIDAE

Upupa epops L. (Hoopoe) **X**

PICIFORMES
(woodpeckers)

PICIDAE

Jynx torquilla L. (Wryneck) **X**
Picus viridis L. (Green Woodpecker) **OR**
Dendrocopos major (L.) (Great Spotted Woodpecker) **BR**
  minor (L.) (Lesser Spotted Woodpecker) **OR**

PASSERIFORMES
(perching birds)

ALAUDIDAE (larks)

Lullula arborea (L.) (Woodlark) **X**
Alauda arvensis L. (Skylark) **BR**

HIRUNDINIDAE (martins and swallows)

Riparia riparia (L.) (Sand Martin) **SP**
Hirundo rustica L. (Swallow) **BS**
Delichon urbica (L.) (House Martin) **S**

MOTACILLIDAE (pipits and wagtails)

Anthus trivialis (L.) (Tree Pipit) **PV**
  pratensis (L.) (Meadow Pipit) **BR**
  spinoletta (L.) (Water Pipit) **X**
Motacilla flava flavissima (Blyth) (Yellow Wagtail) **BS**
  f. flava L. (Blue-headed Wagtail) **SV#**
  cinerea Tunst. (Grey Wagtail) **X**
  alba yarrellii Gould (Pied Wagtail) **BR**
  a. alba L. (White Wagtail) **PV#**

BOMBYCILLIDAE (waxwings)

Bombycilla garrulus (L.) (Waxwing) **WV**

TROGLODYTIDAE (wrens)

Troglodytes troglodytes (L.) (Wren) **BR**

PRUNELLIDAE (accentors)

Prunella modularis (L.) (Dunnock) **BR**

TURDIDAE (robins, chats and thrushes)

Erithacus rubecula (L.) (Robin) **BR**
Luscinia megarhynchos C. L. Brehm (Nightingale) **BS**
  svecica (L.) (Bluethroat) **X**
Phoenicurus ochruros (S. G. Gmel.) (Black Redstart) **X**
  phoenicurus (L.) (Common Redstart) **P**
Saxicola rubetra (L.) (Whinchat) **PV**
  torquata (L.) (Stonechat) **OWV**
Oenanthe oenanthe oenanthe (L.) (Northern Wheatear) **P**
  o. leucorrhoa (Gmel.) (Greenland Wheatear) **X#**
Turdus torquatus L. (Ring Ousel) **PV**
  merula L. (Blackbird) **BR**
  pilaris L. (Fieldfare) **W**
  philomelos C. L. Brehm (Song Thrush) **BR**
  iliacus L. (Redwing) **W**
  viscivorus L. (Mistle Thrush) **BR**

SYLVIIDAE (warblers)

Cettia cetti (Temm.) (Cetti's Warbler) **O**
Locustella naevia (Bodd.) (Grasshopper Warbler) **BS**
  fluviatilis (Wolf) (River Warbler) **X**
  luscinioides (Savi) (Savi's Warbler) **OV**
Acrocephalus schoenobaenus (L.) (Sedge Warbler) **BS**
  palustris (Bechst.) (Marsh Warbler) **X**
  scirpaceus (Hermann) (Reed Warbler) **BS**
  arundinaceus (L.) (Great Reed Warbler) **X**
Sylvia nisoria (Bechst.) (Barred Warbler) **X**
  curruca (L.) (Lesser Whitethroat) **BS**
  communis Latham (Common Whitethroat) **BS**
  borin (Bodd.) (Garden Warbler) **BS**
  atricapilla (L.) (Blackcap) **BS**
Phylloscopus sibilatrix (Bechst.) (Wood Warbler) **X**
  collybita (Vieill.) (Chiffchaff) **BS**
  trochilus (L.) (Willow Warbler) **BS**
Regulus regulus (L.) (Goldcrest) **OW**
  ignicapillus (Temm.) (Firecrest) **V**

MUSCIPAPIDAE (flycatchers)

Muscicapa striata (Pall.) (Spotted Flycatcher) **BS**
Ficedula hypoleuca (Pall.) (Pied Flycatcher) **PV**

TIMALIIDAE (babblers)

Panurus biarmicus (L.) (Bearded Tit) **BR**

AEGATHALIDAE (long-tailed tits)

Aegithalos caudatus (L.) (Long-tailed Tit) **BR**

PARIDAE (tits)

Parus palustris L. (Marsh Tit) **V**
  montanus Conrad (Willow Tit) **BR**
  ater L. (Coal Tit) **V**
  caeruleus L. (Blue Tit) **BR**
  major L. (Great Tit) **BR**

SITTIDAE (nuthatches)

Sitta europaea L. (Nuthatch) **X**

CERTHIIDAE (treecreepers)

Certhia familiaris L. (Treecreeper) **BR**

ORIOLIDAE (orioles)

Oriolus oriolus (L.) (Golden Oriole) **SV**

LANIIDAE (shrikes)

Lanius collurio L. (Red-backed Shrike) **PV**
  excubitor L. (Great Grey Shrike) **WV**

CORVIDAE (crows)

Garrulus glandarius (L.) (Jay) **BR**
Pica pica (L.) (Magpie) **BR**
Corvus monedula L. (Jackdaw) **BR**
  frugilegus L. (Rook) **R**
  corone corone L. (Carrion Crow) **BR**
  c. cornix L. (Hooded Crow) **X#**

STURNIDAE (starlings)

Sturnus vulgaris L. (Starling) **BR**

PLOCEIDAE (sparrows)

Passer domesticus (L.) (House Sparrow) **BR**
   montanus (L.) (Tree Sparrow) **OR**

FRINGILLIDAE (finches)

Fringilla coelebs L. (Chaffinch) **BR**
   montifringilla L. (Brambling) **W**
[*Serinus canarius* (L.) (Canary)] **X**
Carduelis chloris (L.) (Greenfinch) **BR**
   carduelis (L.) (Goldfinch) **BR**
   spinus (L.) (Siskin) **WP**
   cannabina (L.) (Linnet) **BR**
   flavirostris (L.) (Twite) **X**
   flammea cabaret (P. L. S. Müll.) (Lesser Redpoll) **OR**
   f. *flammea* (L.) (Mealy Redpoll) **X#**
Loxia curvirostra L. (Common Crossbill) **V**
Pyrrhula pyrrhula (L.) (Bullfinch) **BR**
Coccothraustes coccothraustes (L.) (Hawfinch) **X**

[ESTRILDIDAE (waxbills)]

[*Poephila guttata* (Vieill.) (Zebra Finch)] **X**

EMBERIZIDAE (buntings)

[*Cardinalis cardinalis* (L.) (Cardinal)] **X**
Plectrophenax nivalis (L.) (Snow Bunting) **X**
Emberiza citrinella L. (Yellowhammer) **BR**
   schoeniclus (L.) (Reed Bunting) **BR**
Miliaria calandra (L.) (Corn Bunting) **O**
[*Tiaris olivacea* (L.) (Yellow-faced Grassquit)] **X**

MAMMALIA
(mammals)

Lists: Evans (1923a); Flowerdew (1980)
Checklist: Matthews (1960, 1982)
* Extinct at Wicken

CHIROPTERA

VESPERTILIONIDAE

Plecotus auritus (L.) (Long-eared Bat)
Nyctalus noctula (Schreb.) (Noctule)
Pipistrellus pipistrellus Kaup (Pipistrelle)
Myotis daubentoni (Kuhl) (Daubenton's (Water) Bat)

INSECTIVORA

ERINACEIDAE

Erinaceus europaeus L. (Hedgehog)

TALPIDAE

Talpa europaea L. (Mole)

SORICIDAE

Sorex araneus L. (Common Shrew)
   minutus L. (Pygmy Shrew)
Neomys fodiens Schreb. (Water Shrew)

CARNIVORA

CANIDAE

Vulpes vulpes (L.) (Fox)

MUSTELIDAE

Mustela erminea L. (Stoat)
   nivalis L. (Weasel)
   vison Schreb. (American Mink)
Lutra lutra (L.) (Otter) [1998]

LAGOMORPHA

LEPORIDAE

Lepus europaeus Pall. (Brown Hare)
Oryctolagus cuniculus (L.) (Rabbit)

RODENTIA

SCIURIDAE

Sciurus carolinensis Gmel. (Grey Squirrel)

MURIDAE

Micromys minutus (Pall.) (Harvest Mouse)
Apodemus sylvaticus (L.) (Wood Mouse)
Mus musculus L. (House Mouse)
Rattus norvegicus (Erxl.) (Brown Rat)

CRICETIDAE

Clethrionomys glareolus Schreb. (Bank Vole)
Arvicola terrestris (L.) (Water Vole)
Microtus agrestis (L.) (Field Vole)

HYSTRICIDAE

Myocaster coypus (Molina) (Coypu)*

ARTIODACTYLA

CERVIDAE

Capreolus capreolus (L.) (Roe (Deer))
Cervus elaphus L. (Red Deer)
Muntiacus reevesi (Zimm.) (Muntjac)
Hydropotes inermis Swinh. (Chinese Water-deer)

REFERENCES AND FURTHER READING

NHWF = *The Natural History of Wicken Fen*. 6 volumes: 1923, Gardiner, J. S. & Tansley, A. G. (eds); 1925, 1926, 1928, 1929, 1932; Gardiner, J. S. (ed.). Cambridge, Bowes & Bowes.

VCH = *The Victoria County History of Cambridgeshire & the Isle of Ely* (1938). Salzman, L. F. (ed.). Published for the University of London Institute of Historical Research by the Oxford University Press, London.

NT (WFLC) = National Trust, the Wicken Fen Local Committee.

Certain seminal or other key works on the Flora and Fauna, not cited in the checklists, are also given below.

Allen, K. R. & Gambles, R. M. (1932). Preliminary Account of the Ephemeroptera of Wicken Fen. *In* Gardiner, J. S. (ed.), *NHWF*, pp. 580–582.

Askew, R. R. (1988). *The Dragonflies of Europe*. Colchester, Harley Books.

Babington, C. C. (1857). *Flora of Cambridgeshire*. London, van Voorst.

Balfour-Browne, F. (1926). The Aquatic Coleoptera of the Wicken Fen Area, Cambridgeshire. *In* Gardiner J. S. (ed.), *NHWF*, pp. 201–214.

Ball, I. (1968). *The Freshwater Triclads of Wicken Fen*. Guides to Wicken Fen No. 6. Wicken, NT (WFLC).

Barber, A. D. & Keay, A. N. (1988). *Provisional Atlas of the Centipedes of the British Isles*. Huntingdon. Biological Records Centre, Institute of Terrestrial Ecology.

Barnard, P. C. (1985). An annotated check-list of the Trichoptera of Britain and Ireland. *Entomologist's Gazette* 36: 31–45.

Barnett, S. F. & Green, R. E. (1972). Bird ticks. *Wicken Fen Group Report* 4: 34–35.

Bedwell, G. C. (1938). Insecta: Hemiptera–Heteroptera. *In* Natural History: Zoology, Imms, A. D. (ed.), in *VCH* 1: 96–103.

Bennett, T. J. (1988). Butterflies and butterfly-watching in Cambridgeshire. *Nature in Cambridgeshire* 30: 31–35.

Benson, R. B. (1928). A Preliminary Account of the Sawflies of Wicken Fen. *In* Gardiner, J. S. (ed.), *NHWF*, pp. 313–323.

—— (1932). Additions and Corrections to the Preliminary List of the Sawflies of Wicken Fen. *In* Gardiner, J. S. (ed.), *NHWF*, pp. 544–547.

—— (1938). Insecta: Hymenoptera. I. Suborder Symphyta (Phytophaga) (Sawflies). *In* Natural History: Zoology, Imms, A. D. (ed.), in *VCH* 1: 162–165.

Bingley, F. J. & Walters, S. M. (1966). *Wicken Sedge Fen, a topographical and botanical guide*. Guides to Wicken Fen No. 1. Wicken, NT (WFLC).

Bircham, P. M. M. (1970). *The Birds of Cambridgeshire*. Cambridge, Cambridge University Press.

Blower, J. G. (1985). *Millipedes*. Synopses of the British Fauna (New Series) No. 35. The Linnean Society & the Estuarine and Brackish-Water Sciences Association. London, E. J. Brill/Dr. W. Backhuys.

Bradley, J. D. (1998; edn 2, 2000). *Checklist of Lepidoptera recorded from the British Isles*. Fordingbridge & Newent, D. J. & M. J. Bradley.

Bratton, J. H. (1990). *A review of the scarcer Ephemeroptera and Plecoptera of Great Britain*. Research and Survey in Nature Conservation Publication No. 29. Peterborough, Nature Conservancy Council.

—— (ed.) (1991). *British Red Data Books: 3*. Invertebrates other than Insects. Peterborough, Nature Conservancy Council.

Brindley, H. H. (1904). The Mollusca of Cambridgeshire. *In* Marr, J. E. & Shipley, A. E. (eds), *Handbook to the Natural History of Cambridgeshire*, pp. 114–138 Cambridge, University Press.

—— (1925). The Mollusca of Wicken Fen. *In* Gardiner, J. S. (ed.), *NHWF*, pp. 154–162.

Brinkhurst, R. O. (1971). *A Guide for the Identification of British Aquatic Oligochaeta*. Freshwater Biological Association Scientific Publication No. 22 (edn 2, revised). Ambleside.

Bristowe, W. S. (1925). The Spiders and Harvestmen. *In* Gardiner, J. S. (ed.), *NHWF*, pp. 104–115.

Brooks, D. & Mitchell, D. (compilers) (1998). *Checklist of the Birds of the Western Palearctic*. London, Birdwatch.

Brummitt, R. K. & Powell, C. E. (eds) (1992). *Authors of Plant Names*. Kew, Royal Botanic Gardens.

Burrows, C. N. R. (1902). British Lepidoptera in 1902. *Entomologist's Record* 14: 284.

Cambridgeshire Biodiversity Steering Committee (1997). *Cambridgeshire Biodiversity*. Cambridge, Cambridgeshire County Council.

Chandler, P. J. (ed.) (1998). Checklists of Insects of the British Isles (new series). *Handbooks for the Identification of British Insects* 12(1): Diptera. London, Royal Entomological Society.

Church, J. M., Coppins, B. J., Gilbert, O. L., James, P. W. & Stewart, N. F. (1996). *Red Data Books of Britain and Ireland: Lichens 1*: Britain. Peterborough, Joint Nature Conservation Committee.

Collin, J. E. (1938). Insecta: Diptera. *In* Natural History: Zoology, Imms, A. D. (ed.), in *VCH* 1: 189–205.

Corner, E. J. H. (1934). The Fungi of Wicken Fen, Cambridgeshire. *Transactions of the British Mycological Society* 19: 280–287.

Cramp, S. (ed.) (1985–92). *The Birds of the Western Palearctic* 4–6. Oxford, Oxford University Press.

—– & Simmonds, K. E. L. (eds) (1977–82). *The Birds of the Western Palearctic* 1–3. Oxford, Oxford University Press.

—– & Perrins, C. M. (eds) (1993–94). *The Birds of the Western Palearctic* 7–9. Oxford, Oxford University Press.

Day, M. C. (1988). Spider Wasps. Hymenoptera: Pompilidae. *Handbooks for the Identification of British Insects* 6(4). London, Royal Entomological Society.

Dennis, R. W. G., Orton, P. D. & Hora, F. B. (1960). New checklist of British Agarics and Boleti. *Transactions of the British Mycological Society (Supplement)*.

Disney, R. H. L. & Perry, I. (2000). A new species of *Megaselia* from Cambridgeshire (Diptera, Phoridae). *Dipterists' Digest* 7: 5–7.

Dolling, W. R. (1991). *The Hemiptera*. Oxford, Oxford University Press.

Donisthorpe, H. St J. K. (1938). Insecta: Coleoptera. *In* Natural History: Zoology. Imms, A. D. (ed.), in *VCH* 1: 104–137.

Duffey, E. (1970). *The Spiders of Wicken Fen*. Guides to Wicken Fen No. 7. Wicken, NT (WFLC).

—– (1971). The rediscovery of *Centromerus incultus* Falc. (*C. alnicola* Schenkel) (Araneae: Linyphiidae), in Britain. *Bulletin of the British Arachnological Society* 2(3): 48.

Dussart, B. & Defaye, D. (1990). Répertoire mondial des crustacés copépods des eaux intérieurs, III. Harpacticoides. *Crustaceana: International Journal of Crustacean Research*, Suppl. 16. Leiden, E. J. Brill

Eason, E. H. (1964). *Centipedes of the British Isles*. London, F. Warne & Co. Ltd.

Eastham, L. E. S. (1932). Wicken Fen Fauna – a Review. *In* Gardiner J. S. (ed.), *NHWF*, pp. 630–636.

Easy, G. M. S. & Kirtland, C. A. E. (1967). *Birds of Wicken Fen*. Guides to Wicken Fen No. 4. Wicken, NT (WFLC).

Elliott, J. M. & Mann, K. H. (1979). *A Key to the British Freshwater Leeches, with notes on their life cycles and ecology*. Freshwater Biological Association Scientific Publication No. 40. Ambleside.

Ellis, A. E. (1978). *British Freshwater Bivalve Mollusca*. Synopses of the British Fauna (New Series) No. 11. London, Academic Press.

Emmet, A. M. (1972). Microlepidoptera of Wicken Fen: an annotated check list. *Proceedings of the British Entomological and Natural History Society* 5(2): 52–74. Reprinted as No. 9 of the Guides to Wicken Fen.

—– (1991). Chart showing the life history and habits of the British Lepidoptera. *In* A. M. Emmet & J. Heath (eds), *The Moths and Butterflies of Great Britain and Ireland* 7(2). Colchester, Harley Books.

Evans, A. H. (1923a). The Fens of the Great Level, their Drainage, and its effect on the Flora and Fauna, V: Of the mammals and birds. *In* Gardiner, J. S. (ed.), *NHWF*, pp. 27–36.

—– (1923b). Full List of Plants growing in the Old Fen Land at Wicken omitting obvious intruders. *In* Gardiner, J. S. & Tansley A. G. (eds), *NHWF*, pp. 50–51.

—– (1939). *A Flora of Cambridgeshire*. London, Gurney & Jackson.

Falk, S. J. (1991a). *A Review of the scarce and threatened Bees, Wasps and Ants of Great Britain*. Research and Survey in Nature Conservation Publication No. 35. Peterborough, Nature Conservancy Council.

—– (1991b). *A Review of the scarce and threatened Flies of Great Britain*. Part 1. Research and Survey in Nature Conservation Publication No. 39. Peterborough, Nature Conservancy Council.

Farren, W. [S.] (1923). The Lepidoptera of Cambridgeshire. *In* Gardiner J. S. & Tansley, A. G. (eds), *NHWF*, pp. 53–64.

—– (1926a). Memories of Wicken. *In* Gardiner J. S. (ed.), *NHWF*, pp. 173–189.

— (1926b). A list of Lepidoptera of Wicken and the Neighbouring Fens. *In* Gardiner J. S. (ed.), *NHWF*, pp. 258–266.

Fergusson, N. D. M. (1986). Charipidae, Ibalidae & Figitidae. Hymenoptera: Cynipoidea. *Handbooks for the Identification of British Insects* 8 (1c). London, Royal Entomological Society.

Fitton, M. G., Shaw, M. R. & Gauld, I. D. (1988). Pimpline Ichneumon-Flies. Hymenoptera, Ichneumonidae (Pimplinae). *Handbooks for the Identification of British Insects* 7(1). London, Royal Entomological Society.

Flowerdew, J. R. (1980). *The Mammals of Wicken Fen*. Guides to Wicken Fen No. 11. Wicken, NT (WFLC).

Frazer, [J. F.] D. (1983). *Reptiles and Amphibians*. New Naturalists' Library No. 69. London, Collins.

Friday, L. E. (ed.), (1997). *Wicken Fen – the making of a wetland nature reserve*. Colchester, Harley Books.

—– & Colston, A. (1999). Wicken Fen: the restoration of a wetland nature reserve. *British Wildlife* 11: 37–46.

Fryer, J. C. F. (1938). Insecta: Lepidoptera. *In* Natural History: Zoology, Imms, A. D. (ed.), in *VCH* **1**: 139–161.

Gambles, R. M. (1932). The Psocoptera of Wicken Fen. *In* Gardiner, J. S. (ed.), *NHWF*, pp. 567–579.

— (1938). Insecta: Psocoptera. *In* Natural History: Zoology, Imms, A. D. (ed.), in *VCH* **1**: 94–96.

— & Kerrich, G. J. (1932). Notes on Neuroptera, Mecoptera and Strepsiptera. *In* Gardiner, J. S. (ed.), *NHWF*, pp. 583–584.

Gardiner, J. S. (ed.) (1925–32). *The Natural History of Wicken Fen* **2–6**. Cambridge, Bowes & Bowes.

— (1928). Wicken Fen. *In* Gardiner, J. S. (ed.), *NHWF*, pp. 371–383.

— (1932). Omissions and Additions. *In* Gardiner, J. S. (ed.), *NHWF*, pp. 644–648.

— & Tansley, A. G. (eds) (1923). *The Natural History of Wicken Fen* **1**. Cambridge, Bowes & Bowes.

Gauld, I. D. & Bolton, B. (eds) (1988). *The Hymenoptera*. Oxford, Oxford University Press.

George, E. A. (1963). The Diatoms of Wicken Fen and Hayley Wood. *Nature in Cambridgeshire* **6**: 39–42.

Gledhill, T., Sutcliffe, D. W. & Williams, W. D. (1993). *British Freshwater Crustacea Malacostraca*. Freshwater Biological Association Scientific Publication No. 52. Ambleside.

Griffiths, B. M. (1925). The Phytoplankton of the Wicken Fen Area. *In* Gardiner, J. S. (ed.), *NHWF*, pp. 116–121.

Griffiths, H. I. & Evans, J. G. (1995). An annotated check-list of British Pleistocene, Holocene and modern freshwater ostracods. *Journal of Micropalaeontology* **14**: 59–65.

Hammond, C. O. (1983). *The Dragonflies of Great Britain and Ireland*, edn 2, revised R. Merritt. Colchester, Harley Books.

Hancock, G. L. R. (1925). A preliminary account of the Ichneumonidae. *In* Gardiner, J. S. (ed.), *NHWF*, 122–139.

Harding, J. P. & Smith, W. A. (1974). *A Key to the British Freshwater Cyclopid and Calanoid Copepods*. Freshwater Biological Association Scientific Publication No. 18. Ambleside.

Harding, W. A. (1925). Hirudinea. *In* Gardiner, J. S. (ed.), *NHWF*, pp. 92–99, pl. III.

— (1938). Hirudinea. *In* Natural History: Zoology, Imms, A. D. (ed.), in *VCH* **1**: 78–79.

Harker, J. (1989). *Mayflies*. Naturalists' Handbook No. 13. Slough, Richmond Publishing Co.

Harris, W. V. (1928). Hemiptera–Heteroptera. Part II. Polyneuria, Onychiophora and Anonychia. *In* Gardiner, J. S. (ed.), *NHWF*, pp. 324–328.

Hartley, B. (1986). A check-list of the freshwater, brackish and marine diatoms of the British Isles and adjoining coastal waters. *Journal of the Marine Biological Association*, UK, **66**: 531–610.

Hawksworth, D. L., Kirk, P. M., Sutton, B. C. & Pegler, D. N. (eds) (1995). *Ainsworth & Bisby's Dictionary of the Fungi* (edn 8). Wallingford, International Mycological Institute, CAB International.

Henderson, P. A. (1990). *Freshwater Ostracods*. Synopses of the British Fauna (New Series) No. 42. Oegstgeest, Universal Book Services/Dr W. Backhuys.

Hill, M. O., Preston, C. D. & Smith, A. J. E. (eds) (1991–94). *Atlas of the Bryophytes of Britain and Ireland* **1–3**. Colchester, Harley Books.

Hillyard, P. D. & Sankey, J. H. P. (1989). *Harvestmen*. Key and notes for the identification of the species. Synopses of the British Fauna (New Series), No. 4 (edn 2). Leiden, E. J. Brill.

Hodge, P. J. & Jones, R. A. (1995). *New British Beetles – species not in Joy's practical handbook*. Reading, British Entomological and Natural History Society.

Hodgetts, N., Palmer, M. & Wigginton, M. (1996). *The Pink Book of Plants – Lists of vascular and non-vascular plant species which are nationally threatened, localised or protected in Great Britain* (First version). Species Conservation Branch Information Note. Joint Nature Conservation Committee, Peterborough.

Hodkinson, I. D. & White, I. M. (1979). Homoptera, Psylloidea. *Handbooks for the Identification of British Insects* **2**(5a). London, Royal Entomological Society.

Hoek, C. van den, Mann, D. G. & Johns, H. M. (1995). *Algae. An Introduction to Phycology*. Cambridge, Cambridge University Press.

Hopkin, S. P. (1997). *Biology of the Springtails. Insecta: Collembola*. Oxford, Oxford University Press.

Hutchinson, G. E. (1925). A Preliminary Account of the Hemiptera–Heteroptera. *In* Gardiner, J. S. (ed.), *NHWF*, pp. 100–103.

— (1926). Hemiptera–Heteroptera. Part 1. Hydrobiotica and Sandalioryncha. *In* Gardiner, J. S. (ed.), *NHWF*, pp. 234–252.

Hyman, P. S. (1992). *A Review of the scarce and threatened Coleoptera of Great Britain*, Part 1 (revised and updated by M. S. Parsons). UK Nature Conservation Publication No. 3. Peterborough, Joint Nature Conservation Committee.

— (1994). *A Review of the scarce and threatened Coleoptera of Great Britain*, Part 2 (revised and updated by M. S. Parsons). UK Nature Conservation Publication No. 12. Peterborough, Joint Nature Conservation Committee.

Imms, A. D. (1938a). Insecta: Odonata. *In* Natural History: Zoology, Imms, A. D. (ed.), in *VCH* **1**: 92–93.

— (1938b). Insecta: Neuroptera and Mecoptera. *In* Natural History: Zoology, Imms, A. D. (ed.), in *VCH* **1**: 103–104.

— (1938c): Insecta: Trichoptera. *In* Natural History: Zoology, Imms, A. D. (ed.), in *VCH* 1: 137–139.

— (1938d). Insecta: Ephemeroptera. *In* Natural History: Zoology, Imms, A. D. (ed.), in *VCH* 1: 205.

Ing, B. (1992). A Provisional Red Data list of British Fungi. *Mycologist* 6: 124–128.

Jackson C. H. N. (1928). The Collembola of Wicken Fen, Cambridgeshire. *In* Gardiner, J. S. (ed.), *NHWF*, pp. 300–307, Pl. VII.

— (1938). Insecta: Collembola. *In* Natural History: Zoology, Imms, A. D. (ed.), in *VCH* 1: 90–91.

Jenkin, P. M. (1928). The Cladocera of Wicken Fen. *In* Gardiner, J. S. (ed.), *NHWF*, pp. 356–365, Pl. IX.

Johnson, R. (1985). *An investigation into the cyprinid hybrid community of Wicken Fen Mere*. Unpublished report, pp. 34–93. Huntingdon, Anglian Water.

Kempf, E. K. (1980–91). *Index and Bibliography of Non-marine Ostracoda*, 1–5. Sonderveroeffentlichungen Geologisches Institut der Universitaet zu Koeln, pp. 35–38, 77.

Kerney, M. P. (1999). *Atlas of Land and Freshwater Molluscs of Britain and Ireland*. Colchester, Harley Books

Kerney, M. P. & Cameron, R. A. D. (1979). *A Field Guide to the Land Snails of Britain and north-west Europe*. London, Collins.

Kerrich, G. J. (1932). Additions to the Ichneumonoid Fauna of Wicken Fen. *In* Gardiner, J. S. (ed.), *NHWF*, pp. 560–566.

— (1936). The Ichneumonoidea of Wicken Fen: Corrigenda and Addenda. *Transactions of the Society for British Entomology* 3: 61–66.

— & Spooner, G. M. (attrib. G. J. Kerrich) (1938). Insecta: Hymenoptera. II. Suborder Apocritica (Heterophaga). *In* Natural History: Zoology, Imms, A. D. (ed.), in *VCH* 1: 165–189.

Kirby, P. (1992). *A Review of the scarce and threatened Hemiptera of Great Britain*. UK Nature Conservation Publication No. 2. Peterborough, Joint Nature Conservation Committee.

Kirk-Spriggs, A. H. (1996). Pollen beetles. Coleoptera: Kateretidae and Nitidulidae: Meligethinae [with check list]. *Handbooks for the Identification of British Insects* 5(6a). London, Royal Entomological Society.

Kloet, G. S. & Hincks, W. D. (1945). *A Check List of British Insects*. Stockport, published privately by the authors.

— & — (1964). A Check List of British Insects, edn 2, revised. *Handbooks for the Identification of British Insects* 11(1): Small Orders and Hemiptera. London, Royal Entomological Society.

— & —(1972). A Check List of British Insects, edn 2, revised. *Handbooks for the Identification of British Insects* 11(2): Lepidoptera. London, Royal Entomological Society.

— & — (1976). A Check List of British Insects, edn 2, revised. *Handbooks for the Identification of British Insects* 11(5): Diptera and Siphonaptera. London, Royal Entomological Society.

— & — (1977). A Check List of British Insects, edn 2, revised by R. D. Pope. *Handbooks for the Identification of British Insects* 11(3): Coleoptera and Strepsiptera. London, Royal Entomological Society.

— & — (1978). A Check List of British Insects, edn 2, revised by M. G. Fitton, M. W. R. de V. Graham, Z. R. J. Bouček, N. D. M. Fergusson, T. Huddleston, J. Quinlan & O. W. Richards. *Handbooks for the Identification of British Insects* 11(4): Hymenoptera. London, Royal Entomological Society.

Lack, D. (1934). *Birds of Cambridgeshire*. Cambridge, Cambridge Bird Club.

Laundon, J. R. (1973). *Lichens of Wicken Fen*. Guides to Wicken Fen No. 10. Wicken, NT (WFLC).

— (1991). Letter to the Secretary, WF Local Management Committee (archives).

Le Quesne, W. J. & Payne, K. R. (1981). Cicadellidae (Typhlocybinae) with a check list of the British Auchenorhyncha (Hemiptera, Homoptera). *Handbooks for the Identification of British Insects* 2(2c). London, Royal Entomological Society.

Legg, G. & Jones, R. E. (1988). *Pseudoscorpions*. Synopses of the British Fauna (New Series) No. 40. Leiden, E. J. Brill/Dr W. Backhuys.

Lewis, D. J. (1932). The Mosquitoes of Wicken Fen. *In* Gardiner, J. S. (ed.), *NHWF*, pp. 548–559 Pl. XIV.

Liston, A. (1995). *Compendium of European Sawflies*. Gottfriedring [Germany], Chalastros Forestry.

— (1996). *Supplement to Compendium of European Sawflies*. Gottfriedring [Germany], Chalastros Forestry.

Lock, J. M. (1963). Recent bryophyte records from Wicken Fen. *Nature in Cambridgeshire* 7: 34–38.

— (1968). *List of the Bryophytes of Wicken Fen*. Guides to Wicken Fen No. 5. Wicken, NT (WFLC).

Lousley, J. E. & Kent, D. (1981). *Docks and Knotweeds of the British Isles*. BSBI Handbook No. 3, pp. 160–163. London, BSBI.

Lowndes, A. G. (1928). The Copepoda of Wicken Fen, with observations on the influence of environment. *In* Gardiner, J. S. (ed.), *NHWF*, pp. 334–345, Pl. VIII.

— (1932a). Ostracoda of Wicken Fen. *In* Gardiner, J. S. (ed.), *NHWF*, pp. 585–589.

— (1932b). A Collection of Fresh-water Entomostraca from Wicken Fen. *In* Gardiner, J. S. (ed.), *NHWF*, pp. 590–594.

— (1938). Crustacea. *In* Natural History: Zoology, Imms, A. D. (ed.), in *VCH* 1: 80–86.

Lucas, W. J. (1925). Insects of the Natural Orders: Orthoptera, Paraneuroptera and Neuroptera. *In* Gardiner, J. S. (ed.), *NHWF*, pp. 65–86, Pls I, II.

—- (1928). Further Notes on the Orthoptera, Paraneuroptera, Neuroptera, etc. of Wicken Fen. *In* Gardiner, J. S. (ed.), *NHWF*, pp. 329–333.

Maitland, P. S. (1977). *A Coded Checklist of Animals occurring in Fresh Water in the British Isles.* Institute of Terrestrial Ecology publication. Edinburgh. Nature Conservancy Council.

—- & Campbell, R. N. (1992). *Freshwater Fishes.* New Naturalist Library No. 75. London, HarperCollins.

Margulis, L. & Schwarz, K. V. (1988). *Five Kingdoms: an illustrated guide to the phyla of life on Earth* (edn 2). New York, W. H. Freeman and Company.

—-, Corliss, J. O., Melkonian, M. & Chapman, D. J. (1990). *Handbook of Protoctista. The structure, cultivation, habitats and life histories of the Eukaryotic microorganisms and their descendants exclusive of animals, plants and fungi. A guide to the algae, ciliates, foraminifera, sporozoa, water molds, slime molds and other protoctists.* Boston, Jones and Bartlett Publishers.

Marshall, J. A. & Haes, E. C. M. (1988). *Grasshoppers and Allied Insects of Great Britain and Ireland.* Colchester, Harley Books.

Matthews, L. H. (1960). *British Mammals.* New Naturalist Library No. 21. London, Collins.

—- (1982). *Mammals in the British Isles.* New Naturalist Library No. 68. London, Collins.

Mendel, H. & Clarke, R. E. (1996). *Provisional Atlas of the Click Beetles (Coleoptera: Elateroidea) of Britain and Ireland.* Ipswich, Ipswich Borough Council Museums.

Michelmore, A. P. G. (1929). The Diptera of Wicken Fen. *In* Gardiner, J. S. (ed.), *NHWF*, pp. 447–478, Pls XII, XIII.

Miller, S. H. & Skertchly, S. B. J. (1878). *The Fenland: past and present.* Wisbech & London, Longmans, Green.

Minelli, A. (1993). *Biological Systematics: the state of the art.* London, Chapman & Hall.

Moore, J. A. (1986). *Charophytes of Great Britain and Ireland.* BSBI Handbook No. 5. London, BSBI.

Morgan, C. I. & King, P. E. (1976). *British Tardigrades.* Synopses of the British Fauna (New Series) No. 9. Academic Press, London.

Morgan, D. (1984). Cuckoo-wasps. Hymenoptera, Chrysididae. *Handbooks for the Identification of British Insects* 6(5). London, Royal Entomological Society.

Morris, M. G. (1990). Orthocerous weevils. Coleoptera: Curculionoidea (Nemonychidae, Anthribidae, Urodontidae, Attelabidae and Apionidae) [with checklist]. *Handbooks for the Identification of British Insects* 5(16). London, Royal Entomological Society.

—- (1991). A taxonomic check list of the British Ceutorhynchinae, with notes, particularly on host plant relationships (Coleoptera: Curculionidae). *Entomologist's Gazette* 42: 255–265.

—- (1993a). 'British Orthocerous weevils': corrections and new information (Coleoptera: Curculionidae) [with new check list of Apionidae]. *Entomologist's Monthly Magazine* 129: 23–29.

—- (1993b). A review of the British species of Rhynchaeninae (Col., Curculionidae). *Entomologist's Monthly Magazine* 129: 177–197.

—- (1997). Broad-nosed weevils. Coleoptera: Curculionidae (Entiminae) [with check list]. *Handbooks for the Identification of British Insects* 5(17a). London, Royal Entomological Society.

—- & Booth, R. G. (1997). Notes on the nomenclature of some British weevils (Curculionoidea). *Coleopterist* 6(3): 91–99.

Mound, L. A., Morison, G. D., Pitkin, B. R. & Palmer, J. M. (1976). Thysanoptera. *Handbooks for the Identification of British Insects* 1(11). London, Royal Entomological Society.

Mountford, J. O., Lock, J. M., Walters, S. M. & Bennett, T. J. (1994). *A Checklist of the vascular plants of Wicken Fen.* Wicken, NT (WFLC).

Muir, R. C. (1951). A report on the birds at Wicken Fen – 1951. *Cambridge Bird Club Report* 25: 24–25.

Mundy, S. P. (1980). *A key to the British and European freshwater Bryozoans.* Freshwater Biological Association Scientific Publication No. 41. Ambleside.

Nellist, D. R. (2000). The National Trust's 100th Anniversary Field Meeting at Wicken Fen 12th–13th June, 1999. *Newsletter of the British Arachnological Society* No. 88.

Nevinson E. B. (1916). Aculeate Hymenoptera and Chrysididae at Wicken. *Entomologist's Monthly Magazine* 52: 90–91.

—- (1926). Hymenoptera Aculeata. *In* Gardiner J. S. (ed.), *NHWF*, pp. 253–254.

New, T. R. (1974). Psocoptera. *Handbooks for the Identification of British Insects* 1(7). London, Royal Entomological Society.

Nixon, G. E. J. (1980). Diapriidae (Diapriinae). Hymenoidea, Proctotrupoidea. *Handbooks for the Identification of British Insects* 8(3d(i)). London, Royal Entomological Society.

Oldham, C. (1926). Additions to the Mollusca of Wicken Fen. *In* Gardiner, J. S. (ed.), *NHWF*, pp. 198–200.

Oliver, P. G. & Meechan, C. J. (1993). *Woodlice.* Synopses of the British Fauna (New Series) No. 49. Shrewsbury, Field Studies Council.

Omer Cooper, J. (1925). The Higher Crustacea. *In* Gardiner, J. S. (ed.), *NHWF*, pp. 140–153 Pl. IV.

—-, Perkins, M. G. L. & Tottenham, C. E. (1928). The Coleoptera of Wicken Fen [Parts I & II]. *In* Gardiner, J. S. (ed.), *NHWF*, pp. 267–297.

— & Tottenham, C. E. (1932). The Coleoptera of Wicken Fen [Parts III–V]. *In* Gardiner, J. S. (ed.), *NHWF*, pp. 489–538.

Painter, D. J. (1994). Some records of aquatic Coleoptera and Mollusca from Wicken Fen. *Nature in Cambridgeshire* 36: 88–91.

Palmer, M. A., Hodgetts, N. G., Wigginton, M. J., Ing, B. & Stewart, N. F. (1997). The application to the British Flora of the World Conservation Union's revised Red List criteria and the significance of Red Lists for species conservation. *Biological Conservation* 82: 219–226.

Parsons, M. S. (1993). *A Review of the scarce and threatened Pyralid Moths of Great Britain*. UK Nature Conservation Publication No. 11. Peterborough, Joint Nature Conservation Committee.

— (1995). *A Review of the scarce and threatened Ethmiine, Stathmopodine and Gelechiid Moths of Great Britain*. UK Nature Conservation Publication No. 16. Peterborough, Joint Nature Conservation Committee.

Paton, J. A. (1999). *The Liverwort Flora of the British Isles*. Colchester, Harley Books.

Paul, C. R. C. (1967). *Mollusca of the Wicken Sedge Fen*. Guides to Wicken Fen No. 2. Wicken, NT (WFLC).

Perkins, J. F. (1957). Two new species of European *Ephialtes* (*Scambus*). *Opuscula zoologica München* 7: 1–3.

Perkins, M. (1928). Cambridgeshire Planarians (Tricladida) with a preliminary list of the Rhabdocoelida. *In* Gardiner, J. S. (ed.), *NHWF*, pp. 346–355.

Perring, F. H. (1968). Vascular plant records. *Nature in Cambridgeshire* 11: 36–37.

— & Farrell, L. (compiler), (1983). *British Red Data Books: 1*. Vascular Plants (edn 2). Lincoln, The Royal Society for Nature Conservation.

—, Sell P. D., Walters S. M. & Whitehouse H. L. K. (1964). *A Flora of Cambridgeshire*. Cambridge, University Press.

Pickford, G. E. (1926a). The Oligochaeta of Wicken Fen. Part I. Lumbricidae. *In* Gardiner, J. S. (ed.), *NHWF*, pp. 215–232 Pl. VI.

— (1926b). Thysanura. *In* Gardiner, J. S. (ed.), *NHWF*, p. 233.

Plant, C. W. (1994). *Provisional Atlas of the Lacewings and allied Insects (Neuroptera, Megaloptera, Rhaphidoptera and Mecoptera) of Britain and Ireland*. Huntingdon, Biological Records Centre.

Pontin, R.M. (1978). *A key to the Freshwater Planktonic and Semi-Planktonic Rotifera of the British Isles*. Freshwater Biological Association Scientific Publication No. 38. Ambleside.

— (1995). Rotifers of Wicken Fen, Cambridgeshire: a preliminary survey. *Nature in Cambridgeshire* 37: 20–24.

Preston, C. D. (1991). Charophyte records. *Nature in Cambridgeshire* 33: 70.

— (1993). Charophyte records. *Nature in Cambridgeshire* 35: 86.

— & Croft, J. M. (1997). *Aquatic Plants in Britain and Ireland*. Colchester, Harley Books.

Proctor, M. C. F. (1956). A bryophyte flora of Cambridgeshire. *Transactions of the British Bryological Society* 3: 1–49.

Purvis, O. W., Coppins, B. J. & James, P. W. (1994). *Checklist of Lichens of Great Britain and Ireland*. London, The British Lichen Society.

Quinlan, J. (1978). Hymenoptera: Cynipoidea – Eucoilidae. *Handbooks for the Identification of British Insects* 8(1b). London, Royal Entomological Society.

Reynoldson, T. B. (1978). *A Key to the British Species of Freshwater Triclads*. Freshwater Biological Association Scientific Publication No. 23, (edn 2, revised). Ambleside.

Richards, O. W. (1980). Scolioidea, Vespoidea and Sphecoidea. Hymenoptera, Aculeata. *Handbooks for the Identification of British Insects* 6(3b). London, Royal Entomological Society.

Richards, P. W. (1932). The Bryophyta of Wicken Fen. *In* Gardiner, J. S. (ed.), *NHWF*, pp. 539–543.

Roberts, M. J. (1985-1987). *The Spiders of Great Britain and Ireland* 1–3. Colchester, Harley Books.

— (1993). *Supplement – The Spiders of Great Britain and Ireland*. Colchester, Harley Books.

Rudd, J. A. (1986). The mosquitoes of Wicken Fen. *Nature in Cambridgeshire* 28: 13–19.

Salzman, L. F. (ed.) (1938). *A History of Cambridgeshire & the Isle of Ely* 1. In the series *The Victoria History of the Counties of England*. London, Oxford University Press.

Sandon, H. (1928). A note on the Microbiology of Wicken Fen Soils with special reference to the Protozoa. *In* Gardiner, J. S. (ed.), *NHWF*, pp. 366–370.

Schwarz, M. & Shaw, M. R. (1998). Western Palaearctic Criptinae (Hymenoptera: Ichneumonidae) in the National Museums of Scotland, with nomenclatural changes, taxonomic notes, rearing records and special reference to the British check list. Part 1. Tribe Cryptini. *Entomologist's Gazette* 49: 101–127.

Scourfield, D. J. & Harding, J. P. (1966, revised 1994). *A Key to the British Freshwater Cladocera with notes on their ecology*. Freshwater Biological Association Scientific Publication No. 5. Ambleside.

Sell, P. D. (1987). The dactylorchids of Wicken Fen. *Nature in Cambridgeshire* 29: 69–72.

Shaw, M. R. & Huddleston, T. (1991). Classification and Biology of Braconid Wasps (Hymenoptera: Braconidae). *Handbooks for the Identification of British Insects* 7(11). London, Royal Entomological Society.

Shenefelt, R. D. (1969–1980). Braconidae 1–8, 10, 11. In *Hymenopterorum Catalogus* (nova editio) **4**: 1–176; **5**: 177–306; **6**: 307–428; **7**: 429–668; **9**: 669–812; **10**: 813–936; **11**: 937–1113; **12**: 1115–1262; **15**: 1425–1872; **16**: 1–384. 's-Gravenhage.

— & Marsh, P. M. (1976). Braconidae 9. In *Hymenopterorum Catalogus* (nova editio) **13**: 1263–1424. 's-Gravenhage.

Shirt, D. B. (ed.) (1987). *British Red Data Books: 2*. Insects. Peterborough, Nature Conservancy Council.

Sims, P. A. (ed.) (1996). *An Atlas of British Diatoms*, arranged by B. Hartley, based on illustrations by H. G. Barber and J. R. Carter. Bristol, Biopress.

Sims, R. W. & Gerard, B. M. (1985). *Earthworms*. Synopses of the British Fauna (New Series) No. 31. London, E.J. Brill/Dr.W. Backhuys.

Smart, J. (1972). *Butterflies and Day-flying Moths*. Guides to Wicken Fen No. 8. Wicken, NT (WFLC).

Smit, F. G. A. M. (1957a). Siphonaptera. *Handbooks for the Identification of British Insects* **1**(16). London, Royal Entomological Society.

— (1957b). The recorded distribution and hosts of Siphonaptera in Britain. *Entomologist's Gazette* **8**: 45–75

Smith, A. J. E. (1978). *The Moss Flora of Britain and Ireland*. Cambridge University Press.

— (1990). *The Liverworts of Britain and Ireland*. Cambridge University Press.

Spooner, G. M. (1930). The bees, wasps and ants of Cambridgeshire. *Cambridge Daily News*, Cambridge.

Stace, C. (1991). *New Flora of the British Isles*. Cambridge, University Press.

Stenton, H. (1953). The soil fungi of Wicken Fen. *Transactions of the British Mycological Society* **36**: 304–314.

Stewart, N. F. & Church, J. M. (1992). *Red Data Books of Britain and Ireland: Stoneworts*. Peterborough, Joint Nature Conservation Committee.

— & — (in press). *Red Data Books of Britain and Ireland: Mosses and Liverworts*. Peterborough, Joint Nature Conservation Committee.

Stroyan, H. L. G. (1984). Aphids - Pterocommatinae and Aphidinae (Aphidini). Homoptera, Aphididae. *Handbooks for the Identification of British Insects* **2**(6). London, Royal Entomological Society.

Thorne, C. J. R. (1971). Grotty leg. *Wicken Fen Group Report* **3**: 17–18.

— & Bennett, T. J. (1982). *The Birds of Wicken Fen*. Cambridge, The Wicken Fen Group.

— & — (1989; edn 2, 1995). *A summary Checklist of the Birds of Wicken Fen*. Guides to Wicken Fen No. 12. Wicken, The Wicken Fen Group and The National Trust.

Thorpe, W. H. (1938). Aves. *In* Imms, A. D. (ed.), The Zoology of Cambridgeshire. *In* Darby, H. C. (ed.), *A scientific survey of the Cambridge district*, pp. 61–63. London, British Association for the Advancement of Science.

Wallace, I. D. (1991). *A Review of the Trichoptera of Great Britain*. Research & Survey in Nature Conservation Publication No. 32. Peterborough, Nature Conservancy Council.

Wallis, A. (1904). The flora of the Cambridge district. *In* Marr, J. E. & Shipley, A. E. (eds.), *Handbook to the Natural History of Cambridgeshire*: 209–237. Cambridge, Cambridge University Press.

Walters, S. M. (1967). *List of the Vascular Plants of Wicken Fen*. Guides to Wicken Fen No. 3. Wicken, NT (WFLC).

Whitton, B. & John, D. (in prep.). *British Freshwater Algal Flora*. London, British Phycological Society and the Natural History Museum.

Wicken Fen Local Management Committee (1986–). *Botanical records*.

— (1986–). *Zoological records*.

Wigginton, M. J. (ed.) (1999). *British Red Data Books: 1*. Vascular Plants (edn 3). Peterborough, Joint Nature Conservation Committee.

Wood, A. H. (1929). The Trichoptera of Wicken Fen. *In* Gardiner J. S. (ed.), *NHWF*, pp. 479–487.

Worthington, E. B. (1928). The Diplopoda and Chilopoda of Wicken Fen. *In* Gardiner, J. S. (ed.), *NHWF*, pp. 308–312.

— (1938a). Myriapoda. *In* Natural History: Zoology, Imms, A. D. (ed.), in *VCH* **1**: 87–88.

— (1938b). Insecta: Orthoptera and Dermaptera. *In* Natural History: Zoology, Imms, A. D. (ed.), in *VCH* **1**: 91–92.

Yu, D. S. & Horstmann, K. (1997). Catalogue of World Ichneumonidae. *Memoirs of the American Entomological Institute* **58**, parts 1 and 2.

NOTES

NOTES

NOTES

NOTES

NOTES

NOTES